The Image of the Heart

THE IMAGE OF
THE HEART

*And the Principle of Synergy
in the Human Mind*

by

Daniel E. Schneider, M.D.

INTERNATIONAL UNIVERSITIES PRESS, INC.

New York   New York

Library of Congress Catalog Card Number: 56–9246

Published under the auspices of

The Foundation for Psychosynergy

Printed in the United States of America

CONTENTS

Part I

THE SONIC IMAGE OF THE HEART

v

Contents

Contents

Part II

THE SONIC ASPECTS OF A SYNERGIC PSYCHONEU-
ROLOGY
HEART IMAGE AND HEART MECHANISM
THE ACOUSTIC ECHO REFLEX

Contents

Foreword

FOREWORD

THE concepts and type of approach to those medical problems which
are known today by the term "psychosomatics" are attracting a great
deal of attention in most of the medical centers of the world. Research
has been active and knowledge expanding in this field for some years,
with interest extending in various directions, centering on one or another of the bodily systems of organs and functions. Naturally in such a
situation there exist diverse opinions, controversial findings and
enough of contradictions to confuse the non-expert. However, science
is still immature in its applications in this particular attitude and attack on medical problems, but undoubtedly with time many hazy aspects will be clarified.

A considerable amount of psychosomatic investigation has been
devoted to the circulatory system. The heart rate is so sensitive to even
slight emotional changes that it was long considered to be the center
of the emotions of fear, anger, and love, and in present-day medicine
there are a number of disorders in which the heart shows an abnormal
activity without any demonstrable lesions to account for them. Modern biology has obliterated fixed lines. The psychic aspects of the individual are also functioning processes which under proper conditions are convertible into certain physical ones. There is also more
than one aspect of the same thing.

This book is a unique presentation which brings into focus some of
the author's novel ideas and experiences in such a way as should stimulate a lively curiosity in medical readers. The author proposes that
there is a sonic image of the heart which has been unrecognized in

consciousness and which, therefore, is approachable psychically as well as physically. This new "synergic" psychocardiology has already influenced favorably the "paroxysmal tachycardia of emotional origin" and has a bearing on the problem of coronary disturbances.

He also points out there is evidence that the sonic image of the heart and other sonic phenomena indicate that a sonic principle determines the operation of the "psychophysiologic apparatus," particularly of the important synergy of the brain-heart relationships. He emphasizes that "psychophysiology" in this concept becomes a new science of *synergic psychoneurology*. Therefore, the *principle of synergy* dominates the fate of psychic and physical survival. For example, the phenomenon of talent is interpreted as such a synergy.

In terms of the concepts in this book psychoanalysis would take on a new development in the direction toward which Professor Freud pointed in his last years. It would become a "psychosynergic analysis" based upon a scientific synergic psychoneurology.

Psychiatrists, neurologists and cardiologists will find this text helpful in their various problems. When new criteria are observed or new interpretations suggested, additional light is cast upon a subject and a better understanding achieved. We are in dire need of such viewpoints and fresh working hypotheses.

Nolan D. C. Lewis, M.D.
Princeton, New Jersey

AUTHOR'S PREFACE

This monograph has been in preparation for over twenty years; yet, while the basic ideas of a new sonic principle in nervous action and of a sonic image of the heart could be conceived and documented in general, the specific new facts were not easy to organize. As a result, the various chapters, written separately as articles, show some overlap which is unavoidable, as well as many gaps which only further work can span.

Up to now, cardiology has been—justifiably—separated from the "psychic." The development of a new *psychoneurologic apparatus,* however, will, it is hoped, make it possible to see new aspects of the human heart both with respect to mind and body. The increasing awareness of the psychic aspects of "heart attack" is no accident.

Indeed, the synergic principle of the image of the heart and the sonic aspects of a synergic psychoneurology may very well simplify a number of *psychoanalytic* complexities, and have ultimately an impact upon psychoanalytic theory and practice. The "heart" as the "seat of the emotions" for thousands of years may have more than a mere "poetic" meaning.

Nevertheless nothing in this book is to be taken to contradict the valid physiologic and pharmacologic practices of cardiologists. On the contrary, cardiologists and neuropsychiatrists may find areas of mutual interest here, of benefit to the long-suffering race of man.

I should like finally to express my gratitude to Dr. Milton Mendlowitz, of the Mount Sinai Hospital, for his thoughtful suggestions throughout the course of this work.

Daniel E. Schneider, M.D.

ACKNOWLEDGMENTS

Several of the chapters included here were first published as articles in the following journals: *Growth, Journal of Nervous and Mental Disease, Journal of the Hillside Hospital, Journal of the Mount Sinai Hospital,* and *The Psychoanalytic Review.* The author thanks the Editors of these publications for their kind permission to reprint these papers.

The Image of the Heart

PART I

The Sonic Image of the Heart

THE IMAGE OF THE HEART AND THE SYNERGIC PRINCIPLE IN PSYCHOANALYSIS (PSYCHOSYNERGY)—THE DEFINITION OF ANXIETY

INTRODUCTION

THE history of science is the history of changes in our fundamental views of the universe and its nature. No matter what outcry, physics and mathematics have moved us steadily forward into the relativistic world which prejudice and fear would have denied to us. Progress is inevitable always, despite whatever entrenched interests want to reenact the historically clownish role of King Canute. Ever since Man stood erect and looked at his hand with its uniquely opposable thumb, no one has been able to bar him for long from the triumph of using whatever new tool might advance his personal comfort and his transcending voyage of discovery. Repressive institutions of all kinds would do well to contemplate this simple fact.

So too with the discovery of the tools of psychoanalysis. *New* tools have a way of digging up new *facts*. Those who manufacture the old tools also have a consistent history. Out of very material interests—not the least of which are their old defensive delusions—they tend to regard as sacred all organizational forms which seemed to promise the eternity of the old tools. Those who wish to make advances in psychoanalysis itself must take this historic conflict into account.

Today, for example, it is becoming increasingly clear that the science of psychoanalysis—together with other medical sciences such as that of nutrition—is becoming one of the foremost sciences of *longev-*

ity, as well as a science of human relationships with all its attendant successes in self-expression and self-assertion. The moment that psychoanalysis became "psychosomatic" it made a very practical juncture with problems not only of general health but also of *survival.* Analysis gave insight to the "accident-prone" person; it called attention to and tried to check and transform the myriad guises of masochism inherent in the pain-pleasure principle.

Survival is more basic than "adjustment." To survive is to win time. To survive in a state of physical health and psychic liberation is to enrich that time in a potentiality that has been realized by a long span of friendship, love, sustained effort and creative results. To know that one has the possibility and opportunity—however uncertified—to survive with so enhancing a perspective is to achieve a degree of hope and security that no amount of temporal personal riches, no matter how well hoarded, can proffer. The synergic principle in psychoanalysis—or, simply, psychosynergic dynamics—is devoted to that goal of longevity and creativity.

The principle of synergy is that of a "working together" in the human mind—and therefore psychosomatically—of all the components of survival. It includes not only a new view of the heart as a psychic organ of central importance; it looks upon the entire process of identification and one's talents as *directional*—or, better, as *cybernetic,* i.e., as a *steersman function* in human affairs. And, once one views the process of identification in this light, then it becomes important not only to make "good identifications"—to establish valid ideals—but to establish ideals adequate to a *true definition of self,* dedicated to its own individual and discriminate direction in the "voyage" of life. For, *it does no good* (however "good" one's identification may be) *to survive living someone else's life.* If human progress means anything, our ability to exist together in a moral society has for its prime purpose the triumph of the sense of individuality equipped, because of its very individuality, to pause as the Samaritan paused and to share as beings who speak the gift of the word.

Central to the principle of psychosynergic dynamics is a new view of the human heart as a psychic organ.

THE IMAGE OF THE HEART—ITS SYNERGIC ROLE

It is Freud who gives us the necessary clue—one which he himself might very well have pursued had he not had so many other more obvious aspects of anxiety to elucidate in the great welter of data available and pressing for elucidation at that time in the history of psychoanalysis. In his *Problem of Anxiety,* Freud (1926) points out that the heart and lungs are the organs most definitely productive of actual physical sensations peculiar to anxiety—and that, in addition, anxiety has a distinctive character of unpleasurable emotion—*a note of its own* is the way Freud puts it, making a musical or *sonic* attribute of the emotion of anxiety in his word "note." It was highly intuitive to use that word—*note.*

For, *the heart does produce its image in consciousness in large part by the sound that it makes.* It makes its presence felt in many other ways—each having a phasic quality like that of music—or, more pertinent to the heart, of *rhythm,* as in the various registrations of the pulse throughout the body, or again more specifically, in the "palpitation" of anxiety in which the heart rings out the alarm we feel like a clapper in an alarm clock. One patient described this "leap" of the heart in the chest like the sudden "kick" of a baby in the uterus when the mother "feels life"—a very important aspect of the various disguises by which *the image of the heart has hidden itself subtly.* Hence our esoteric dictum that there is no image of the heart in consciousness, a view which we now must change.

It is important to clarify this concept at once. No image of an object can be "registered" in the cortex of our brain unless that image stimulates specific organs at the end (*end organs*) of specific neural pathways that carry the composite qualities thus perceived to the sensory cortex. None of our internal organs do "register" in this way—except the heart, and to a much, much lesser extent the lungs. (For all practical purposes, the lungs may be considered as non-registrant except under certain situations of great stress—because we *do* breathe, and the sensations of "lungs" is mainly contained in the registering changes of tone produced by our respiratory muscles—by that tone and by a certain "lightness" or "heaviness," however intermingled with changes in the activity of the heart.) In this way, Nature ensures our internal organs a certain merciful autonomy—and by the same token frees our brains and our minds from the violent necessities of the vast and complex physiologic processes which take place every second of our lives.

Except for the heart. And here, Nature has produced an exception to the rule by making the heart perceptible *via a special hearing mechanism*—a mechanism which does not disturb the smooth functioning of internal autonomy and yet operates as an emergency information "corridor" through which the image of the heart may register upon the brain *sonically and rhythmically* and therefore emotionally. Every child knows that, in terror, his heart will not only "leap to his throat" but also "pound in his ears"; anyone who has ever had excessive fatigue will perceive this sound in a quiet room; or, in a swollen angry mass of inflamed tissue, the heartbeat will make itself evident in the throbbingly painful pulse.

For, *this is a mechanism of survival—this sonic image of the heart* given rhythm by its pulse felt everywhere in the body and given volumetric dimension by the sensations it produces within the chest. It appears in dreams indubitably though disguised; this concept has a thousand corroborations in our everyday language and in all languages spoken by man; "the heart" is where love resides, and the nucleus of all our meanings is "the heart of the matter," etc.

But it is to the synergic role of the image of the heart in psychodynamics that we must pay immediate attention. Here the meaning and affect of anxiety become clearer—we understand its peculiar note of insistent imminent catastrophe. Here too we perceive, however dimly, at last an important road to the fact that *premature coronary death* occurs predominantly in males up to forty years of age and that anxiety—in particular the violence of castration anxiety, as well as other kinds of "stress-anxiety," predominate in the male. We are able too, once we accept the concept of the image of the heart, to perceive the possibility that premature coronary disease is the result of *a continuous attack upon the heart from six years of age onward,* the major manifestation of a particular kind of neurotic development in childhood. (In this respect the life of Edgar Allan Poe is most suggestive;

he had "heart attacks" beginning in his twenties and was dead of his fourth attack by forty; with tremendous intuition, not only in his verse but also in his remarkable short story *The Tell-Tale Heart,* he projects the "image of the heart." This story will be analyzed in detail in this series of studies.)

The *physiologic* theories of coronary disease increase with each season both in numbers and in contradiction. . . . Take for example the recent "cholesterol" hypotheses. To hold causative a substance which, even if it is withdrawn from the diet, *will still be manufactured by the body* as Nature's "cement" for arterial patching, is to say that Nature is intent upon destroying the very structure she is repairing— a contradiction both in theory and in fact.

It is furthermore important to emphasize that when we speak of the image of the heart as existing in the textures of consciousness for the synergic purposes of survival and ego defense, we are not referring to an "abnormal condition"—we are not referring to the many "hysterical" or "neurasthenic" heart syndromes which have been described nor to that "cardiac psychosis" which comes as a result of various kinds of cardiac disease, decompensation, or defect, in a precariously poised neurotic personality. We are speaking instead of a distinct, however varying from individual to individual, image of the heart resident in the textures of consciousness at the very root of the human ego, obeying certain basic synergic necessities of survival and determining by its nature, extent, disguises and excursions *later quantitative difficulties* in making the proper identifications in life, in truly *defining* one's Self, and in establishing one's *directions* and, other things being equal, one's *longevity.*

The most simple manifestation of the principle of synergy in the mind of man as determined by the image of the heart is the so-called *psychosomatic syndrome,* many varieties of which exist; so many have in fact been described, the term is almost losing its specificity. But the clearest way to regard these syndromes is as *defenders of the heart.* Every analyst knows that the psychogenic syndrome, say, of ulcer is a particular *resolution of anxiety.* In the production of ulcer—not infrequently associated with other "psychosomatic syndromes"—the ego is spared a *constantly running anxiety* by the substitution of the symptom, an actual ulcer in the gut wall. If now we recognize that these are *deep* anxieties that are being stimulated and that the heart image at the root of the ego must first and foremost preserve the integrity of the entire body's circulation in relation to ego function, then a very simple defense exists. *The early pains of the nursing or feeding crises are reinstituted, the ego utilizes the pain to justify a deep helplessness and a new feeding regime, in a total regression* that has roots not simply in the desire for breast but even deeper *for prenatal narcissistic magic and shelter from those impulses which might otherwise make "the heart burst."* I repeat: every analyst of experience has surely remarked upon the fact that *each of these psychosomatic syndromes revives a very considerable root extending back into the most primitive past* when "viability" was first established in the mother's uterus and when at birth *the first act of ego independence is the burden of its own heart work.* Indeed, this has been one of the most stubborn problems of analytic theory—this unsuspectedly strong "narcissistic root" into the past; it is one of the reasons why analysis had to become a much longer process than was at first hoped; this was why "working through"—constantly "ironing out" similar aspects of various ego problems—had to be instituted; this is why some "analyses" are interminable: the root desires for magic and the accompanying helplessness away from the analyst are intractable; or, as the "interminable" patient will say—only in the analysis does he get "heart's ease." These facts, it is here maintained, point to the existence of a *synergistic principle* that has hitherto not been recognized—the desperate principle of the need to survive at all costs—the principle over which the image of the heart holds sway.

Or take, for example, the heart syndrome of *paroxysmal auricular tachycardia* which might indeed be named "the neurosis of the runaway heart"—several cases of which will be described in this series of studies. Up to very recently—indeed in most places in the country—this condition has been treated not by the psychoanalyst or psychiatrist as it should be; it is treated by the general practitioner and the cardiologist—and yet every experienced physician knows that for the most part (there are important exceptions) it is a syndrome of emotional origin best treated by sedatives and reassurance together with such adjuncts as quinidine, etc. *Again, as in premature coronary death, it is a syndrome which predominates in the male,* though attacks in women are not uncommon. The attack itself is telltale: abruptly, apparently without warning, the heart rate of the paroxysmal attack *leaps* into a range anywhere from 140–250 beats per minute (it may go as high as 350 per minute)—a range which is precisely within the limits of the *intrauterine rate of the foetal heart.* It is so clearly a "heart in flight" as almost to beggar discussion. For here, the heart symbolizes, naked of defense, *an ego threatened with dismemberment,* as in certain violent forms of rape-dismemberment-murder, so that the paroxysmal onset—so abrupt—recapitulates the hiatus of birth in the regressive direction, toward magical shelter. As a matter of fact, patients with this syndrome will describe the beginning of an attack as the result of a certain kind of breathing belonging to fantasies of birth. But in this syndrome, the meaning of its occurrence is clear only when one recognizes that here *the heart is the child,* in symbolic language; or, the image of the heart dominates the synergic principle determining the survival of the ego and its many defenses in terms of fright, flight, and fight.

We thus arrive at a very greatly simplified definition of anxiety—a problem that could not hitherto be solved. *Anxiety is the disturbed synergy between the image of the heart and the ego in general.* In this way anxiety "warns" the ego, as Freud put it, of approaching danger, either from outside the ego or from within. It is *not* that, *accompanying anxiety,* there are commonly heart (and lung) sensations—as Freud thought, and hence arrived at an impasse in his attempt to solve the actual nature of anxiety; it is rather that there is normally a synergy —a working together—of the image of the heart and the rest of the ego for the purpose of survival. And *sometimes the dyssynergy is so great that an actual physical sensation* of heart "palpitation" results; more often this is relatively slight and instead there is the well-known vague sense of "foreboding"—of "imminent disaster" of an ill-defined kind, but with its characteristic *note* nonetheless. For "heart's ease" is never so difficult to obtain as in a human being who believes magically, consciously or unconsciously, that his *survival* will be cut short—

that his days are numbered by an angry God—and that "castration" in terms of *foreshortened time for the ego* is his *impending doom.*

It is in the dream—the dream is the royal road to the unconscious—that the image of the heart may be clearly seen, however subtle and masking its disguises.

Take the dream symbol of the *hourglass* with its two chambers and its back-and-forth circulating "sand." Such a symbol may be interpreted as many different things depending upon the context of associations and the textures of actions embedded in the gemlike facets of the dream. At the same time, no matter what sexual "radiance" the hourglass symbol sends out, it is basically and indubitably a dream image of the heart. *Observe that its walls do not beat as the heart walls beat,* and this is its secret! The heart appears in dreams as a *flask* or a *vessel* (cf. the word "blood vessel") or a double vessel like the hourglass but *always with walls that are stationary and static,* no matter how dynamic the action of the symbol (e.g., as in the dream symbol of the *pump*). The reason for this is in accord with everything we know about dreams and about the heart—*the heart image appears in response to the magic wish for restful cardiac standstill*—for its walls to rest while the machinery of the circulation operates nonetheless. An organism that could achieve this would be practically "immortal," if "a man is as old as his heart and his arteries!"

But, in addition to the wish for magic cardiac standstill which helps to disguise the image of the heart from consciousness, there is another and even more cogent disguise, a technique of wearing a coat of many colors in many different kinds of light. The heart—as all colloquial speech in every human tongue tells us—is psychically a dual organ. In the symbolizations of our dreams, the heart is not simply a circulating work-machine, it is also the basic wellspring of erotic feeling and as such may represent practically every aspect of sexuality. For example, many years ago, Jenny Waelder Hall (1935) in Vienna reported the analysis of a boy with "heart pain" and she was able to show that "heart" also meant "genital." In the same case, although Jenny Waelder Hall did not draw the connection, the boy connected in his mind the fluttering of the heart, as seen through the thin chest wall of one of his boy friends, with "babies." This occurred in the boy's mind when he and his friend were interrupted at a game of *making babies*—twenty or so "babies" a day. In other words, in children the heart may not only equate symbolically to genital; it may also, as we have already noted in paroxysmal auricular tachycardia, symbolize the "unborn child." Indeed this is one of the ways in which the male with pregnancy fantasies may "feel life"—and such a repressed imaginary "baby" as the heart would be incapable of emerging unless (*as is frequent in the male child's fantasy*) the child emerges *in the precordial area between the breasts*. It is not surprising therefore to find in the analysis of men with the "coronary character," complaining of mild precordial or radiating pain traveling down the left arm, that they feel *throttled* by the various "walls" of their life—so deeply, literally at the level of birth, does the first act of postnatal existence identify the newly independent heart with the very ego itself. For the moment of birth is not simply the first breath of air, the first sensation of light and the external sounds of the world—the moment of birth is that profound circulatory hiatus which marks out the first freedom of the mother from the child—the child's heart beats fully on its own at the same moment that its ego takes its first root in outside reality.

Thus a male patient, in his late forties, with the typical money-mad, hard-driving, ambitious, hurrying characteristics of the "coronary man," could never sleep on his left side *from earliest childhood on*. His rationalization was not only the disturbing sound of the heart beating in his ear and the wonder "would it ever stop?" but also the terror that, in the left position, his other organs would crowd his heart and stifle it. He was the baby of his family—his heart was the baby of his body. Everything in his psychology rotated around this deep identification of himself with his mother "pregnant" with his own heart. A thinly concealed, violently defended, severe passive homosexuality and paranoid attitudes rounded out the portrait of the "coronary man."

In summary, these clinical observations, to be presented in much greater detail subsequently, suggest that, *in the male particularly*, castration threats of childhood and other developmental events may drive him not only to equate heart with genital but even to identify heart with "child"—with his own perpetually unborn ego to which everything not immediately gratifying is an insult *in a continuous attack upon the heart from at least six years of age onward.* The result may be "heart pain" in childhood itself, as Jenny Waelder Hall's (1953) case showed—and it may be associated with severe night terrors in childhood, as one would expect. Sleep—even in adult life, is fitful —with a "troubled heart." Finally, recent U.S. Army statistics bear this orientation out most strikingly. Enos, Holmes, and Beyer (1953) —officers of the Army—studied the incidence and severity of coronary disease among U.S. soldiers killed in action in Korea. Three hundred autopsies were performed and the coronary arteries dissected. *The average age of this group was 22.1 years.* In 77.3 per cent of the cases, some *gross* evidence of coronary disease was demonstrated that varied from "fibrous" thickening to complete occlusion of one or more of the main branches.

Such a trend is statistically significant of long-standing stress, long before the sudden shocking premature coronary death in the late thirties or early forties in the men involved.

How closely the birth process of circulatory and ego transition is mirrored in the transference situation and how much it marks out *the role of the image of the heart*—the *sonic* image—in the dependent attitudes of the ego may be seen from the following situation and dream close to the end of an analysis:

A woman whose analysis, it was agreed one day, would come to an end in July—a month before her birthday—dreamt on that night of decision that she had been riding on a pleasant jaunt in the caboose of a strange little locomotive. Quite suddenly, the little locomotive stopped, backed up and went off on a spur track which ended abruptly and the jaunt was over *with a bump* sooner than she thought it should have finished. *All this time,* as the locomotive backed up and went off on the terminal spur, she could hear the regular *chug-chug-chug* of the locomotive—not only *in* her ears—but as though, too, her ears were up against the body of the engine. The pulsing sound was the most prominent thing in the dream.

There can be no doubt that the dream, among other things, symbolizes the end process of pregnancy and intrauterine life. The dream delineates her premature "rebirth"—the conclusion of her analysis one month before her birthday. The sound is not only the beating of her own heart in her ears but also the beating of her supportive mother's heart (here the analytic "locomotive"). This would seem to be clearly suggestive of the idea of *the sonic image of the heart.*

Once one becomes aware of this factor in dreams, the symbols of this category mount up literally into hundreds of thousands of permutations and combinations. It is as though the basic image of the heart at the root of the ego—composed of sensations of sound and rhythmic power—extends itself into every aspect of language, music and design —into symbols of songs as well as symbols of engines and strangely constructed flasks of all kinds. And this is the way "anxiety" warns us: the sonic image of the heart has its tendrils in all our associations of any dangerous essence—*and the dyssynergy between the image of the heart and the rest of the ego*—the recoil of the heart image and all its "branching arteries of thought and feeling"—*is the meaning of anxiety,* a meaning so long sought, in psychoanalytic theory.

A brief note here on Otto Rank's theory of the "birth trauma." We can now see even more clearly why Rank's concept of birth as basic to the neurosis is in error, as Freud stated in his *Problem of Anxiety* (1926).

The problem of birth transition, as is shown in the dream just described, is that of separation from the shelter, nutrition, *and the circulation of the mother.* The first act of the human postnatal ego is also the last "act" of the intrauterine child, namely: its first breath, its first outcry as it established for all time the closure of the foramen ovale and *its own independent circulation and its own heart work.* The heart "leaps" to its new "plateau" and to its new task—and new and definitive images begin to impinge, however vaguely, however magically, upon its perception at the very same moment. It is a hiatus of bright light, loud sound, lower temperature and a revolution within heart, lungs and brain—an individual *Genesis,* the prototype of all danger—all narrow straits navigated—of all "anxiety"—a word whose very derivation points always to this *transition of the heart.* It is for this reason that Freud—not Rank—was correct; the problem is that of the condition and effect of *separation* from the "beloved" object for male and for female; and this makes castration the cataclysmic threat it is to the male; he faces this threat an entire lifetime.

Observe now that this very hiatus, this very epoch of separation, **is** at once *dual* in all its implications: it is not simply the increased heart work (for which the child is now prepared); it is increased heart work plus the discomforts—if discomforts there are at the transition—of *separation the forerunner of the castration threat.* The image of the heart thus becomes the first and basic ego-sexual image of independence and separation—to the healthy child, and of "rejection" and "castration" to the mentally sick child. How much the heart "sounds" its terror in the ears of the child being born we shall never know; but we can safely predict that *the image of the heart* will be etched into place, with individual variability, at this point of our existence to dominate our psychosynergy, and to sound the warning of anxiety, in all later experiences having the significance of dangerous transition from within or from without—from within *to* without.

The psychosynergic action of the image of the heart at the root of the postnatal ego has a relation to sleeping and dreaming as well; its role in survival is mediated in many ways and in none more important than in the still poorly understood psychophysiology of sleep; at this point, we can do no more than state that there is evidence that *the essence of the terrified awakening in night terrors is due to the severe effect upon the conduction mechanism of the heart* of certain kinds of psychic traumata inflicted upon the child during the day. *And this kind of trauma would over many years*—by affecting the very conditions of circulation in the heart—*produce the psychic components of injury to the coronary arteries.* Thus Jenny Waelder Hall's case of "heart pain" in a child was also and mainly *a case of night terrors.* In subsequent studies in this series, evidence will be presented in detail with reference to this crucial factor. But we can now, immediately, see the significance of *the dream as the guardian of sleep* in relation to heart rest and to longevity. For, the traumatized child who *must awake to reassure itself of its integrity*—who cannot "dream out" the impulses of conflict—is a child then whose heart will be under continuous attack from at least six years of age onward. In this connection evidence has been collected, in the course of these studies, indicating that a certain number of the "coronaries" have long-standing insomnia of very severe degree.

But in order to establish, with as much conclusiveness as possible, *the concept of the image of the heart as the basic psychosynergic mechanism of the postnatal ego,* the following case—and dream—is cited:

A single man of forty-nine with a known cardiac defect proven since childhood—an interauricular septal defect—with actual abnormal admixture of arterial and venous blood, but well compensated, arranges to take a woman for an affair to an apartment in the top story of a "walk-up" building. They walk up the long flights together and he—out of fear that he will be "rejected" if he shows his respiratory distress by slowing down—does not rest at the landings and continues steadily with her up to the top. He knows she is aware of his discomfort since she perceives it and is furthermore acquainted with his heart condition. But she seems—to him—sadistically to challenge him because she does not *insist* upon his climbing slowly or resting on the long ascent. Jokingly, when she saw him puff on the way up, she said: "Shall I carry you up?"

They enter the apartment. He sits down on a sofa—his heart dancing in his chest and beating in his throat—he is utterly spent and frightened. She sits down on a chair across the room. Still concealing from her the high degree of his fear, he lies down, as though casually, on the sofa,—and in a moment—not intending to—he falls asleep. When he awakens forty-five minutes later, she is gone and does not return. In the interim, he dreamt.

He dreamt that he was installed, curled up and "dozing with one eye open," in one *compartment* of a huge flask or bottle, a great perfume bottle, literally Gargantuan in size, with a very, very long neck and a *heart-shaped* lower portion. Air came in via the long neck—to be apportioned out, strangely enough by the woman herself, who stood upright within the Gargantuan bottle, in such a way that her head and shoulders were thrust upward into the inlet part of the neck—at its junction with the "heart" of the great flask. By her position in the center of the bottle, she could alter the pressure and direction of the air coming in the long neck; in this manner *she could shut off his air* and give the vital oxygen *to her child who lay curled up in the other com-*

partment of the flask on the other side of the woman. **The great test**
of the dream was: "Whose air will she shut off—mine or her child's?
Who will be loved more and be permitted to survive, her child or I?"
Or, as he later put it, this was the heart of the matter and the matter
of the heart.

In this dream it is at once clear that the "two compartments" are
deceptively like a uterus with a "twin pregnancy," and most analysts
would assuredly, and justifiably, on the basis of standard theory interpret the dream as one of great helplessness, "intrauterine narcissistic
aggression," and intense sibling rivalry with a death wish for the rival
child. Certainly the woman can be easily conceived of as the hostile
mother, neglectful and cruel (she had remarked satirically: *shall I
carry you up?*). This "two-compartmented container" bears a considerable resemblance in this respect to the *hourglass symbol* discussed
before.

But a little care and accuracy will reveal that this is no simple intrauterine fantasy—though thousands of dreams are interpreted every
day in this light. There *is* a reason for its having *a connection* with
intrauterine life in which the mother assuredly breathes for the child,
and *the position* of the man and the child in the dream is assuredly
that of the foetal posture. Nevertheless discriminative study shows
that it can only be *his own heart at magic cardiac standstill* which is
pictured in the dream; in this way—*by standstill and survival,* a paradox magically resolved—he tries to reach back into the narcissistic
perfection of the past. *Indeed this is why he fell asleep*—for only sleep
could have provided *both rest and tension release via the mechanism
of the dream.* Here is the very powerful relationship between sleep
and the image of the heart, and the action of the conduction mechanism which is allayed and sedated by sleep; the situation of this dream
is the very reverse of night terrors—as a matter of fact it is possible to
coin the phrase: "day terror" for this set of circumstances. *The principle of psychosynergy is here seen to operate in an indisputable laboratory demonstration.*

Examine this "perfume" bottle and its architecture. Like the hourglass, it is neatly divided into two precise compartments. The human
heart does have its two compartments (the "right" heart and the "left"

heart) while the uterus does not. Observe further the position of the woman *in* the bottle, controlling the supply of air. She is *within* the heart-shaped flask—it is *not within her;* nor is this an inversion of that image of her uterus to deny his helplessness (the general kind of objection that would be offered). Rather it has another and more basic meaning connected with the long air-inlet (the neck of the bottle) which he instantly called an "air-passage—like the one in the neck"— namely the *trachea,* indicating the emphasis here on the *lung* portion of the image of the heart (the trachea or air-inlet is frequently tagged on; the hourglass symbol specifically erases the trachea to accent the circulating "blood"—*sand*). While the air-passage might be taken conceivably to mean the vaginal outlet from the uterus—and the long, long neck mean the seemingly interminable passage of birth, then we would still have the "two compartments" to deal with in that case. We cannot have it both ways.

But what stamps this dream even more clearly as the image of the heart is the particular and individual dilemma of this man's life— specifically, the dilemma of the compartments or "heart chambers." He had, it will be remembered, an *interauricular septal defect,* the septum which, in part together with its ventricular portion, divides the heart into two compartments. As a result of this defect a portion of the blood which should have gone into the lungs for oxygenation was instead with each beat of his heart pumped directly into the left auricle to mix with the arterial blood returning from the lungs.[1] From childhood on his problems in life centered around that desperate defect of the septum dividing his heart. *The position of the woman in the bottle is precisely the position of the septum;* his *survival* is determined by the way she moves, to right or to left. And, because of his neurosis, she is as dangerous to him—with her "sexual defect"—the vaginal opening in her body, as is the defect of the septum itself. *He fell asleep in order to avoid sexual intercourse*—he was deeply afraid that this particular woman with her particular kind of sexuality *would destroy him.* The issue was desperate. He was having a "day terror" and, *resolving it psychosynergically,* he fell asleep and dreamt *in order to live.*

[1] The admixture is in both directions through the defect.

We can now evaluate the "intrauterine" portions of the dream which are layered upon and condensed into the image of the heart. Her remark during the climb—*Shall I carry you up?*—and her preoccupations with her own child whom she *has borne* and therefore "carried," link his own "heart problem" to that of mother and to a time when he was within mother and she did his heart work and breathing for him. The "intrauterine fantasy" is made necessary *only because of the image of the heart at standstill*—the magic of eternity.

Finally, we become aware how much *too invasive and pervasive an image of the heart will produce quantitative and directional problems* so that *the later synergies* of hererosexual identification, talent and realistic thinking with the image of the heart will be *disbalanced* in terms of the latter's constant "warnings" and need for literally mountains of security, reassurance, wealth, and magic—the underlying needs of the "coronary man." For, add the threat of "castration" to such an image of the heart, and the entire conduction system and arterial stability of the organism must be put under premature and pathologic stress.

Here again one is impelled to recommend a study of the life of Edgar Allan Poe as a classical case of an almost "malignant," because so invasive and pervasive, image of his heart—and hence his impotence, his addiction, his poetry to the heart and his stories of "night and day terror," and inevitably his own premature death at forty of his fourth "heart attack." Marie Bonaparte's (1949) very voluminous tome on Poe's life and works unfortunately completely missed its most important opportunity.

A Brief Outline of the Psychosynergic Dynamics of "Heart Attack"

Against the background of the foregoing considerations, the premise is here offered, in the very briefest outline form, that—except for certain relatively rare exceptions of congenital, inherited, or infectious arteriolar disease—*premature coronary death in relatively young men is the result of a most severe, though masked, continuous onslaught against the child and the image of the heart from six years of age onward*, the heaviest blows falling within the first three years of postnatal life, and gradually "covered over" by six to eight years. Indeed, such a child may be considered as having had a childhood neurosis of terrifying proportions, against which a certain kind of compensation is marshaled so that the child is described as having been "perfectly normal." The analysis of case histories and the *in vivo* analysis of such men in the analytic situation invariably shows that *they have never had normal lives,* that on the contrary almost every moment of their existence in adult life is *shot through with fantasy,* a fantasy generally concealed from every one, particularly from those nearest and dearest, i.e., from wives and children, and for very good and cogent reasons. Such men quite generally—*before their first coronary attack* —will avoid psychoanalysis with vehement denunciation of all psychologic approaches. One of their "characteristics" upon which they openly pride themselves is their "objectivity" and their "realism" which in private they consider a genius for "superreality."

Indeed it is by now common knowledge, no matter what appearances are put upon the shockingly premature death of these unfortunate men (and rarely women), that they have these basic telltale traits, as they mature into adolescence and adult life—so much common knowledge that we find them listed in the "health columns" of newspapers. These traits—apart from their association in a number of cases with diabetes and hypertension—are the following:

(1) They are under a peculiar "controlled tension"; this tension itself spells security—and relaxation, paradoxically, spells danger. Even if they have a coronary attack which warns them of an urgent necessity to change their entire mode of existence, their "goals" and their values, they generally cannot wait to "get back to work"—and will thus not uncommonly have *a second and fatal attack* within months or a year.

(2) They are generally—however "sweet" their manner—in *a physical hurry* which, if thwarted, will produce outbursts of intense hate. (A wife giving a history of her dead husband's characteristics will suppress this almost universal detail.) Their *hurry* is not uncommonly contained even in *a hurrying gait*—they are fond of making an impression with a very "intent kind of walk," indeed their gait is a sort of signature to their personalities. They believe they are hurrying

toward something, whereas unconsciously, they are *hurrying away from a deeply concealed dread.*

(3) They are ridden by ambition in a way peculiar to them—in a way belonging to their intense and secret fantasy. Their attitude to money or to fame or to work itself is distinctly different from the attitudes commonly held by most relatively and more healthily ambitious men. This difference is marked out by the fact that severe or fatal attacks occur just after "success" as well as after "humiliation." In the legal situations of life, for example, the "accuser" is as likely to develop an attack—particularly if his accusation is successful—as is the "accused." The accuser who will have a "coronary" will develop paranoid terror before his attack; the accused will develop crushing guilt and worthlessness following the humiliation of the accusation itself— *for he must never be accused of anything.*

From the psychosynergic point of view—as is theoretically to be expected—too invasive and pervasive an image of the heart will produce a heavy reliance both upon "conspiracy" and upon "deceit," upon conniving and upon evasion, upon *a fatal magic,* in brief. And, as the work of Edgar Allan Poe tells us, it stimulates the imagination to dwell upon every kind of above-ground and underground torment and dissolution of self—setting free impulses of such primitive quality that the resultant self-condemnation must constantly be "watered down" *if one is to avoid suicide itself.* Thus, not a few people who will ultimately have absolutely or relatively premature coronary attacks will secretly wrestle with suicide—the way out of this dilemma is one or another attempt at *self-purification.* And, both for the "accuser" and the "accused," therefore, the matter of self-purification is of the essence; the humiliated has been denied his immunity from accusation; the accuser has exposed himself to a seemingly deserved destruction—hence his paranoia.

One such patient who had an anginal syndrome as the final development of an entire galaxy of "psychosomatic syndromes," including hay fever, rose fever, asthma, sinusitis, constipation, vertigo, and tinnitus, etc., came into analysis only by coincidence, so to speak. He was a very "realistic" business man; it took him several months to admit that every day of his life as far back as he could remember was occupied with wild "success" or "hero" fantasy. He had amassed considerable money and had always believed that what he wanted to do was to retire—every day of his life was spent calculating how much money would accrue if a certain rate of interest could be achieved. Like all such men—whether their "coin" be money, prestige, or power—there was never enough; and the coin was cherished for itself, not as a medium of exchange whereby life might be lived more fully. This particular man, in his forties, discovered that he had calculated his "interest" up to two decades in advance. His thinking process was almost entirely magical though he had always assumed it to be "practical"—it rested upon his identification with his mother, whereas his *working* activity, as a routine, rested upon his identification with an uncle. He prided himself on being known for his *"very fast, very purposeful walk"* which he liked commented upon by all and sundry. It was part of his great "efficiency" and "superrealism." In three years of analysis, all of his psychosomatic syndromes disappeared—and the conquest of the anginal syndrome itself followed from his recognition of the terrified, invasive and pervasive image of the heart which had prevented him from ever knowing who he was really and what he wanted to do with his life. All else in life—such was the nature of his mother's thinking process—had to be subordinated to the "practical" aspects of money.

The three traits cited thus far—the "controlled tension," the "hurry and hurrying gait," and the constant need for "self-purification" or "immunity"—are all illustrated in this man, one of whose dreams demonstrates the deeply primitive impulses at work *in the production of anginal pain*. He was awakened one night with pain over the precordium following this dream:

He dreamt that he sat down to table and that his wife served him a cooked dog for dinner. On close inspection, he saw that it was his very own dog which was to eat. Abruptly the dog opened his eyes and rolled them up, as though pleading for pity. Nevertheless the dreamer stuck the prongs of his fork into the flank of the dog—and *at that juncture* awoke with precordial pain of a "sticking" variety.

The curious thing about the dream was that it led to a deeply concealed fact. The patient's brother had died of heart disease and the patient had to sleep *in that brother's bed with him.* By coincidence, his dog had been named with a name very similar in sound to that of his dead brother. From earliest childhood, he had—because of the voluble concern about his brother's heart—been aware of the fact that a human being has *a heart which can stop.* He lived in constant terror of his own heart stopping—a terror which seemed to have disappeared by the time he was eight years of age—even though his brother did not die until three years later, and at night, in that very bed in which he slept, so that one morning he awoke to find his brother a corpse. Yet for three years he had ceased to have any preoccupations with his own heart; what remained was a residual conviction that, *for one reason or another,* he would not live past his brother's age. Sticking the prongs of the fork in the dog associated in his mind with the phrase of our competitive business age—*dog eat dog.* This actual dramatization of cannibalism disturbed him until he was brought to realize that this was a re-exposure of the manner in which he had identified with a brother terrified of his heart disease; by eight, the patient had completed his identification (cannibalistic incorporation) with his dying brother and *repressed very powerfully* all conscious connections with the idea of heart failure. Nevertheless, every one of his numerous "psychosomatic syndromes" could be shown to bear a relationship to this epoch which strengthened his conscious determination to be like his mother who had lived to a ripe old age—at least to *think* as she did. The anginal pain is the *retaliation*—the recoil of his own prongs in the flank of the dying dog. *Dog eat dog* does him no good, since he too may be eaten.[2] But the most crucial factor of all—and one also operating in the childhood of Edgar Allan Poe—was the factor of *hunger.* In his childhood, he had often been acutely hungry—and at night, now in his adult life, the moment he came home and had his dinner, he had to keep eating compulsively all evening until just before he went to bed. (He couldn't bear doctors who told him to diet because he knew that *he had to keep eating and smoking* all night until he was overcome by sleep.) This did not disappear until he realized that his

---

[2] I.e., his heart may be eaten; the prongs of the fork were "teeth." Compare this with the expression "Don't eat your heart out." There are many people to whom the eating of the heart of fowl or beast (chicken, beef) is violently taboo.

image of the heart had made him utterly dependent upon his mother, and that hence the feminine and passive homosexual elements in him had *enormously increased quantitatively*—with only a sick brother and a remote uncle to counter the feminine influences, since his father had died before he was born.

(There is in brief a tremendous difference technically when one can impart the concept of the image of the heart to a human being who is motivated by it and who has spent a lifetime trying to "quiet" it. And, similarly with all the major "interpretation posts" of psychoanalysis. A patient comprehends quite naturally the intrauterine magic situation when it is explained to him as a situation in which *mother's heart does the work* which he fears his own body can not do. There is a profoundly powerful relationship here to the unsolved problem of *transvestism*—and the recently mutilating Danish surgery; for in the analysis of "coronary" types, one finds, coherently enough, partial transvestite impulses, as one would expect from the psychosynergic approach to the basic goal of survival. For if, symbolically, *the heart is the child,* then the transvestite is an extreme example of modeling his *body after mother's* and thus acquiring her "heart"—instead of the genitals and pride of manhood.[3] In this manner psychosynergic dynamics may lead to a better technique of handling the transvestite than has hitherto obtained.)

(4) In addition then to the traits of "controlled tension," "hurry and hurrying gait," and "self-purification or immunity," we may now add the evidences of a "healed split" in the identification processes of childhood, giving rise to partial transvestite impulses which are utterly concealed and denied. The "coronary man" gets married to avoid and dispel this problem within himself—and hence comes his vehement denunciation of all psychologic approaches—hence his "superrealism" and the trait of "superpaternalism," a particularly annoying trait which may produce constant disturbances not only in the handling of his children but also in his business associates. Not a few cases of

---

[3] This formulation holds for adults of both sexes. The "passive attitude" may be defined, in one sense, as wanting mother's heart to do all the work. Conversely, the state of *mobilization* is the most difficult to achieve—and the most desirable answer to the state of "passive masochism."

"coronaries" are men who cannot work together with others because of their "superpaternalism" and their "superreal genius."

It is important to stress that the "coronary" man is neither manic-depressive nor schizophrenic—he is rather a product of a profound psychic "scar" which needs to be resolved by the most thorough analysis. For as long as it exists, the patient will be the victim of a curious duality in his life which, however much he seems "devoted to one subject," nevertheless tugs at him in perpetual conflict. These men, for example, never have "hobbies" the way other men have. It does not matter whether the "hobby" is an athletic game such as tennis or golf, or an art such as painting or music. The "hobby" becomes a desperate issue, and so much energy is devoted to it in secret fantasy concerning it and in other ways, that they finally are forced to "hurry" to their "vocation" in a most rapid and "purposeful manner," as already detailed.

This is the typical story of a man now dead of a coronary at forty-two as described by his closest friend: "When he played golf, if the shot didn't go right, he would go into a violent rage and fling the golf club away with all his might. . . . He had a coronary attack a year ago. The doctor told him to stop smoking. It would have been easier for him to have cut his tongue out—he kept right on smoking two to three packs of cigarettes a day. . . . He would always say his sense of reality was absolutely beyond question." Every one knows this description—hence the popular belief that "heart attack comes from worry and aggravation." The burden of this paper is the opposite—the worry and the aggravation originate from the very early "heart attack" in the life of the child, from the conditions of his birth, from the conditions of his feeding, from the conditions of castrative threats directed against him and the cumulative effects of his "night terrors" *and* "day terrors," from the magic thinking that thus arises to becloud a lifetime.

Even if the patient be an accomplished scientist, he is not immune from the internal threat of magic thinking which has to be kept under constant revision; hence the trait of "controlled tension."

(5) The fifth and final dyssynergic attribute in the analysis of the "coronary man" is the blow to his inborn talent which in general he must in one way or another deny or destroy. As a "superrealist" even

if he is highly gifted—and frequently he is very highly endowed—he can never permit his talents to interfere with his drive toward a "goal." For the psychic split and the psychic scar involve particularly the freedom of spontaneous "inspiration." The very upsurge—the very "creative thrust" from the unconscious, as it was named in my studies of the psychology of the artist—is met not by a wholehearted "creative mastery" but instead by a "superreal" caution—by a strangely self-suspecting, again self-purifying "let's see what we have here" until the spontaneous feeling is quite completely dissected away into lifeless fragments. (In Edgar Allan Poe we have an exception which proves the rule: his addiction to drugs and to alcohol made it possible for his creative impulses to get "by," though his sexuality never could; his wife died virginal.) All the evidence gathered at this writing indicates that *the man who dies a premature coronary death has a personality the very antithesis of the creative artist.* And this jibes with the fact, now well known, that "heart attack" is the scourge of the professional worker—the "hurrying" physician, the "controlled tense" precision scientist, the "self-purifying or humiliated" attorney, the "superrealistic" business man.

A simplified view, then, of the psychosynergic dynamics of premature coronary disease is that at the end of their oedipal development, the human beings susceptible to this disease, will, at great cost, finally turn into "normal" heterosexual identification but only as a "healing shell" over a quantitatively powerful passive feminine identification with mother; this latter is itself not the eruptive force which threatens the shell of heterosexuality; the eruptive force is the too invasive and pervasive image of the heart whose "branching arteries of thought and feeling" too continuously ring the alarm in the voyage through life— one of the greatest "alarms" being the deep tendency to an inner transvestism or one or another mutilation of the ego—in order to have "mother's heart"—a state of conflict directly releasing very primitive impulses and a corresponding retaliation upon the conduction mechanism (as in paroxysmal auricular tachycardia) or upon the arteries supplying that mechanism (anginal pain). A sufficient number of such "eruptive alarms" with such an effect upon the cardiac synergic mechanism and its arteries, day after day, year after year, should not surprise us if it produces, as the Army statistics quoted above show conclusively, *gross coronary disease in 77.3 per cent of cases whose average age is 22.1 years!*

This orientation to the problem of "heart attack" in no way invalidates medical research into *abnormal* cholesterol metabolism; indeed it perhaps increases its importance particularly because of the need for the "smoothest patch" possible, if patch there must be at the point of stress and strain in the arterial or arteriolar wall. At the same time, our psychosynergic approach does indicate that all such physiologic research work will have to take into account that part of the human body which is above the chin; it will have to take into account the psychosynergy of the image of the heart and its later dynamic relationships to identification, thinking and talent developments of the human ego.

For, the entire nervous system exists not so much for "reflex coordinations" as once we were taught; it exists for the integration of power and the realization of potentiality in order that the *synergies* it institutes between "brawn and brain" should result in "mind" and in *survival* with all that maximum life has to offer a healthy mind in a healthy body.

Chapter II

THREE DREAMS OF THE DISGUISED
HEART IMAGE

PERHAPS the fundamental reason why the basic and synergic image of the heart in consciousness has been disguised in dreams is the fact that it is first and foremost a sonic image with certain vague, almost amorphous, but nevertheless tangible, even tactile components. A thing heard as the heart's beat is heard—felt as the heart's beat is felt in palpitation or in the pulse at the various peripheries and planes of the body is capable of creating a sense of pressure or heaviness in the entire chest because of its effect upon the lungs (the sense of "volumetric" expansiveness and lightness or constriction and heaviness). Such an image must, of deep physiologic and psychic necessity, be synergically compounded with the other more defined and definitive effort and emotional images of the ego. Indeed, the principle of synergy, devoted to survival and longevity, demands such a compounding; otherwise "the bells would not toll"; the image of the heart as it spreads pulsewise through the ego warns by tending to retract and to separate from[1] the other images in the ego; it refuses to concur— whether out of neurotic or real assessment of whatever danger—it refuses to concur with the ego in its impending course and direction; in such a situation one may express this feeling in its various gradations all the way from "not wholeheartedly in favor" to "downright anxious" or "abjectly terrified" depending upon the inner tempest and the tolling of alarm.

It is not necessary to recite the interminable list, in all languages

---

[1] This moment of retraction and separation of the image of the heart from the rest of the ego is the moment of anxiety.

spoken by man, of this compounding—as expressed by intuitive human speech—of the image of the individual heart with the other images of one's personal universe. What is necessary, however, is the recognition of the innumerable sonic branchings of this basic synergic compound in language and thought structures of all kinds. For example, there is little doubt that the sonic function of rhyme—which we see disturbed in the clang association of mania[2]—carries this self-preserving sonic synergy up to the finest and most complex aborizations of our plastic or routine thinking, however illuminated by our vision, and however we think of reality as visual, enhanced by the seductive coloration of outer light. If nothing else, the etymology of the word "anxiety" foretells this fact of sonic-respiratory alarm, derived as it is from *angor*, meaning strangulation, i.e., the compressional danger to the heart (and lungs) as the natal child passes through all "narrow straits," out of the mother's body at birth into life and out of life through the strait-passage at death. As Freud taught us, this "separation anxiety" of birth and death—not any birth trauma or death fear as such—is basic, and so reaches its acme during mortal existence, in the masculine terror of the image (and actuality) of separation from the male genital—"castration anxiety." Thus it is that in waking the heart actually carries the burdens of its image compounded and compounding with the external world as the outwardly oriented and outwardly perceptive ego moves in that world.

This is the psychic essence of "neurocirculatory integration." A particular set of perceptions may thus raise the blood pressure, set the heart to racing or produce that curious sense of a "stuffed bosom" which Shakespeare correctly designated in Macbeth:

> Canst thou not minister to a mind diseased,
> Pluck from the memory a rooted sorrow,
> Raze out the written troubles of the brain
> And with some sweet oblivious antidote
> Cleanse the stuffed bosom of that perilous stuff
> Which weighs upon the heart?

[2] It may be said, in an entirely new formulation, that the manic's terrified heart has leaped "out of his throat" into his mouth, i.e., into his speech. Similarly in the mild mania of love, it is said "the lover wears his heart on his sleeve."

And, as is most evident in what is called "the stroke" of old age (or of high blood pressure), the actual sonic signaling system of anxiety can be broken down by destruction or paralysis of the word area of the brain (aphasia) with paralysis of half of the body (hemiplegia) and a fall in blood pressure telling us where the brunt of the burden has fallen over the years—the area subserving the integration of sonic images and body effort (the internal capsule of the brain).

From this point of view, one perceives the function of sleep in a new way with a heart-purpose "to ravel up" the unraveled "sleave of care"—i.e., to release the image of the heart from its compoundings, and so to give true heart rest. Hence the wisdom of Freud's adage: the function of dreams is to guard sleep—to which we now add: and sleep releases the image of the heart from the burden of its compoundings. The night terrors of children who are thus awakened may be associated with heart pain (see the case of Anton quoted in Chapter I). And, from this we may see that the actual pacemakers and synchronizers (the conduction bundle of His) of the heart within the central partition of the heart chambers stand in dynamic synergic relationships to the image of the heart within the ego. In night terrors, this disturbance of synergy is so intense that release demands awakening; the ego can not "dream it out" while asleep.

In a very important sense, then, not only will there be dreams in which the heart image (with magically stationary "resting" walls) will appear in one disguise or another, but also all dreaming—and our theory of dreams and the neuroses—must include sleep among other aspects of the defense of the image of the heart.

Otherwise dreaming and sleeping would have no synergic restful purpose, as daily rebirth, and the principle of synergy in psychoanalysis would be lost to us. In these dreams, especially in night terrors, we may see the effect of changes in heart rate, blood pressure, heart fatigue, heart synchronization—once we learn to insert the multiple meanings of the image of the heart. Night terror teaches us the prototype of all hallucination; the image of the heart controls the key to waking consciousness. When the image of the heart "compounds" itself with reality images, it "engages" the external world once more and we awaken; when the image of the heart tends to "retract," we experience anxiety; when the image of the heart is able to be "released," or rather to release and to relinquish the image of the world, we fall asleep.

The three dreams which follow illustrate the intense compounding of the image of the heart with the image of the genital, with all the implications of such compounding for the comprehension and treatment of the human being.

1. Dream Sequence After a Coronary Attack and Permanent Coronary Damage in a Hypertensive Patient Under Serpasil Therapy

A few weeks after a coronary attack and its fierce heart pain with resulting slight but definite permanent alteration of the electrocardiogram, a man in his forties, under serpasil therapy for a moderate hypertension, had this first dream:

My young daughter is dancing around the room holding a curious vase in her hands as she leaps and swings around. It is a large vase, broad at the top and narrowing to a point at the bottom, with an odd lid at its top, covering it.

As she dances with it, there comes squirting streams of water out of its top portion and its sides not through the lid but through the walls of the vase—streams ejected in short spurts.

As she continues to dance, she shakes it, and it is clear that there is something inside the vase responsible for squirting the streams of water through its walls. She shakes it hard, and a small mouse leaps out of its lid and falls to the ground stunned.

It is a strange-looking little mouse. It has a kind of machinery—a group of rods or tubes sticking out from around its mouth as though it had squirted the streams of water through them.

My young daughter, who cannot bear to see things hurt and suffering, cries out that it is in agony and that I should do something about it.

I stamp my foot on it until I crush the life out of it and I feel sick to my stomach with a horrible feeling as I stamp it to death.

A more complete dream image of the heart than this vase is difficult to obtain, the nearest to it in completeness in my experience being the "great perfume bottle dream" described in the case of interauricular septal defect (Chapter 1). The word *vase* is of course a variant of *vessel* or the Latin *vasa*. The streams of water coming magically through the stationary walls of the vase are surely in part short-hand descriptions of pulsing arterial flow. Note also that the "mouse" which is a "squirter" (colloquial: "young squirt") must be in a certain position within the vase for the streams of water to come out rhythmically from the top and sides—not from the bottom—of the vase. The "mouse" must be in a central position within the heart, the position of the pacemaking, synchronizing mechanism (i.e., the "spark" of life and the "rods" or "tubes" around the mouth of the mouse—a kind of "machinery"—are not only "squirters" but also associated with "sparkers" and "piston rods"). Indeed life is made possible only because this pacemaking and synchronizing conduction bundle of the heart catches "the spark of life" in the uterus from its mother and its life "catches on," so to speak, to give rise to a new heart and a new individual.

The same symbolizations express this man's sexual dilemma: the "vase" is a combined vagina-uterus; the "mouse" a penis or foetus. The powerful role of the image of the heart as an influence upon sexuality—and in a dynamic equation with it—is nowhere clearer.

On the day of the dream he had been extremely worried because of the pain in his heart on effort; and as is common in all human beings with real or imagined severe heart disease, his terror that he would die during intercourse began to mount. He feared that his sex life was at an end. He happened to pass a newsstand displaying a popular psychologizing book on heart attack which contained a chapter explaining the fallacy behind the fear of sexual intercourse after a coronary. In his own particular case this fear was heightened by the fact that he had a moderate hypertension which however was controlled by serpasil therapy. He complained that serpasil therapy, however, made him feel impotent.

That night he had intercourse successfully and there immediately followed the above dream in which his dilemma with his wife is displaced in terms of his daughter who is maturing toward womanhood and beginning to attract young men.

He had jocularly remarked that day that he would be glad to trade his daughter (and her pets) for a son. In the dream—which illustrates fusion of genital and cardiac images so decisively—the vase is not only great "blood vessel" or "bloodvase"; (i.e., heart); it is also a sexual organ, and the streams that spurt from it are his dream conception of feminine orgasm. The "mouse" in its sexual connotation is the "young squirt," i.e., the male genital of the young rivals for his daughter's sexual love. By displacement to his daughter, he expresses his fear of rival men and their impregnating power if he can no longer have intercourse with his wife. His stamping of the "mouse" to death is thus his way of squelching the new dangerous sexual desires of his daughter and the rival male sex organ, with which she excites herself, i.e., "dances" full of life and has orgasm, either in present masturbation or future intercourse. (If he had a son he would be in no such danger, so far as his own incestuous wishes for his daughter and his rivalry are concerned.) By the same token, the "mouse" is again the "sparker of life" in that it generates within the uterine sex organ of the woman that new "sparking" heart mechanism which makes possible a new child. (He had discussed the idea of another child with his wife before the coronary attack—an idea which must now be stamped to death, both for a permissible child with his wife and an impermissible child by incest with his daughter.)

All these sexual wishes and heart fears had been repressed when he mobilized enough courage to have intercourse, and so they reappeared in the dream.

Of the greatest interest in this dream is the actual idea formation that makes the "mouse," which is a condensation of mainly two words, an "oral-circulatory" condensation:

$$\frac{\text{MOU(TH)}}{\text{MOUSE}}$$

A further aspect of it was the idea of a small rat and its connection with the word image of:

$$\text{RAT(E)}$$

with which he was very much naturally concerned during intercourse.

The dream in its over-all heart-genital symbolic equation shows the usual deep conviction in these hypertensive patients of the "phallic woman," i.e., a woman with a penis "inside"—the residual effect of the dominating mother with whom they identify and so suffer all the castrative restlessness of an unresolved fear of the loss of the sex organ, a restlessness which must be actively combated in the treatment of the patient with hypertension and especially in the "coronary case," prophylactically, and after heart damage has occurred.

This factor of a deep identification with a phallic woman (covered over by a late masculinity as described for the "coronary man" in Chapter I) is sharply seen in the next dream, the next day, after he had received a copy of "The Image of the Heart" (Chapter I).

He had not come to see me professionally concerning his heart and neurosis until after reading this chapter on "The Image of the Heart." Indeed, as is common with "the coronary man," he had rarely been ill, nor had he treated himself considerably when he was ill, and rarely slept more than six hours a night in his adult life; he had always been "on the go." (These men have a restlessness which is almost suicidal and designed to prove their masculinity over and over again, although all the premature "coronary men" I have known have shown a surprisingly uniform though thinly concealed feminine attitude toward life. As already described, they persist in a controlled tension covering magic thinking, a physical hurry, a constant need for self-purification, a superrealism and superpaternalism, and a crushing of all true talent.)

After having been given a copy of "The Image of the Heart," he had a dream which at first he could remember only in the following sentence:

> I called an old carpenter of about sixty-eight years of age to come and fix a box for me.

He said there was "something else" he couldn't remember; he would consult with his wife because he had told her the dream in detail; he had been so struck by it. He returned with the dream completely recalled:

It wasn't a box. It was a cat. The dream was this: My wife and I were driving in our car; in the dream we had a cat along. The cat leaped out of the car and her tail was cut off and bleeding.

I called the old carpenter, a man I admire very much, and he came and fixed her up—sewed the tail back on to the cat. But, for some reason, I forgot the cat and remembered only calling the old carpenter to fix the box.

What had actually happened that day was that his wife and he had been riding in a car; but they had a dog along, not a cat. The dog had leaped out of the car and his tail had been injured. They took the dog to the veterinarian and the dog's tail had been partially amputated. On that day he had received the article on "The Image of the Heart."

No simpler illustration of the basic feminine identification with the mother is possible—together with the unbearable terror of castration characteristic of such men, as illustrative of the "scarred, healed, split identification" described before, particularly to be seen in the "coronary character" of Edgar Allan Poe (see Chapter I).

There is, however, a subtler point here than merely that of the customary interpretation of "identification with the phallic mother," as will be seen when the facts of this dream sequence are assembled in relationship to the known coronary damage.

*   *   *   *   *

For example, there is no doubt that in the above dream the carpenter who fixes the "box"="cat" is surely the analyst who has written the article on the heart, namely myself, but also his father, a builder by trade. Observe too that the substitution of "box"="cat" for the male dog, whose tail has actually been amputated, is a denial of real male castration and the substitution of a female phallus to remedy the situation, i.e., to preserve at all costs the "pussy's tail," the basic view of self as a woman. Furthermore, the process of his repression is in part visible by his forgetting the entire dream except for the carpenter coming to "fix the box."

But this is only a part of the repression and the dream; a much larger and more important set of facts come into view when we compare his two dreams:

In both dreams an animal leaps out of an enclosure—the "mouse" out of the vase, the "cat" out of the car.

In both dreams the enclosure is in motion: the daughter "dances" the vase around; the man himself is driving a car—therefore a moving enclosure.

In both dreams, because the enclosure is in motion, the animal is injured in its leap; the mouse with its mouth machinery is stunned; the cat's (anal-genital) tail is cut off.

In both dreams a man is distinctly and definitely called upon to do something for the injured animal. His daughter shrieks for him to do something about the mouse's agony; a carpenter is called to fix the "box-cat." In both dreams a woman is present—his daughter, his wife. His daughter called for him to help; he called for me.

In both dreams a piece of apparent "magic" of the body is performed—the mouse with the mouth machinery squirts streams of water through organic walls; the carpenter reattaches a lost portion of the cat to its body.

These facts give us further confirmation of the synergy between the physiologic pacemakers and synchronizers of the heart and the neuro-psychic image of the heart in the patient. He is now dreaming in images that, however elaborated, fused and compounded with genital images, betray the basic and injured image of the heart.[3]

These two dreams (and thousands like them) illustrate that:

[3] If the pacemaking sinus node is cut out from a mammalian heart and is divided into the smallest possible parts, one still sees rhythmic contractions. According to Pick (1924) this specific tissue can be revived twelve hours after death. He describes the case of a child from whom, twenty-three hours after death, the papillary muscle with an at-tached Purkinje fiber was transferred to a nutrient solution and showed contractions of 2 per minute; after oxygenation, its frequency was 22 per minute, and contractions in-creased in amplitude. Kubliako (1902) reports the case of a child of three months of age in whom he was able to demonstrate sinus node pacemaking activity twenty hours after the child had died of pneumonia. Kubliako believed that the region of the sinus node remains viable for *seven days after* death.

This area is connected with the sensory vagus (the entire auricle is richly supplied with vagus fibers) and so with the labyrinthine-sonic system, the tractus solitarius, and therefore with the sonic image system. It is unconceivable that this all-important cen-ter of animation should not send afferent impulses up the vagus to the brain where it becomes sonically and visually symbolized in images expressive of the heart.

I believe that this contains the answer to the "animals" of night terrors and the "ani-mals" of acute paranoid alcoholic hallucinations: the heart's pacemakers and synchro-nizers (the "animation" mechanism) discharge their burden in this way, a way which necessitates the mobilization of being awake.

(1) the cardiac conduction mechanism lying in the septum between the heart chambers which, as pacemaker and synchronizer, makes life possible is a neurosexual tissue; and

(2) that it is a hitherto unseen integrative "arbiter" between the image system of the brain on the one hand and the sexual drives on the other; otherwise the two dreams could not be so remarkably parallel, point for point, symbol for symbol;

(3) that it is here in this very mechanism that the synergy of self-preservation on the one hand and the impulse to sexual pleasure and reproduction on the other are locked in a struggle; and finally,

(4) that it is precisely the pattern and daily outcome of this struggle which determines heart work and coronary artery damage (taking into account special physiologic factors). As for the effect of healthy sexuality almost all people are aware of the remarkable slowing, and "calm" of the heart after sexual orgasm.

*   *   *   *   *

Return to the comparison of the two dreams and observe their differences which also illuminate the image of the heart and its influence. In the second dream the carpenter (father, analyst)—assuredly the superego—is the kindly repairing figure; in the first dream, when he is called upon by his daughter to do something, he, the ego, must crush "the mouse that made the heart go," with its curious oral machinery.

(How often the human child asks concerning all moving machinery as it projects the mystery of self-propulsion and self-pulsation—*But what makes it go?*)

In the first dream the ego solves the problem with sadomasochistic castration and death; in the second, the kindly superego repairs and restores. The second dream, hopeful of repair and survival, denies the dream and the fact of damage.

In the first dream the magic is done by the "animal"—oral—the rods and the tubes; in the second dream the magic done to the animal is anal-genital, the resewing of the tail.

Both make up a root ego image of cardiac propulsion and pulsation, fused with genital erection and orgasm.

Both represent the magic mobile power of life. For the cat "makes the car go," just as the mouse made the vase squirt. The cat became the "box"—because this called to mind an ignition box—a box of his childhood, in the old-fashioned motor cars of the past, and a magic tool box, i.e., the vagina which makes his "car" go.

The dream image of the mouse in the vase and of the cat in the car thus are together an oral-anal ego image of predominantly cardio-sexual components.

There is no other way for the ego to symbolize this quintessential pacemaker-synchronizer portion of the cardiac image of the ego—except as an animal which motivates both action and hunger, action and sexuality. Cf. the derivation of the words *animal, animate, inanimate, animus, animosity,* and finally the term *unanimous,* i.e., literally meaning not divided into hostile, warring factions. There is no other way for the ego to symbolize the actual beat of the heart except as the animal leaping—here, ominously leaping out of action to castration and death, unless "repaired by the old carpenter." This leap is nothing more or less than that original evolutionary leap out of the inanimate into the animate and into its individuation, as the next dream in another case will show.

2. The Dream of Impregnation: Symbol of the Animal Leaping Into Enclosure

Over a period of twenty years in neuropsychiatry and psychoanalysis, this writer has frequently observed in women the dream about to be described. Whenever all its ingredients are decisively present, it is a practically infallible indication of pregnancy and a viable foetus. Though it varies, it is a typical dream—and it symbolizes the opposite of the dreams described above. Here, the small animal leaps into an enclosure not out of it.

A young married woman who has missed a period reports her dream as follows:

> I had a dream that there was an open shoe box, and suddenly a purring lively kitten tied with a pink ribbon around its neck jumped into the box.

Immediately, the sides of the shoe box began to fold over by themselves and they apparently developed a zipper which automatically zipped the shoe box tight and I could feel the frightened kitten beating in and against the sides of the box.

The interpretation of the dream was that she was pregnant. Pregnancy was confirmed. She was ultimately delivered of a normal female child. This type of dream, in its simplest form, is amazingly similar from patient to patient; sometimes a rabbit dives into a burrow which automatically closes over its head; sometimes a small kangaroo leaps into a self-sealing pouch.

The elements of the above dream contain all the factors of the image of the heart already described in the "coronary personality" except that here the elements point to the beginning not the ending of animation and individuation.

(1) The "small lively kitten with a pink ribbon around its neck leaps into" the enclosure. (The mouse and the cat leaped out).

(2) The enclosure is a "shoe box," i.e., it is used to contain an instrument of motion, e.g., a shoe (contrast with the danced vase; the car.) (A shoe has a given size and shape and the human foot bespeaks individual evolutionary development.)

(3) The sides of the shoe box develop a zipper. (Compare with the lid on the vase; the box which the carpenter will repair.)

(4) A "zipper which automatically zipped the shoe box tight." (Compare with the oral machinery of the small mouse; or the water squirting magically through walls. Compare also with the colloquial expression: "to be undone," i.e., destroyed.)

(5) "I feel the frightened kitten beating in and against the sides in the box." (Compare with the daughter's cry that there is something in the vase.)

When one recalls the development of the heart embryologically, one becomes aware that "the automatic zipper" can only be the description of the forerunner of the heart, each little "tooth" of the zipper representing not only the very rapid beats of the two embryonic arteries lying side by side, one on each side of the midline as a zipper lies, but also the actual establishment of the fundamental animation process (cardiorespiratory pacemaker-synchronizer) by which those beating arteries will ultimately fuse, thicken, coil and descend from the neck area of the foetus to become the heart and to lay down what might be called the "track of the heart." (Compare with "my heart leaped into my throat.") In brief, the kitten leaping into the box and the automatic zipper is the representation of the forerunner of the neurosexual pacemakers and synchronizers of the two arteries-to-be-come-the-heart. Once this happens—once this tissue is laid down and operates—a viable child should develop. A new life has "caught on," and all the subtle changes in the mother's body are summated in this very primitive dream image of the heart. Observe: the kitten "beats" in and against the sides of the box, as it will later beat, as a heart, against the sides of its own chest wall. The word "shoe" also associ-ated by rhyme in this young woman's mind to "who"—indeed the purring kitten leaping into the "who-box"—is the ultimate symbol of the beginning of an animated individual. And finally, recall how the word "purring" is also used in our automatic age in which we speak of the "purring motor."

That this dream is also a simple expression of impregnating sexual intercourse is obvious, and indicates again genital and cardiac image fusion.

In all three dreams, the image of the genital may be found masking the image of the heart, masking it by fusing with it because the entire aim, to nature, of the sexual drive is reproduction—a process to which the pleasure-pain principle is subsidiary, just as survival of the repro-duced individual becomes the paramount synergic principle of life.

3. DREAM OF THE FUSED HEART-GENITAL IMAGE IN A PATIENT WITH RHEUMATIC HEART DISEASE AND SEVERE EJACULATIO PRAECOX

A single man of thirty with a history of rheumatic combined aortic and mitral valvular insufficiency and cardiac enlargement presented himself for treatment for severe ejaculatio praecox. He had had in-tercourse frequently. Quite potent, after the first premature orgasm, he was able to indulge in intercourse several times a night thereafter with a delayed orgasm. However, the first orgasm had remained se-verely praecox. There were a number of character disturbances, a neurotic fear of being unloved, and a violent all-pervading ambition.

He had several friends who had died of rheumatic heart disease, and the fear of death hung over him. In addition, whenever he was in a situation promising great success, particularly when he was on the verge of gaining money at cards or at business, he would have short bursts of violent tachycardia, almost abruptly paroxysmal, except that they subsided the moment the trial of winning was over. During these bursts of tachycardia, his heart was "in his throat"—and at the same time, hammering against his chest.

He reported this dream:

> I had a wet dream last night. In the dream I was lying flat on my back having a tremendous sense of sexual excitement. My penis began to throb with a terrible violence as though it would leap away from my body. The sensation was frightening, though violently pleasurable, and so I put my hand on it to quiet it and hold it down.
>
> But as I touched my penis, its throbbing and leaping became worse and then I realized it wasn't a penis but a bullfrog which had somehow gotten into my groin between my legs and was throbbing and thrashing around.
>
> Then I had a sexual emission and woke up.

The day of the dream he had had a particularly severe stimulus to his heart. As usual, he gave no overt indication to the outer world of his bursting tachycardia, beating in his throat.

The throbbing bullfrog is again the heart masked by the image of the genital. A "bull-penis" was a great part of his fantasy. Both his father and a friend whom he loved very passively had very large genitals.

Like Edgar Allan Poe, he had fantasies of a "tender, sad, pallid girl" on whom he would use, in his imagination, the "bull-penis." The girl was a projection of himself and mother linked together.

But there was an even more cogent association, proving that the "bullfrog" is a child, an unfinished foetus within the body of his own deeply repressed feminine longings.

The "bullfrog" associated in his mind to a scene from Jacob Wasserman's "World Illusion" in which the hero is repelled by the idea of sexual conquest of the heroine in the forest because a slimy frog jumps out of a forest pool beside her, and leaps upon her elegant silken dress. The "frog" is described by the patient as "goggling up" at the two lovers whom it separates by its appearance from the "underworld of slime," its heart beating visibly in its throat—so it seemed to him in his mind's eye, as he recalled the book.

The synergistic symbolic equation—heart = (animal leaping) = genital = unfinished child—is therefore indisputable. There can no longer be any doubt that there is—albeit and however masked by fusion—an image of the heart in consciousness, and that the pacemakers and synchronizers of the heart make their influence felt psychically, and are in turn extremely sensitive synergically to all the ramifications of the image of the heart—as it penetrates the entire sonic structure of the brain and mind, particularly with respect to word structure and thence to the verbal residues of the dream. Ordinarily the heart is under automatic control but, in the case of anxiety, certain situations bring the entire cardiac conduction mechanism under the impact of specific word structures and image formations; i.e., there is a shift from the heart's obedience to the metastable factors of repressional equilibrium to the immediate functional sonic factors of word structure and situations recalling the "separation anxiety" of birth.

This approach solves the problem of anxiety hitherto unsolved; as stated before, anxiety is the disturbed synergy between the image of the heart and the rest of the ego. Indeed severe schisms may grow up, stimulating schizophrenic processes, around the need to defend the image of the heart as separate from other ego interests.

In preparation, finally, for a study of the paroxysmal tachycardias, predominantly the auricular types, but also the more fatal ventricular type, the following episode of "voodoo death" as told by Walter B. Cannon, the Harvard physiologist, is of great interest to show how much the image of the heart stands in dynamic relationship to the pacemakers and synchronizers of the heart. "Voodoo death" is quite explicitly a death resulting from a terror which can disintegrate the pacemaking and synchronizing of the heart. Cannon describes a documented episode in which a Negro in an African locale discovers, after a year has passed, that his host, whom he has now revisited, a year before fed him at dinner a taboo wild hen. His host, a liberated man, laughs as he serves the taboo hen again, now revealing its nature for the first time and observing that the religious Negro had survived a whole year proving that the taboo was mere superstition.

The superstitious Negro African died of sheer terror in twenty-four hours at the idea of having eaten unbeknownst to himself a taboo wild hen a year before.

Proven cases of a paroxysmal ventricular tachycardia as a result of terror have recently been described in the medical literature, and thus it is known that certain forms of taboo terror can cause cardiac death.

The "wild hen" is again the "leaping small animal" of the three dreams described (the mouse, the cat, the bullfrog). It is as taboo in Africa, as food, as a mouse and a cat in Western culture. (The frog as food was terribly taboo to the rheumatic patient described above. He was an orthodox Jew; frogs legs revolted him—he described eating them as "eating a child.")

The reason for this heart (and lung) symbolization as an animal leaping (including the same implications in a wild, i.e., uncontrolled, hen) is entirely neurophysiologic as well as psychophysiologic. And when this is understood, it becomes instantly transparent why taboo terror should destroy the ego via paroxysmal ventricular tachycardia.

It is not merely that the function of fear is to mobilize the resources of the animal for either fight or flight. Taboo terror, it is true, represents a violent overmobilization in which the flight is expressed entirely by the heart running and the rest of the body immobilized in an acute helplessness. (Indeed, slowly deteriorating schizophrenic catatonia can be looked upon as a counterbalance to paroxysmal ventricular tachycardia so that the heart slows and is spared over a long time as opposed to the "running heart" and "quick death" of taboo terror, in which one is practically eaten up by one's own voracious oral magic.)

The dynamic paradox of the eating of the wild hen in Cannon's case is, in psychic terms, that the "leaping animal" which controls individual life, i.e., the normal heart pacemaker-synchronizer, is psychically destroyed, internally devoured. The taboo animal respected and not eaten controls group aggression and oral evil magic. Eaten, it devours its eater from within. The magic moral is—as always—"do not break group taboos which appear to have been devised for individual survival." In neurophysiologic terms, the entire sonic (vagal) regulatory apparatus crumbles.[4]

Finally the symbolism of the "leaping animal" as seen from the genetic embryologic viewpoint supports fully the concept of the cardiac pacemakers and synchronizers being a portion of a central integrative apparatus, a neurosexual tissue capable of acting directly with the sexual system, and also capable of stimulating sonic image formation.

Recall in this connection the facts of embryologic development.

(1) The heart is actually the ultimate fusion of two centrally placed arteries lying one on each side of the midline of the foetus.

(2) They lie originally, as arteries, in the neck area of the foetus and only later fuse, coil and descend into the chest.

(3) When they first "appear" as arteries, they take shape out of that area which is later to become the head and neck sonic apparatus, the gill-cleft area; they always thus retain their connection with the vagus nerve and the sonic system.

(4) The cardiac pacemakers and synchronizers arise from the midline of the neck area and are comparable—relatively gigantic though they become—to the tiny ganglionic nerve cells regulating smooth muscle; here they become adapted to cardiac striated muscle.

These peculiarities of the synchronizing-pacemaking tissue, arising not from the arteries but from midline areas to become incorporated in the partition between the arteries, and the fact that it transmits, like every nerve, a most complex periodic electrical impulse (the EKG), indicates that it is not only directly influenced by the sonic-respiratory midline neural area but is also an integral portion of that area and apparatus indispensable to animation; i.e., only when the sonic respiratory neural system and the cardiac pacemaker-synchronizer become mutually vitalized or "electrified" has animation and sexually viable individuation been assured. In this cardiac animation it must be recognized that the foetal heart is the foetal "breather"; the lungs do not really function till birth and it is at birth that the heart be-

[4] This illustrates the psychophysiologic advantage of the concept of a-sonic barrier as determining nervous integrity (Schneider, 1953); certain idea structures can conceivably shatter functional nervous integration—to use a physical analogy, much as a sound, by resonance, can shatter glass.

comes completely a heart and the lungs fill with air for the first time.

A rather startlingly clear case now to be described in the following section will illustrate the clinical import of the fused sonic image of the heart and the principle of synergy which the heart image dominates. Careful clinicians alert to new advances in psychoneurologic theory will recognize in this patient many of their own most difficult (and least satisfactorily understood and treated) cases of impotence and talent inhibition.

The principle of psychosynergic dynamism dominated by the image of the heart, as illustrated by this case, bids fair to alter the course of psychoanalysis and the evolution of its technique.

Chapter III

THE DISGUISED IMAGE OF THE HEART IN A CASE OF SEVERE SEXUAL IMPOTENCE AND TALENT INHIBITION—THE CASE OF THE CLOCK CHIMER (PAROXYSMAL AURICULAR TACHYCARDIA IN FATHER AND SON)

THIS patient, a man now in his forties, married for twenty years, the father of two children and once a promising creative talent, presented himself with the statement that just before coming he had read the article on "The Image of the Heart" (Chapter I), and it had made a profound impression on him.

He had seen three analysts over a period of fifteen years, for a severe sexual impotence and an increasing immobilization of his considerable creative ability.

At age twenty-two, he had met his wife. She had, as a matter of fact, become attracted to him because of his creative work which by now had gradually dwindled. With her during their courtship he had been sexually virile, capable of more than one orgasm a night and he had been a hard-working productive person.

Abruptly, as they were about to marry, her mother interfered and tried to get the girl (now his wife) to meet other richer, more "aristocratic" men.

In anger he had packed his bag and gone to a hotel in another town. As he got into his room, a small room, and leaned over to open his bag, he was aware that his heart suddenly was beating very quickly. He

45

felt weak, strange. He lay down on the bed and did not know what was happening to his heart or why. As if "by magic it had started" its racing and "by magic it stopped."[1] It was easily twice its normal rate. Later, he had finally married the girl.

He had told his previous analysts of his rapid heart, but he recognized he had told them it was a "rapid palpitation" which he linked up in some ways with the fact that his father had had—he had thought —a "nervous heart," and his father had finally died several years later of a dissecting aneurysm of the aorta, while driving a car. When his father had first developed the "nervous heart," mother had moved out of father's room. At about this time he had begun to masturbate.

The first analyst did him "no good at all" and had felt that the patient needed a more active therapist and had suggested the second analyst.

During the treatment with the second analyst he improved considerably for a while but under the criticisms of his wife who resented his "passivity"—a word they had both learned from analytic terminologies—his analytic improvement repeatedly "came undone." His first recourse was to urge his wife to go to the second analyst to get her to cease her criticism of him which he thought made him impotent in spite of considerable improvement.

As his wife improved and learned to restrain her criticism, his own improvement was now volatile—at times stable, at times unstable; he would become sharply inhibited, "turn green," be unable to work and then improve again.

The second analyst recommended a third analyst for him. The third analyst was much older, very kind, very gentle, very passive and helped him a great deal. His wife meanwhile still felt that he had never been restored to what he had been, though she concluded her own analysis very satisfactorily. She still resented the recurring episodes of his impotence and maintained her feeling that he had never really regained control of his creative ability. She had ceased to criticize him so violently for his "passivity" but also had "no love for such passivity." She insisted he was really not a "passive man," and urged him to keep trying to recover his capacity sexually and artistically.

1 In other words, a typical attack of paroxysmal auricular tachycardia.

He had then read "The Image of the Heart" and recognized the facts listed below. While he had never clearly communicated them to the various analysts, neither had they ever clearly questioned him about his own "rapid palpitation" or his father's "nervous heart paroxysms."

The following facts now emerged in a new context:

(a) He had never been impotent nor creatively inhibited until that paroxysmal cardiac episode in the hotel room. From that point on he had become "passive."

(b) The episode in the hotel room had been a classical case of paroxysmal auricular tachycardia—abrupt leap to at least twice the normal rate, abruptly starting, abruptly stopping.

(c) He recognized he had and was having at least one such attack a year; together with this there were all kinds of precordial pains and complaints, especially when driving a car, and when about to engage in the sexual act.

(d) He now realized that he had failed to tell his analysts that his father also had true paroxysmal auricular tachycardia. He remembered his father lying down, pressing his hand to his neck to stimulate the vagus, the house dark and "as though in mourning," and he recalled his contempt for his father whose attacks came on after losing everything in the crash of 1929, and finally his mother's "leaving father's room." Originally proud of his father, he too turned away and left his father to die in the darkened room.

(e) After he had read "The Image of the Heart" he had said to himself: "Now let's see. When did we have our heart attacks?" and then realized how he had linked himself (and his impotence) to his father. That night he was impotent. The next night, on learning that I would see him the next day, he was potent.

(f) He recounted a curious symptom about clocks and time which he had also failed adequately to tell his other analysts. He had several chime clocks in his house and of course his own watch. One of his major rituals—and one to which he was a complete prisoner—was his compulsion that all the clocks must chime precisely together. He went around the house interminably checking these chime clocks; he couldn't work otherwise.

(g) His children also had to "work right"; he never gave them a "breather"; they were never allowed time to come to him for help; he had to go to them to supervise all their work; it was his necessity; his duty. His children, like the chime clocks, had to "work on time" and together with him. They were all his "tickers." Everything that represented his heart had to "chime together." He exerted remorseless tyrannic control of them.

(h) He frequently was afraid to sleep on his left side for fear of compression of his heart (as in the case described in Chapter I).

(i) As a child he had had severe night terrors.

(j) After seeing me, he had several dreams in which different women were destroyed or disciplined, all connected with his mother's leaving—(at first he said "our")—his father's room. In this way he now discovered for the first time where his deep hostility to his wife came from—namely, his unconscious violent hatred of his mother for "leaving father's room," i.e., really for leaving father to die and stimulating his own guilt in the satisfaction of his oedipal wish.

(I have seen repeatedly the same phenomenon, with very violent anxiety in persons with childhood night terrors and/or enuresis, namely a recognition of a deep and irrational hatred of the mother thus accused of killing father and exposing the son to oedipal castration by getting the son to concur in the abandonment of the dying father. This sense of guilt is always associated with impotence and creative inhibition—and terrifying anxiety. It is the keystone of an intensely masochistic character structure.)

(k) He now recognized that in all his analytical work previously, though he had been helped considerably, something had been "missing." He had never solved or understood his "clock-chiming symptom" before, nor his impotence.

(l) It was clear he had fused heart and genital in one image, ever since the hotel room episode. The interference of his future mother-in-law functioned precisely as his own mother's hostility to father had functioned—except that he never saw that he had brought the image of cardiac death with him to bed. Or, in other words, if a woman—his wife—were to criticize him particularly before the sexual act, it would not be "criticism"; rather his wife would walk out on him and he be left in the dark to listen to his racing heart or to die a cardiac death while driving a car—as his father died. He let his penis fall as a substitute sacrificial offering to preserve his heart.

(The symbolization of "heart failure" while driving a car is an extremely common masculine fear of our day; in this case very heightened, its symbolic equation to death during intercourse is obvious. Compare with the dreams of the leaping cat and fears of the hypertensive "coronary man" described in Chapter II.)

(m) His imagination had become constricted because he recognized that his fear of death had been greatly heightened and his ego had thus become dyssynergic. His talent could no longer operate until he could once and for all convince himself that his heart rhythms were all right; until he could stop attacking himself for his mother's desertion of his father, for his own contempt of his father until his children "worked right"; until all the clocks chimed together.

The change which has come about in this patient as a result is astonishing to those of us who have been brought up with the theoretic notion of an inborn "passivity." He is assertive, virile and has returned to full-scale artistic work.

The theoretic conclusions are that the appraisal of the human mind must take into account the basic principle of synergy, so important to the integrity of the ego and its talent expressions on the one hand, and its cardiosexual imagery on the other. The heart and the genital while linked together by the neurosexual aspects of the cardiac pacemakers and synchronizers, must nevertheless enjoy an autonomy, if anxiety and the compulsions derived from it are to be overcome.

A creative human being cannot spend his life in the necessity to make all clocks chime together as a prerequisite for work and sexual joy and love.

Chapter IV

THE IMAGE OF THE HEART AND THE
CENTRAL PROBLEM OF ANXIETY

EVERY one at all versed in the history, theory and practice of psycho-analysis is aware of Freud's long struggle with the central problem of what has been called for centuries, "anxiety"—an emotion distinct from fright, terror, uneasiness, and yet, however distinct, nevertheless partaking of some of the attributes of these other tangential emotions. Apart from all other bodily feelings, anxiety is also called, more col-loquially, a "heaviness" and an "agitation of the soul."

One further knows how Freud's failure to solve completely the cen-tral problem of anxiety was—and is—connected with the other several major dilemmas of psychoanalytic theory and practice. Indeed the fail-ure to solve the central problem of anxiety may be said to have roots in all those obstacles, because it has roots in our ignorance of the functioning of the brain.

The first of these dilemmas is the nature of the "psychophysiologic apparatus," i.e., *the way in which brain activity is transformed into the mind* and into character, into the qualities of "conscious, precon-scious, and unconscious"—into dynamic characterologic entities which have, in our period of analytic history, been called "ego, id, and superego."

"Anxiety" is one of the basic results—and causes—of so-called "id-ego" conflicts. Yet the central problem of anxiety remains unsolved as long as we do not really know whence it comes physiologically nor how it transforms itself into an impact upon our mental organization. We do now know that the ego itself comes to assume a specific "char-

50

acter" because "anxiety" forces us to build "defenses" against internal psychic impulses which threaten our necessities of social control or against external "real" threats to our integrity and shelter.

The unsolved relationships of anxiety to a host of *paradoxes* so far as its origin is concerned, include not only "real danger," "neurotic helplessness," "birth trauma," "castration anxiety," and once upon a time "increase of libido," but also a number of other situations, such as that of the "traumatic neuroses" where Freud saw clearly that the pain-pleasure principle was not the most basic element of brain activity as it transformed itself into "mind" or "character."

It was necessary to go "beyond the pleasure principle" (in the book by that title) in which Freud brilliantly perceived that there was a curious integrative "barrier" which had to be postulated for the action of the nerve cell itself, a barrier we have already described elsewhere in terms of sonic psychophysiology (cf. Part II). In brief, again, the source of "anxiety" went back to something in the way the actual irritability of protoplasm was determined and guarded. If those "guards" broke down, the organization of the ego was shattered; the integration of "mind" and of brain activity failed; the convulsive and other (psychosomatic) phenomena of a no longer controlled nervous irritability took place.

These questions are at the frontier of psychoanalysis. It is necessary only to go through Freud's *The Problem of Anxiety* (1926) to see the long courageous theoretic struggle so replete with his individual integrity. Certain addenda to that volume further illustrate the insoluble nature of the problem up to now as long as the word "anxiety" remains something only vaguely defined.

THE CENTRAL PROBLEM OF ANXIETY

Here is a condensed record, a digest with commentary, if you will, of Freud's "twistings and turnings" in that illuminating, brilliant incessant quest known as *The Problem of Anxiety* in the English title for *Hemmung, Symptom und Angst*. This review is essential at this point in order to contrast its theoretical difficulty with the simpler concept of anxiety as dyssynergy between the sonic image of the heart and the rest of the ego.

Freud begins by stating that the relationship which inhibition bears to anxiety is such that exercise of the function (inhibited) would give rise to anxiety. Inhibition thus is an internal automatic psychic avoidance of the threatening impulse.

He admits that anxiety which arises in repression is not simple. The ego is the real locus of anxiety, but he rejects the idea that the cathectic energy of the repressed impulse becomes converted into unpleasure or anxiety. Anxiety is not created *de novo* in repression but reproduced as an affective state in accordance with a memory picture. In man and creatures related to him the act of birth is the initial individual experience of anxiety. This again dovetails with the heart changes of birth. The first and very intense attacks of anxiety occur prior to the differentiation of the superego, i.e., the superego comes into existence in part as a whole system of automatic avoidances, permittances, and prohibitions. He points out that it is not at all a question of any indefinite fear but of a definite anxious expectation, e.g., that of being bitten by a horse as in the case of little Hans. Thus, the patient who insists upon having an "amorphous" anxiety is one who is repressing his specific anxious expectation.

He shows that because of castration anxiety, little Hans renounces aggression against his father and that the motive force behind repression is castration anxiety. *Here it is anxiety that causes repression* and not, as he earlier stated, repression causing anxiety. (This change in theory fits the dyssynergic sonic image of the heart, as well. The ego must attempt, and generally succeeds, by repression, to bring about a modicum of synergy once more.) He stresses that anxiety never emanates from the repressed libido, as he once thought. Tentatively he concludes that this seems a contradiction, and one not simple to resolve . . . saying *Non liquet*. It does not solve! (But it can be solved by recognizing the phenomenon of synergy and dyssynergy.)

He goes on next to remark that anxiety now appears (in phobias) as a complication which conceals the true state of affairs. He observes that there is a plenitude of neuroses in which no anxiety is manifested. This also fits with our new concept; in many neuroses, the dyssynergy is handled by an actual split in the ego (cf. below).

In the phobias, conversion hysteria, and compulsion neuroses—in all three, he assumes, castration anxiety is the motive force behind the struggles of the ego, but only in phobias is anxiety manifested and acknowledged. He asks how, in the other two, the ego has preserved itself from anxiety? (Our answer is that in phobias the dyssynergic image of the heart is *not* defended adequately; the "animal" is the projected sono-visual image of the heart in terror.)

He turns back to repeat that as soon as the ego has recognized the danger of castration, it *gives the signal of anxiety*. He does not state— nor has anyone else done so—just how the ego gives the signal of anxiety. Through the medium of the pain-pleasure mechanism, he believed (this he later corrected in *Beyond the Pleasure Principle,* 1920), it inhibits, in a manner still obscure to us, the threatening process in the id. The anxiety of the phobia is therefore facultative. It makes its appearance only when its object is actually perceived as in the "horse" or "wolf" or "rat"—substitutes for the castrating father. (Or, we would say, from our new vantage point, the "animal" reminds one of *how the image of heart and genital become antagonistic* with all the "separation fear" this induces.)

He tries to refine the definition to mean that anxiety is the reaction to a situation of danger; and that it is circumvented by the ego's doing something to avoid the situation or retreat from it. Symptoms are therefore created in order to avoid the *danger situation* of which anxiety sounds the alarm.

Again he feels that he has arrived at a new conception of anxiety as the reaction to a loss, a separation. The first anxiety experience, of the human being at least, is birth. But unfortunately, birth is not at all experienced as a separation from the mother. He observes that reactions to separation are known to us. We experience them as grief and mourning, not as anxiety.

Anxiety, he repeats, acknowledging his dilemma and struggle, is not a simple thing to grasp. He has, he feels, arrived at nothing but contradictions. He now prepares to bring together in an unprejudiced manner everything that can be said about anxiety.

He dismisses the physiology of anxiety. The analysis of the *psychologic* anxiety state provides, then, as its attributes: (1) a specifically unpleasurable quality, (2) efferent or discharge phenomena, and (3) perception of these. Anxiety is a specific state of unpleasure accompanied by motor discharge along definite pathways. An increase of excitation underlies anxiety. One may be inclined to see in the anxiety state a reproduction of the trauma of birth, but there is such a thing as anxiety without a prototype in birth. However, this later objection, if pursued, would take us from psychology into biology.

Precisely because anxiety as a reaction to situations of danger has a biologically indispensable function to fulfill, it may have been contrived in different organisms in different ways. He feels that because anxiety arose as a response to a situation of danger, it will be regularly reproduced thence forward whenever such a situation recurs.

He proceeds to the premise that anxiety thus seems to be a reaction to the perception of the object, and there at once spring to mind the analogies that castration anxiety has, also separation from a highly valued object as its content, and that the most basic anxiety of all, "the primal anxiety" of birth, arises in connection with separation from the mother.

This, he states, is how neurotics behave: that although in their mental apparatus there have long since developed all the agencies necessary for dealing with a wide range of stimuli, although they are mature enough to be able to gratify the greater part of their needs themselves, although they know perfectly well that castration is no longer practiced as a punishment, he observes that they nevertheless behave as though the old danger situation still existed. They remain under the spell of all the old causes of anxiety. (Our concept gives us no difficulty here; as long as there is a basic dyssynergy between the image of the heart and the rest of the ego, "anxiety" must arise, over and over again, from internal and external sources.)

He asks whence comes the element of permanency in these reactions to danger? Whence springs the preference over all other affects which the affect of anxiety seems to enjoy? And finally, he concludes with the almost despairing questions: What is the source of neurosis, what is its ultimate, its specific, underlying principle? "After decades of analytic effort," he states, "this problem rises up before us as untouched as at the beginning."

Not content to be overcome by these paradoxes, Freud continues the struggle. In an addendum he notes down an ever more incessant search, a wider perception of the problem. He stands on the brink of solution but is barred from complete satisfaction. Yet his definition, as far as it goes, is brilliant. Above all, it fits to what is seen in practice.

Anxiety, he feels, is the original reaction to helplessness in the traumatic situation.

He states that we know the difference between true anxiety and neurotic anxiety; a real danger is one which threatens via some external object, neurotic danger via an instinctual demand. He stresses that in relation to the traumatic situation, against which one is helpless, external and internal danger, reality danger and instinctual demand coincide. (Or, in our terms, the traumatic situation is one in which the dyssynergy is increased by internal and external forces at the same time.)

He observes that we can understand certain of the enigmatic phobias of early childhood—the fear of being alone, of the dark, of strangers—as reactions to the dangers of object loss; with regard to others—fear of small animals, thunderstorms, etc., there is the possibility that they represent the atrophied (i.e., implying prehistoric) remnants of an innate preparedness against reality dangers.

(We explain the fear of small animals and thunderstorms as projections of the sonic image of the heart under conditions of severe dyssynergy with the rest of the ego.)

However, for the sake of the history of psychoanalysis and our new psychosynergic dynamics, we must follow Freud to what is practically his last utterance in which just before his death he struggles once more with the old, unsolved problem of anxiety, this time, however, strikingly *in terms of a split in the ego*. Nowhere else does Freud reveal himself as the Titan that he is, in so few words. For there is no doubt that "anxiety" can produce as well as result from just that splitting process, and, as such, "anxiety" continues to be the central problem of neuropsychiatry.

In his final work, *An Outline of Psychoanalysis* (1939), he speaks very little of "anxiety" as such. In his concern for an even wider, more elementary perspective, he is now devoted to the task of bringing together the doctrines of psychoanalysis and to state them "in the most concise form and in the most positive terms." In the final portion of this last work, he returns to "anxiety" spurred on by his old striving to solve the problem of psychosis via the subject of a "split in the ego." He points out in this last work that the concept of a split in the ego applies not only to psychoses, but also to the neurosis (as I have postulated for the "coronary character"). He pointed this out in the neurotic cases of *fetishism, an elaborate device to avoid castration anxiety,* as in men who act as though they have not perceived the lack of masculine genitals in women.

Side by side with this attitude which is a defense against castration anxiety, they have another attitude which is the correct one. "The two attitudes," Freud notes, "persist side by side through their whole lives without affecting each other." He goes further and insists that this "split"—the result of castration anxiety—is not limited to cases of fetishism. (And indeed, it is not. Dyssynergy between the image of the heart and the rest of the ego quite commonly is solved by neurotic ego splitting.)

Freud's last words on this important phenomenon stress the fact that these two attitudes, contrary to each other, and independent of each other (*split*), represent a *universal characteristic of the neuroses,* and that one of them belongs to the ego and the other—the opposing, repressed one—belongs to the id. And, he adds, *whatever defensive efforts the ego makes in warding off dangers,* its defense is *never complete* or unqualified, because the other attitude of self leads to psychic complications. (In brief, the dyssynergy is only *institutionalized* within the ego by this self-divisive technique, from our point of view.)

Freud has come closer to the solution of the problem of anxiety; anxiety may go so far—particularly castration anxiety, as well as the loss of love, and dread of the superego—as to create a "split in the ego." In fact, here Freud hovered over the concept of synergy and dyssynergy but failed to recognize the sonic image of the heart.

At the end Freud knows the consequences of anxiety more than any man on earth. From the first days when he adduced the connection between castration anxiety and coitus interruptus to the last day when he adduced the connection between castration anxiety, fetishism and a split in the ego, he has struggled to elucidate the essential source of anxiety—its persistence in spite of later maturity, its existence at the root of the phobias, the hysterias, the compulsion neuroses.

But the solution of the problem of "anxiety"—this strange, evocative propelling emotion, so distinctly different from outward fear, objective terror, grief and mourning—the solution of the essence of the problem of anxiety evades him. He has embraced it and defined it as no other man and he is, at the end of his life, the physician, the neuropsychiatrist, finally trying to bring to a solution all that he has gained on the age-old problem of the "split in the ego." But, he must leave the true solution to the future, as all of us must in so many of our problems; for the solution of the problem of anxiety depends upon a new concept of the functioning of the brain—one to which the sonic image of the heart belongs.

THE IMAGE OF THE HEART AND THE SEPARATION DANGER OF DECAPITATION AND DISMEMBERMENT

We have already redefined anxiety by describing it as that emotional state which results *whenever the sonic image of the heart is dyssynergic with the rest of the ego*. It is this dyssynergy which we feel as a "warning," as "palpitation," as the "sounding of the alarm." This is an unequivocal psychodynamic definition; there is no possible contradiction involved in our meaning. There are only the questions as to what is the sonic image of the heart? What is the normal synergy between the sonic image of the heart and the rest of the ego? Specifically at *what point do they become dyssynergic?*

Here it becomes clear why Freud could not solve the problem; it involves recognition of the heart and the brain as sonic mechanisms; it waits for the development of a new concept of nerve-cell action, involving sonics—those periodic forces which have become so important to modern science. *For the heart is a sonic machine,* and together with its pulse propagated everywhere in the body, it produces a sonic image of itself, usually subtle and sub-surface; indeed, the entire perceptive and moving envelope of the body must be recognized to have a fundamental sonic arterial beat, however minute; we are not made of porcelain, marble or granite; we are living, resilient tissues kept alive by a sonic machine, capable of producing a steady periodic force, the heart and its pulsing arterial system which branches from the heart as the limbs branch from the torso. Our skin surfaces are capable of "drum" effects. Indeed, when we get to the problems of that sonic range which we call "audibility," it becomes evident that the activity of the heart belongs to an *internal sonic system* whose audible sounds are usually "covered over" by our ability to perceive external sound which relatively predominates or "masks" internal sound. But in an experimental "dead space"—a room so perfectly sound-proofed that neither ceiling, floor or walls can convey external sound to the ears—the internal noise of the body is actually so much of a "roaring, rushing, hissing" chaos *that great anxiety* is experienced by the person in the "dead space." One would expect it to be so. To be in a "dead space" is *one of the ways of making the sonic image of the heart dys-synergic with the rest of the ego,* which is thus disconnected from its normal ways of masking the internal sonic chaos of the body caused largely by heart-blood-breathing action. (It is curious that the term "dead space" has arisen in sonic terminology—a "dead space" is a coffin and a grave and too is productive of sonic chaos.)

These facts have a special application to the sonic problems of deafness. Another sonic phenomenon—an awareness of internal sonic chaos—can be observed in our everyday psychoanalytic practice. Most analysts have seen patients who, at the moment a correct interpretation is given, take refuge in *a sonic device;* they say: "Music is running through my mind." Among a great number of instances is one case, an ex-soldier who said: "When you touch my anxiety, a fugue runs through my head—and to me a fugue is an attempt to bring order into confusion, a musical skirting and intellectual organization of the edge of chaotic sounds and of the sounds of chaos."

*   *   *   *   *

The sonic image of the heart, then, is an image made by its *periodic* forces, either audible or tactile; audible as when heard beating in the ear, tactile as when felt in "palpitation" and even perhaps in stimulating other senses, such as *seeing* the heart beat in the neck, temple, wrist, belly. To be sure, it is not perceived in the same full rounded way one perceives an apple; *it is in part a projective image;* it is nevertheless perceived, and in such a way, already described (Chapter II), as to be compounded with other external objects of the ego and so projected in various denotative and connotative proportions not only obviously as in the symbols of objects and feelings: "ticker," "hour-glass," "valentine," "hearty," "disheartened," "stout-hearted," "heavy-hearted," "whole-hearted," "half-hearted," "sweetheart," "pump," etc., but also in many more complex and powerful ways in our word and thought structure. In all our dream and artistic imagery, it plays a very special but very *elusive* role. Thus a great flask in a dream is apt to be a portrayal of "magic cardiac standstill" which nevertheless keeps the dreamer *alive without heart work.*

For example, recall all those struggles which Freud had in his attempt to relate anxiety—not to Rank's theory of birth trauma—but to the process of birth itself as a prototype of separation, of loss of love, of castration anxiety (separation from the instrument of love) and at the same time as a protoype of danger, without his ever recognizing the image of the heart. To find the image of the heart explicitly in any of these *anxieties* is very rare; it is the *dyssynergy* which makes the anxiety—the dyssynergy between the image of the heart and the rest of the ego. Yet, to perceive the relationships of word and thought structure (exclusive of some 347 words in our language directly using the word "heart" in compound form) is to understand precisely how the sonic image of the heart has been involved in each of the great *danger* situations of life, the great transitions, of which birth and death are the most obvious, and how it is woven into the textures of our consciousness up to the highest elements of thought. In this way, it functions to give us "alarm" or "ease," at whatever level.

*   *   *   *   *

THE NORMAL SYNERGY OF HEART IMAGE AND EGO IMAGE

The elements of the heart image, then, are so involved and compounded in the experience of danger with sound, word, and (secondarily visual) thought structure, that *it tends to separate out as an image only at the point of separation danger thereafter.* And it is this which *warns* us because the *image of the heart is in dynamic equilibrium with the heart mechanism itself at all levels of internal develop-*

ment, and with all the implications of external danger. In this way we get also the three main forms of anxiety: "palpitation," sense of constriction," "waves of fearsome helplessness" (panic).

This sensation of separation danger is the most basic element of anxiety and is connected with the helplessness and trauma at the point of helplessness as Freud showed. The sonic *image* of the heart in relation to the *mechanism* of the heart parallels the image of the ego in relation to the mechanism of the head and limbs. And, just as the image of the heart and the image of the ego are normally integrated and synergic at the psychic level, so too the arteries and limbs (including the head) are integrated and synergic at the body level; it is the function of the autonomic nervous system to effect this limb-artery synergy.

Therefore, separation danger is *always dismemberment* danger; the limbs are threatened when the artery is threatened; the image of the heart and pulse registers the total integration.

All anxiety, every valid word that Freud has ever adduced about anxiety, is comprised of various portions of the threat of dismemberment in one form or another. Children before puberty rarely talk about their "hearts" but they do have a direct concern with dismemberment; death appears to them as a dismemberment; castration anxiety is a separation danger; birth is a separation danger, loss of love is a separation danger, exclusion from a group (breaking of a savage taboo) is a separation danger: i.e., loss of "belongingness" with death and starvation in the jungle—to be pursued and destroyed, eaten, ultimately as a beast; and all of them are *dismemberment,* either in terms of individual integrity or *membership* socially.

Nothing therefore is more equivalent to the dyssynergic image of the heart than the threat of dismemberment in all its implications. For this strikes at the fundamental heart-limb structure of the ego.

(Edgar Allan Poe's *The Tell-Tale Heart* is a story of a *dismemberment murder* in which the mad murderer is driven to confession by virtue of the remaining torso hidden under the floor, suddenly sending forth the sound of its still magically beating heart—really the beating of the murderer's heart in his own ears as he is questioned by three detectives. Cf. the more detailed analysis of this story in Chapter IX.)

Moreover, dismemberment is symbolically the essential helplessness of the moment of birth because, until the foramen ovale of the heart closes, with the end of the umbilical circulation, the child is functionally only a torso, only a body; and it is "dismembered" from the mother. Immediately after birth the child begins to be aware, but it can not control either its limbs or its head—in contrast to four-footed animals. The heart has not yet *in utero* connected itself to the lifelong task of guaranteeing the essential oxygenation of the brain; as we know, once born, should the heart fail in this task outside the uterus *even for a period of minutes* (loss of oxygen as opposed to loss of consciousness), the human being is perpetually for life physiologically "decapitated," i.e., rendered a neurological cripple—a "vegetable"—with mental deficiency and deterioration.

Decapitation is reflected as massive dismemberment or separation danger—for the brain governs the members—and the heart must supply the brain with that minimum oxygenation or else the ego stands in danger of being decapitated, virtually if not actually dismembered. To round out the facts of "anxiety," as Freud himself mobilized them, the head of the body symbolizes the head of the penis and vice versa. Anxiety thus is revealed as the *rupture of a quintessential synergy between the sonic image of the heart and the images of the limbs, including the genital, and the head itself.*

At the psychologic level great "anxiety," i.e., a quantitatively great dyssynergy, can and must produce a set of defenses and distortions and "traits" forced to bind up the ego once more, specifically to ward off threats; in the presence of so extensive a dyssynergy, a considerable split in the ego can occur, just as Freud postulated, as the result of the necessity to defend oneself, to mobilize oneself, to quiet a constant state of alarm. As a matter of fact, when in analysis, anxiety is stimulated, we get our greatest—however unpleasant—opportunity to see the neurotic split in the ego. The successful, courageous treatment of these sometimes unavoidable crises in analysis produces dramatically good changes in character, however painful the anxious epoch. As Otto Fenichel (1941), perhaps one of the greatest analytic therapists of modern times, has pointed out, these crises can be handled preventively in most cases by the proper *dosage* of interpretation.

In premature coronary disease this division of self is particularly sharp; it is covered over by a series of fetishistic reactions precisely as Freud described for the neurotically split ego; indeed, it is the awareness of such potential anxiety that keeps the "coronary man" away from adequate psychotherapy in time.

At a glance, then, we perceive why premature coronary disease should be and is more common in men; it is the male in general—and the fetishistic man in particular—who is likely to suffer the acute "separation danger" of "dismemberment" in all its forms, in his social and sexual role. This is even more true in men whose fetishes of and defense against their chosen seemingly phallic women depend upon the possession of money, the fulfillment of great ambition, etc., i.e., in which the ego and the heart are chained to the external objects of the world and are pushed and pulled by each flow of outer circumstances. The divided selves of the "coronary man" and his feminine "secret person" *before his first attack*—these are becoming common knowledge. The "coronary man" lives in two worlds and spends his life bridging them.

Psychically as well as physiologically, this concept of anxiety as a dyssynergy between the image of the heart and the rest of the ego (in contrast to the nonanxious, subtly blended and projected sonic image of the heart which is woven into the scaffolding of thought) is accurate and valid down to the finest detail of the three great groups of "anxiety" neuroses: the compulsion neurosis, the hysterias, and the phobias. In order to complete our description of anxiety, it is necessary to understand completely the relationship of "memberment" and what we may call "membery" (memory) to what we call "thought structure" and "feeling tone." For all these things hang together: memory, accessible and repressed, the structure of thought and feeling tone, "separation danger" or "anxiety," the synergy of talent and imagery; fetishism and dyssynchronization of the heart. Here begin the psychosynergic dynamics of longevity.

Chapter V

THE INTEGRATION OF MIND, MEMORY AND "MEMBERMENT"—THE SIGNALING SYSTEM OF ANXIETY

To begin our portrait of the signaling system of anxiety, it is necessary to understand some aspects of that synergic psychoneurology by which the human brain becomes "the mind." We shall begin with the highest function of the "brain-becoming-mind" and the place of the sonic image of the heart in it: namely, the *sonic function of human speech,* whose cybernetic attributes of communication and control determine our social destiny. For *the mind is sonic.*

It is unavoidably important here to stress the difference between our approach as based upon the processes of brain-becoming-mind and that of all other "classical neurology" and "classical psychiatry." While this may seem tedious, it will be rewarding for our immediate purposes of exposition. (In much greater detail, this is the subject of Part II.)

Classical neurology is built upon "the reflex" which, however valid to the mechanics of function, is from the standpoint of a synergic psychoneurology only at best half a unit. The synergic psychoneurologist, true to his basic premise of the "brain-becoming-mind," must see the "reflex" as only a part of the synergy of movement and of mind. (Every contraction of the heart is a synergy and not a reflex.) Even the Pavlovian view is forced to add something to the reflex, namely *conditioning.* For, the reflex of a dog has little to do with the striving of a man.

Modern neurophysiologists are becoming more and more aware of the importance of the synergy of nervous action. Thus Fulton, in the introduction to his fine textbook on neurophysiology, stresses that while *reflexes govern muscles, synergies govern movements.*

In turn, classical psychiatry is built upon concepts of necessarily static types of *breakdown* of mind, well-established categories of symptoms for purposes of care, differentiation, prognosis and study.

By contrast, synergic psychoneurology is concerned with the units of build-up and thus with growth, not mechanically, as "one reflex built upon another" or "one muscle tied to another," but with the units and combinations of synergy, i.e., the plastic ways the various members, organs, parts and areas of the body and mind work together at every stage of growth from birth to death. In particular, a synergic psychoneurology is based upon the synergy of the image of the heart and the rest of the ego—and upon the physiologic synergy of the arterial "limb" of the heart and the actual limb of the body. It is thus clear that the very principle of synergy means the ability to use the various kinds of energy—electrochemical, sonic and mechanical—in order to survive and develop. It is this energy of transformation, this *synergic quantum* which is basic to our view, in contrast to the reflex.

Psychoanalysis has, for many years, sought a genetic (growth) concept of neurology or psychophysiology or a "psychophysiologic apparatus." *Synergic psychoneurology may be defined as the science of the genetic psychophysiologic apparatus.* The introduction of the sonic image of the heart, therefore, has two aspects. It introduces not only psychosynergic dynamics and the growth of the heart image intermingled with the growth of thought and feeling. It also introduces the various problems of the synergic psychoneurology of the heart and body, i.e., the manner in which the heart, at every stage of growth, "works together" with brain-becoming-mind—the ways in which the heart as a projected and compounded image functions in the very thought structures of words and the tensions of feeling. Synergically, and cybernetically, as any good steersman mechanism does, the signaling system of anxiety must be able to "sound the alarm at narrow and dangerous straits" which threaten to break up the ship of self, at the bodily as well as at the brain level. This dyssynergy too, in our text and context, means *stress and ultimate breaking down,* as any intricate machine—and certainly the living human organism—does when its parts undergo strain and finally stop working together. Thus the epileptic reaction of the traumatic neurosis, or the convulsion of idiopathic epilepsy, is a psychoneurologic dyssynergy. So too, most severely, is the psychosis.

*   *   *   *   *

If it is now recognized that we regard the process of "brain-becoming-mind" as basic, then we must at once pay attention to those sonic manifestations of transformational energy which we call "words"—the result of that new portion of the mammalian brain called "the speech area" or, in neurologic terms, the Island of Reil, and the concomitant of a new orientation of the members of the mammalian body, namely, the human erect posture and human handedness.

Consider for a moment the historic case of Helen Keller, known by now to all humanity. Words finally come to her but through vibration which is called "subsonic" acoustic energy (and perhaps also by certain "subultrasonic" forces). The periodicity of vibration felt through the fingertips can therefore be used as a sonic (subsonic) "nucleus" of thought. The qualities of smell, touch, temperature, pain (as well as dreams) can be mobilized by a deaf-blind-mute person to build the structure of thought around that sonic nucleus. The periodicity of vibration produces a sonic pattern upon which a phonic pattern can be built—around a "sonic nucleus"—which functions like an internalized "Morse code."

It must be realized thus that what we call the quality of developing consciousness is the state of being receptive to the perceptive exercise of all senses built around the sonic nucleus of thought, communication and control. And as every one can demonstrate to his own satisfaction, the moment the sonic "nucleus" is removed from the pattern of conscious thought, the pattern tends to disintegrate and we fall asleep or "go blank." Hypnosis rests upon substitution of the sonic nucleus of the hypnotist for the sonic nucleus of the subject. It is apparently practically impossible to exist rationally in a "pure visual" or "pure tactile" or "pure olfactory" state of consciousness without the dynamic center of the sonic nucleus of thought. To do so is to lose consciousness or to be dominated. "Mass hysteria" is such a phenomenon, and the blaring megaphones and agitational sonic changes are deliberately contrived to produce *a single compelling sonic nucleus* for the thoughts of the entire crowd. Psychoanalysis, like hypnosis, rests upon the essentially sonic technique of "free association" whereby the sonic nuclei of experience and fantasy are exposed and re-molded.

If we now return to the sonic image of the heart—and to the heart as a pulsing sonic machine—we recognize that the projective, blend-ing, compounding image of the heart is woven into our "states of con-sciousness" which also depend upon our "members," i.e., upon our body and limb structure, upon our evolutionary gift of the erect pos-ture, upon our stance, our standing, and our understanding.

The assumption of the erect posture, we know, has freed the hand and given us the tool of the opposable thumb. The finer and finer movements of our hands and of our vocal cords—and their synergies —as they work together around the sonic nucleus of conscious thought and perception patterns have built our advancing civilization.

If these considerations are valid, the field of etymology—*the science of word history and developmental word forms*—now becomes an adjunct science of the field of synergic psychoneurology. For if separa-tion danger always starts the "tolling of the bells"—the palpitating re-traction of the sonic image of the heart from the sonic structure of the ego, of the body surface and its moving members—then we should find a connection between the derivation of the words for *limbs* or *members,* and the words for *anxiety.* For to threaten one is to arouse the other; both are tied together at the mental level by the sonic sig-naling system nuclear to consciousness. In other words, separation danger ought to be connected to the word *anxiety* by definite sonic traces. In this way we survive; we have "intuition"; the finest ramifi-cations of our thought structure are woven synergically (and ordinar-ily silently) to the sonic image of the heart.

The historical traces of these word connections between *dismem-berment* and *anxiety* do indeed exist, as the etymologic evidence shows. There is a constant cross-reference in the history of language and in evolving word forms between the terms: *mind, memory, limbs,* and *heart* on one hand, and *mind, memory, limbs* and *anxiety* on the other. *Anxiety* thus is *dyssynergy* between limbs and heart; it is not to be equated *to* heart, except when the heart's action itself indicates or describes the consequences of that dyssynergy.

In this very sketchy etymologic discussion, it must be recognized that for thousands of years, the circulation of the heart and the function of its arteries were not known.

Not until the seventeenth century, when our present language forms were practically established, did the great Elizabethan Englishman William Harvey discern the true meaning of the dynamics of the heart. The first recorded studies of arteries and veins were made in 300 B.C. by Erasistratus, but neither he nor Galen in 100 A.D. (who distinguished between bright arterial blood and venous blood) had any real idea how the heart worked. Even after Harvey, the entire scientific picture of the heart and its arterio-venous tree, as a sonic machine pulsing in a closed circulation all over the body, was not proven until fifty years later when Malpighi with the newly discovered microscope demonstrated the existence of the capillaries linking arteries and veins.

As Harvey discovered the motion of the heart, so is it our task to elucidate the hidden sonic image of the heart and its normal synergy with ego and limbs.

In this work etymology now has a place, a scientific, psychiatric place and a synergic psychoneurologic task; and, in this etymological study, it must be recognized that the word "heart" pertaining to an external object is not necessarily an internal sonic image. By "internal sonic image" we mean the projective symbolizations of the heart as the result of previous or repressed dyssynergy. At the same time, the word "heart," particularly in its collaterals or compounds, can be used to express various facets of "mind" or even of "anxiety" such as in the phrase: *palpitation of the heart.*

The etymologic facts can be summarized thus:

(1) There are an enormous number of "direct" and "indirect" heart words indicating our awareness of *the heart as an object* and an organ for centuries going back to the very beginning of speech.

(2) There is a most extensive network in word derivations of heart-limb integration which seems almost to amount to an etymologic law.

It is as though the sonic image of the heart as an *internal image* were a keystone of thought and the dynamic sonic center of the signaling system of anxiety.

(3) There are in English, as a rapid count of Webster's will reveal to anyone, no less than 347 words using the word "heart" itself in word compounds. This does not include other indirect heart words such as "courage" from the French *coeur* which in turn derives from the Latin *cor, cordis*.

Let us list the etymologic forbears of the English word "heart." Here we observe at once that in practically every Caucasian language the word for "heart" is surprisingly uniform (taking into account vowel inversion). Every one containing the letter "r" and either "d" or "t" sounds (as though each great racial group were aware of the sound of the heart) and an immediately preceding or following vowel most common "a" or "e."

Heart

M.E. harte, herte, heorte
O.S. herte
O. Fr. herte, hirte
D. hart
O.H.G. herza
G. Herz
O.N. hjarta
Goth. hairto
L. cor, cordis
Gr. cardiac, ker
G. Ir. cride
Lith. sirdis
O. Sl. Srudice
Arm. sirt.
Hittite. Kardi
Skr. srad

A Few Derivations

Latin: cor, cordis

French: courage
  cord, chord (music)
  record—(remember)

Italian: non te scordar di me (forget)
  discord
  accord, according to, concord
  cordial

Greek: ker
  cardiac
  credo
  credit, discredit, accredit
  credence
  creed—credible, incredible
M.E. crede—credulous, incredulous
A.S. creda—creant, grant
L. credo—create
O. Ir. cretim (I believe)
Skr. sraddha, faith
  (placing of heart upon)

It can be seen that a very great number of words branch out directly from "heart" of which the above is only a very small segment, many more than if the heart were merely an organ or limb of the body. An entire book on this subject (indeed a series of etymologic works) would not exhaust its branching in and out of the various languages.

(4) But more significant is the "heart-limb" organization of vocabulary. Take the word "record" above, one of the meanings of which is "remembrance," others being "the act of witnessing," "evidence," "knowledge," "extraordinary performance," etc. A "recorder" also means a "witness."

There are other connections of interest, namely words for *limb* and *witness* whose roots derive from one Greek word, *meros,* meaning "thigh," and also become the basis for the word *mermeros* or "memory" or "anxious." The word for "mind" derives similarly, as shown in the accompanying diagram. This diagram is only a brief and inadequate segment of the signaling system of anxiety.

COR (HEART)	MEMORY	MEMBER	ANXIETY
Record (remembrance)	*MEMOR, Latin,* Mind	*MEROS,* Greek, *THIGH*	*MERMEROS Greek,* anxious
RECOR*DER* (witness)			
C*REE*D	*REMEMBER*	MEMBER, limb or genital	ANGST, *German*
CORDIAL	*MARTYS, Greek*	SMARATI, *Sanskrit,* he remembers	ANGOR, *Latin*
ACCORD	witness or rememberer		
CHORD (music)	*MOURN*	MARAIM, *O. Ir.,* I remain	ANGINA, *Latin*
(S*CORD*AR, *Italian,* put out of tune, disagree, cause discord)		NIGHT*MARE,* (incubus that sits upon the chest)	ANGINA PECTORIS (*L.*) pain in chest)

FORGET

(Non te scordar di me, *Italian,* don't forget me)	(Vergessen, *German,* let go the holding of, let go the handgrasp)
	(Oblivisce, *Latin,* to forget)
	(Oublier, *French,* to forget)
(Obbliare, *Italian,* to forget)	Obliterate, wipe out, erase

Of interest too is the fact that the English word for "remember" is based on the body and the word for "record" based on the heart also includes the act of writing and performing. The word for "forget" which in other languages—and English is essentially *obliterate*, nevertheless in Italian is also a *negative aspect of the heart,* namely the word for *discord.* In brief, the positive aspect of the "heart," "record," is to remember, the negative aspect is to forget (*non te discordar di me*).

Both *remembering* and *forgetting,* then, partly derive from the *heart.* But at the same time the *memory* and the *mind* as words are akin to a Greek word for "anxious," namely *mermeros.*

The pattern is unmistakable. Etymologically, the word for *heart*—like the word for *anxiety*—is linked to the members of the body, and the pattern cuts across all language differences.

Similarly *creed* or *faith,* which is the activity of belief involving the intellect, in part means "heart" almost directly.

But of greater interest is the fact that "to forget" is really "to obliterate," i.e., to wipe out the memory of that which had been *recorded.*

We must now examine the sonic psychoneurology of the heart image which this indicates in a further study of the word for *forget.*

$$* \quad * \quad * \quad * \quad *$$

To "forget"—so important to psychoanalysis because it is linked to "repress" and thus to the unconscious—is directly related to the new limbs of man. Thus "get" is to "seize" or "grasp"—in German *gessen* (*vergessen* is forget)—also means to *prehend,* to *catch,* or *anticipate,* and then *via apprehension its meaning moves to the* "apprehensive" or "anxious."

Prehend or *prehensible* pertains directly to the new evolving hand of the ape and man. And its relationship to "repress" is thus of interest. "Repress" comes from the Latin *primere* which means to *command,* i.e., the force of the so-called superego. Or, one *forgets* (*lets go of*) what one *represses* (*is commanded to.*)

As with *prehend, comprehend, apprehension,* so too with *memory, mind* and the Greek word *mermeros* (anxious).

A similar development, but not the same shift, occurs with respect to the words for erect posture—i.e., standing, "to stand," "to understand" as in the German *stehen, verstehen.* So too the phrase: "I cannot stand it," i.e., *endure.*

Therefore, when we get to the words for the "unemotional brain," these are all words which have to do with other than sonic functions. Thus "intellect" derives from the Latin word "to read"—a visual integration—as does the word for "reason." Hence intelligence is something built up largely visually around the sonic nucleus of words pertaining to the *heart* as a nuclear image of prehension and apprehension, anger and anxiety, the remembered and the *mermeros,* the dependent (clinging, hanging from) and the independent (standing on one's own two feet), etc. Or, simply, the usage of the ages, the poetic expression "mind and heart," is one of the utmost simplicity—and accuracy—in describing the differentiation between intellect and emotion. To this it is necessary only to add that the *sonic* is more fundamental than the visual and that the "heart" reaches into the "mind" it supports.

*   *   *   *   *

To return, however, to our study of the signaling system of anxiety. It will, first of all, be evident that the roots of these various words are like, say, sensitive magnetic needles—e.g., the root "prehend"—to which small quantities of sonic energy are applied, i.e., the prefixes "com—" or "ad" so that the "needle swings" to *comprehend* or to *apprehend* from *accord* to *discord* to *concord.* Each swing, however small, makes a different pattern, bringing into play different muscular stances or attitudes of the ego and thus creating different circumstances or situations.

We have defined anxiety as a dyssynergy between the sonic image of the heart (as opposed to the object-word "heart") and the rest of the ego. Ordinarily blended and disguised, practically by fusion with the image of the genital (the private member from which one must not be separated), only when a separation danger threatens does the sonic image of the heart retract from its usual fusion with the ego image, especially with the image of the genital; and at that moment "it palpitates us" or we suffer palpitation. We develop the *angor,* i.e., the constriction around the chest and belly, the sense of apprehension, of oppression—"the perilous stuff that weighs upon the heart."

Yet the signaling system of anxiety, except for the very tenuous connection between the words for "heart" and "forget" (*Don't forget me —non te scordar di me*), shows no definite integration between "anxiety words" and "heart words." However, there is every kind of connection between *dismemberment, memory* and *mind,* and "anxiety" on one hand, and *dismemberment, memory, mind* and "heart" on the other. To use a mathematical analogy, two things, "anxiety and heart" are "equal" to the same thing (dismemberment, memory and mind) and yet etymologically are not synonymous with each other. And this is surely among the reasons why the sonic image of the heart, and the principle of synergy has remained so long undiscovered, though the curious branching of the heart derivations indicates its deeper meaning.

How is this paradox to be explained and resolved?

*   *   *   *   *

The paradox is to be resolved—with a new ingredient—along the general lines and direction in which Freud went. The human brain, as all neurologists know, is composed of two brains merged together— one, the nonspeaking, primitive one, is nearer to the archipallium (caudate nucleus, basal ganglia hypothalamus); the other, the *speaking* one, the more recent (larger cerebral cortex, frontal and prefrontal lobes, Island of Reil) is concomitant with the development of speech and larger frontal lobes, and is called the neopallium. (A portion of the neopallium derives from the archipallium.) In certain neurologic states, the attributes of one brain can be seen to dominate over the attributes of the other; certain drugs stimulate these changes in domination. What Freud called the id, and the ego, we shall now call (for purposes of a synergic psychoneurology) the archi-ego[1] and the neo-ego as another aspect of our premise of "brain-becoming-mind." The terminology thus belongs both to time-honored neurologic and psychoanalytic entities or:

Psychoanalytic		Synergic Psychoneuro- logic	Classical Neurologic
Id	(Nonspeaking)	Archi-ego	Archi-pallium (primate cortex)
Ego	(Speaking)	Neo-ego	Neo-pallium (human cortex)

[1] The archi-ego comprises also the activity of the primate cerebral cortex, e.g., the nonspeaking mammalian brain of the great ape.

This change in terminology is not arbitrary; it will soon be seen that it is necessary, logical, and accurate, particularly with respect to the phenomena of words in relation to patterns of behavior. It is not meant to displace analytic terminology, but rather to amplify it.

The point is simply that the signaling system of anxiety which we have been studying thus far belongs to the later ego, the neo-ego, because it is a word-sonic or rather phonosonic ego. It is the neo-ego which gradually, beginning at three years of age, becomes phonosonic, speaks in a new efflorescence of vocabulary, giving words to external objects in a much different manner than it did before three years of age, when it had indeed already learned words, but not in the same way. Or, up to three years of age, that period which analysis has designated as "pregenital," the nonspeaking archi-ego with its primary emotional processes and incomplete neurologic motor coordination (nervous fibers are not completely insulated in cord and brain until three) *dominates.* The archi-ego from birth to three is therefore essentially a sonic receptive organism which must be *commanded and carried,* whose words are much less expressive than its sign language.

Indeed, the much talked about oedipus complex—the dynamic center of psychoanalytic theory for half a century—can now be seen as the period of transition from the "primitive beast man" (he—it has been theoretically suggested—had only a five-year life cycle) who was at the mercy of the elements and small ground animals capable in their wild state of tearing a gorilla to pieces. (Cf. the childhood phobic fear of rats and thunderstorms.)

*   *   *   *   *

We can now resolve our etymologic paradox, a resolution which throws a new light on the transitional oedipal period from three to five in which archipallic function is "layered over" by neopallic domination and the archi-ego is "put on a leash" by the neo-ego. The intellectual and characterologic significance of this transition is not only sexual; it is also sonic and phonic. *The phonosonic signaling system of anxiety is created, as a substitute for the actual heart fear,* nameless and now obliterated, in accord with the neo-ego principle of synergy for the sake of survival.

The evidence when assembled in this light is incontrovertible. In the earliest archi-ego state from birth to the utterance of the first word, *the threat of dismemberment is so acute to an incompletely myelinized nervous system, that it can only be expressed by flight of the heart and an awareness of helplessness (waves of fear-panic) which must be forgotten and, in its place, is created the phonosonic signaling system of anxiety, when the neo-ego takes over.* In brief, there are *two* heart images *all* the time after three years:—one (the archi-ego) retracting, palpitating, throbbing, roaring, sonic, *wordless* image of the heart ordinarily silenced and integrated by being projected outward and blended into some external object (flask, hourglass, chime clock, engine, animal); and another neo-ego *image and word* for *heart* as an object or as a feeling. The two images of the heart are utterly different; they betray their connection with each other in various ways, however, particularly in their etymologic relationships to the words for limbs, *memory, mind, dismemberment, remember,* and *forget.*

Just as the terrors of primitive man can be seen in the night terrors of our own children, so too much research work on children has shown that they think of the fear of death in terms of dismemberment, and sadistically love to dismember their dolls, butterflies, clocks, etc., in part to satisfy their curiosity as to what makes it go, in part to destroy the animation of that which they cannot make and so control. But while the child will not and can not speak of the heart generally, he may later draw a picture of the heart. The sicker the child is the more it will draw the heart, or call attention to it. Jenny Waelder Hall's case (1935) of Anton, which has been mentioned in Chapter I, actually had "heart pain" and Jenny Waelder Hall pointed out correctly that "heart" was "penis" symbolically. But also we have shown that in that case it was "baby"; and it may also have a variety of other symbolic guises.

We must repeat that the transition from three to five is not only genital but also phonosonic. Perhaps a better way to put it is that it is genital and phonosonic at the same time, and the relationships between sexual development and phonosonic function become of first importance, as I have already mentioned in a study of the psychophysiology of the sonic system. Indeed, there is every reason to believe that the terms "cathexis" and "libido," words invented by Freud years ahead of his time, really describe sonic energy transformations within the nervous system.

Our paradox is thus resolved; in archi-ego sign language "decapitation-dismemberment fear" is "heart fear," *as a sound and as a feeling not as a word*—a sound and a sensation to which the word "anxiety" is later attached because the development of the steersman and repressor functions of the neo-ego ("superego") system commands us to forget it; if we forget it, it becomes shifted to the idea of the integrity of our limbs and of our erect posture. *In brief, anxiety reappears whenever ego resource, coordination, achievement, pride, and sexuality are threatened.* This shift from archi-ego to the neo-ego conceals the sonic image of the heart which is thereafter normally blended into and synergic with the rest of the ego. And dyssynergy between them becomes synonymous with "anxiety" and makes the heart "palpitate."

APPLICATIONS TO A CASE OF SUDDEN "CORONARY DEATH" WITHOUT PRE-EXISTING DISEASE

I have never seen a premature coronary death—an acute coronary closure—without any pre-existing disease, except in personalities suffering from a particular kind of intensely primitive identification with their mothers of such a nature that any real emergence from the "body" of the mother is tantamount to "decapitation-dismemberment" terror, i.e., to acute cardiac dyssynergy, or acute cardiac standstill.

A recent example in a man of forty-four, "never sick a day in his life," is a case in point. A confirmed bachelor, he decided to marry a woman he had loved "from afar" for many years. He was in perfect physical condition, not "fat and bald," but slim, and he did not indulge to excess in tobacco or alcohol, avoided "high cholesterol foods," had normal blood pressure, etc. Just previous to his death he made an appointment to change his insurance policy benefiting his mother to benefiting his new wife. The first harbinger of coronary distress, transitory "acute indigestion," began after he made the appointment with his insurance agent. He "dropped dead" forty-eight hours later, the night before he was to make the insurance change. A post-mortem showed nothing but acute coronary closure and no pre-existing disease.

A knowledge of this man's inner controlled tensions, as I have described elsewhere in the "coronary man," his actual living a thinly covered archi-ego life and career, would not be noticed by most observers. His "secret" feminine self too was covered over except for one curious trait by which he betrayed himself; he was "more expert than a woman" in his knowledge of soaps for washing male and female garments. I have already mentioned the concealed tendency to transvestism in the "coronary man," however "executive" he may appear. These men have been described psychoanalytically as having "hostile identifications" with mother, i.e., identifying with the bad traits of the mother. This, however, is inaccurate. The identification with the mother is much more primitive; at all levels, primitive good as well as primitive bad. It is perpetual symbiosis at the level of decapitation-dismemberment terror. It is as though they hover on the brink of a sudden shift back to the short-lived archi-ego. Such men, it would seem, must not marry, at a late age, without analysis.

*   *   *   *   *

The man just described had no conscious acute "anxiety" until the last three days, but he did have all his life a kind of "machine-gun speech" and a furious but controlled rage. These phonosonic characteristics betray the fact that there is a severely "split" identification. I have already indicated that the severe schism in the coronary man borders upon, but is not the same as, the psychotic split; however, the psychic elements do show the same tendency to split off the sonic nucleus of thought pattern because the "coronary structure" is not firmly "tied together" at archi-ego: neo-ego levels of differentiation. The sonic energies thus released may be conceived as taking a direct route like the firing of an "internal bullet" to the tractus solitarius down the vagus to create cardiac dyssynergy or cardiac standstill, with acute closure of the coronary arteries—or even via the accelerator nerves to produce the "functional" tachycardia, flutter and fibrillation of the auricular type so well known to cardiologists. For sonic energy is the very energy of life; fertilization sets off its existence and operation and starts it oscillating in the "motion of growth" (cf. Part II); with this energy the "ego" (in our term, the full neopallic neo-ego) dominates the "cathexis" of ideas; sexual development releases a large amount of this sonic energy for character and career; it makes its impact on the pacemakers and synchronizers of the heart as already described; it is released to some degree ("free-floating libido") in anxiety where the sonic nucleus of ideas is reduced by any dyssynergy between the repressed sonic image of the heart and the rest of the "membered" ego.

The tendency to cancer may follow the same principle of sonic energy transformation as Freud long ago hinted. Cancer is a disease of advancing age when nervous energies of restraint weaken and the original sonic energy of growth may be "shot out" and converted into abnormal cellular growth.

Chapter VI

REPRESSION AND THE IMAGE OF THE HEART— THE CYBERNETIC-REPRESSOR FUNCTIONS OF THE EGO ("SUPEREGO") AND LONGEVITY —THE NEUROTIC FEAR OF HEART STOP (CARDIAC STANDSTILL)

To complete our portrait of a new synergic psychoneurologic apparatus which involves the sonic image of the heart integrated with the "members" of the ego, we must establish the relationship of the image of the heart to "repression" which is a curious form of command —forgetting. The "superego" does the practical commanding and enforcing of forgetting. It thus establishes the inhibition of an impulse; this inhibited impulse, if released, would in turn produce anxiety. For we have already shown by pursuing our synergic psychoneurologic premise, that it is as though in infancy the sonic image of the heart becomes too easily dyssynergic, produces severe anxiety and must become repressed in part by growth itself. Furthermore, it has long been recognized on clinical grounds that what has been called the "superego" is not and can never be purely the "incorporated" image of the parents and of external forces. The individual growth and constitutional make-up of the child must be taken into account. His "selector, minimizing and maximizing" inborn tendencies are factors. Every analyst knows how much more severe the superego is than the activity of the parents really indicates. The sadism of the superego and masochism of the ego are always disproportionate to outer reality. And sadomasochistic forces are extremely important to problems of neurotic exertion, exhaustion, "accidents," and so to longevity. The

78

factor of growth and the conditions of growth—e.g., myelinization—must in part determine this "superego severity," this "splitting power" of the superego, wherever there has been an infancy (before three years of age) filled with terror for whatever reason of actual threat or inborn sensitivity. This is what is meant by the "pregenital trauma." So to speak, the gradual completion of the neo-ego, operates in part like "the lid" to a Pandora's box which, *if reopened,* brings back the "pregenital" (birth to three years) injury and dyssynergic image of the heart. Such a regression may result in an unavoidable depression or schizophrenia which is refractory no matter what psychotherapy is utilized.

The distinctions between *suppression* and *repression* must be kept clearly in mind. In suppression the idea is held in abeyance; its syntax is not broken; its meaning remains and holds; it is pressed away from the center of consciousness toward the edge of consciousness (the hypnagogic periphery of the preconscious); it may ultimately either be "repressed," i.e., drawn into the unconscious or come back to center, be taken into account either by itself or as a compound and be discharged as an "expression." (In the language of the modern sonic calculator, a suppressed idea is analogously held in a short reverberating "ultrasonic" delay line, until it is "wanted" and is "commanded" to come forward. Until then it is "pressed back" and waits its "summons.")

The process of repression is different; repression acts as though a chemical change acted upon the reverberating circuit.[1] It is not only pressed back; its syntax is broken. As Freud put it (and no one has since explored it in the light of modern scientific advances) "preconscious connecting links" are taken out; Freud explains that the preconscious—to us an area of *sonic* transformation—is more directly connected with hearing and speech. The breaking of the links of syntax pushes the idea "over the edge" of the preconscious into the unconscious. Freud (1925) compared the operation of the conscious-

[1] The metastable equilibrium of growth at each stage of life can function analogously as an "ultrasonic delay line"; a *sonic* idea can thus be drawn out of conscious range for an indefinite time. In our previous monograph, *The Growth Concept of Nervous Action,* it was shown that the creation of such a metastable equilibrium (there called the "tension-relaxation" equilibrium) is the regulating principle of nervous action.

preconscious to the "mystic writing pad," that child's toy in which one writes on a semitransparent gray-white adherent film into a darker colored or black impressionable surface beneath it so that the writing on the film is temporarily and perceptibly grooved to the under surface; when the film is "peeled," the writing disappears from the surface film; it has been "repressed."

This "breaking of the preconscious links"—so casually treated and thoroughly neglected by psychoanalytic theory since the death of Freud—is no small event; it is the event which makes possible the existence of the human mind. Without it we should long ago have been extinct; our own impulsiveness would have destroyed us both from within and without. (It is not inconceivable that our primitive precursors in the species of the "ape-man" have a short life span for reasons connected with their less repressive organization, i.e., a lower order of general conservation of self and less automatic protection against impulsiveness.)

Just how does this "breaking of the preconscious links" occur? Into what medium in our brain cells is the conscious-preconscious "writing" impressed? For the repressed idea—like the suppressed idea, though under different conditions—does not vanish without a trace; it too can be summoned back by the gradual sonic technique of "free association"; indeed, if it comes rushing back too abruptly the result may be psychosis, for in this way powerful sonic energies break through the ego and disrupt its defenses and shatter its integrity like glass can be broken at a distance by resonating sonics.

Repression then—in obedience to the principle of synergy and survival—depends precisely upon the shift from archi-ego to neo-ego organization which obliterates heart fear and the fear of heart stop *before there is a name for it.* Otherwise we should all be anxious hysteric paranoid creatures; the roar and palpitation of our hearts in terror would dominate every action. We would not grasp and comprehend; speak and write; stand and understand; echo and originate; imitate, propose and initiate (cf. Part II). We should see separation danger everywhere in the traumatic terms of decapitation, dismemberment, castration and their derivatives. We would not love for longer than the moment of pleasure; we would hate, kill, devour. We would not survive.

The secret of the mechanism of repression, therefore, lies in the process of growth itself—as Freud showed—which provides the mechanism for breaking preconscious links in the meaningful syntax of ideas. Even the factor of repression—like the *style of dreaming*—is individual to some extent.

(This unpredictable individual factor of growth and inheritance makes for the psychic fingerprint. Hence all those theories of the mechanizing "basics" which have recently flourished since the death of Freud are so limited.) The "basic" *organ inferiority* of Adler, the "basic" *birth trauma* of Rank, the "basic" *personality structure* of Horney, the "basic" *oral-masochistic neurosis* of Bergler—and a dozen other "basics" both within and without the "official" precincts of psychoanalysis all fail to recognize that Freud constantly and tentatively avoided *all psychologic "basics"* because of his awareness of the multitude of archi-ego and neo-ego forces at play in man as the two integrate and interact in a vast kaleidoscopic manner. It is not "psychology" which is ever "basic"; brain function and growth determine the behavior of man, which is differently cast in different ages, generations, places and cultures.

Two Kinds of Repression

We must realize, then, as Freud pointed out, that there are two kinds of repression—the primary and the subsequential. The primary acts as a *gravitational* force pulling all subsequent repressions into its orbit. These stages of repression are actually manifestations of the functional power of the superego and of the stage of growth. For the purposes of a synergic psychoneurology we suggest the addition of the terms: steersman-repressor to "superego." The cybernetic and economic terms *steersman-repressor* at least tell us how the "superego" operates to bring about subsequential and primary repression. It operates in accord with the differently equilibrated frameworks of growth and experience, creating a cybernetic-conservative structure called "character." At each level of growth, direction and repression differ in their proportions. The superego sanctions the expression of certain impulses and permits certain "ideal" images to become directional (the steersman), and as part of this activity represses certain other impulses rendering them unconscious (the repressor). In growth we include an archaic heritage in the directional and repressive potentialities of man. In experience we include the parental and instructor images and certain tangible forces of still accessible, still effective tradition images as among the steersman-cybernetic and repressor-conservative functions.

In his *Problem of Anxiety, Freud* (1926) said: "I have elsewhere stated that the majority of repressions with which we have to do in the therapeutic work are instances of *subsequential* repression (*Nachdrängen*). They presuppose *primal* repressions (*Urverdrängungen*) *of an earlier date which exercise over the more recent situation their gravitative influence* [my italics]. But far too little is as yet known concerning this hinterground and those primary stages of repression. . . . [The very stages with which we are concerned in the matter of the sonic image of the heart, particularly in view of their gravitational pull upon later "subsequential repression." Freud goes on:] "At the present time it is impossible to decide whether the erecting of the superego perhaps creates the demarcation between primal and subsequential repression. *At all events, the first, and very intense,* attacks of anxiety occur prior to the differentiation of the superego [my italics]. It is entirely reasonable to suppose that quantitative factors, such as a stimulus of excessive strength, with the failure of the safety device protective against too powerful stimuli (*Reizschutz*), are the more direct causation of primal repression" (pp. 20–21).

For "primal repression" has one simple purpose: *to protect the synergy of the heart as an actual mechanism* by creating the basis for defense against the otherwise constantly disturbing *dyssynergic image of the heart* in relation to the rest of the ego which we call "anxiety." Freud emphasized this fact: anxiety causes the repression, not the other way around.

And the great word capacity of man which aids the subtle and highly flexible defense system does so by providing us with a communicative signaling system of anxiety, an instrument of conservation and control. Indeed, the question as to the ultimate source of the neurosis which Freud asked resides here because of the gravitational pull of primary repression upon subsequent repression. For only by *excessive* repression to subdue the dyssynergic image of the heart can the neurosis be perpetuated, just as the psychosis follows from the severe weakening or fracture of repression. In brief, there is optimum normal quantity of repression.

A new and shortened psychoanalytic technique for which we have all been searching may also be here. For, if what has been said thus far is true, the prime concern of analysis, so far as it is concerned with longevity, will be to pursue "the track of the heart," along the lines which repression lays down as it gives its defensive structuralization to character. Whether this be true or not, certainly an analytic concern with heart overwork will have to study this new orientation of repression and the heart.

In this process the "superego" (steersman-repressor) emerges as that new force which is cybernetic and repressive also in obedience to the principle of synergy and survival.

Note Freud's remark that the first and very intense episodes of anxiety occur prior to differentiation of the superego—including the steersman-repressor functions of the ego. Freud cannot decide whether or not the formation of steersman-repressor functions marks the dividing line between primal and subsequential repression. The concept of the sonic image of the heart permits us to answer this question in the affirmative. The action of heart image and heart mechanism as we approach a buried excessive primal repression in analysis tells the story. The ego acts as though it were about to be dismembered; the heart "palpitates"; waves of fear set in.

In brief, the formation of the steersman-repressor (superego) marks an important part of the process whereby the terrifying aspects of the image of the heart are repressed. This is the entire *biologic survival* purpose of "primal repression" (whether excessive or not) and superego formation (whether "cruel" or not). From this epoch-making transition, *man* emerges, no longer the beast which is *guided* by the leap of terror in its beating heart, or by the pleasures of the archi-ego as it hunts for its unrepressed and unrepressible immediate wishes for food, shelter and sexual release.

Or, in other words, primal repression, though it may be excessive, is self-conservative in its *aim;* if excessively constrictive in a neurotic childhood, it aims to preserve *human* life; nevertheless subsequential repression—always tied to it—may continue this tendency to such excess as to produce all the well-known inhibitions of a constricted, really unlived life. One may become afraid to "put one's heart into" anything.

It is in this way finally that we can comprehend the disguised heart image in the various genital-animal images of the dream, already analyzed in Chapter II.

In a severe neurosis, the originally *conservative* primal repression (which reflects the final merging of the archi-ego and neo-ego) now becomes as punitive as the steersman function fails to be liberating. The signaling system of anxiety may now be so hypersensitive that anything endangering the "limbs" (or genital) will immediately interfere with the steersman. The moment the steersman is weakened or perverted, the sense of the direction of an identity is disturbed. The repressor grows correspondingly overactive—becomes a suppressor as well—because the primitive instinctual impulse which threatens must be held back by sheer counterforce. The image of the heart may become more violently dyssynergic with the rest of the ego because repression ultimately weakens. Anxiety appears, or rather reappears. In paroxysmal tachycardia where the fear is dismemberment (as at birth), the heart itself responds by automatic flight back to the intrauterine rate.

Endanger a limb—any limb—in an implication of separation danger, and anxiety therefore appears. Every strong "anti-separation" force protects the heart; the pleasurable genital in a secure ego calms the heart. Let the steersman call out *"Danger!—but I cannot tell from what source"*—and anxiety returns full blast. The heart "trembles," the limbs "quake" as the primitive impulse and the forgotten injury pound at the repressor.

The ego feels threatened on all sides.

Let the repressor fail and—with defenses broken—panic, infantile helpless fear, sets in. If the panic continues in spite of all therapy—or because the panicky individual is in love with that which seems to his disturbed perception to castrate him or to threaten his death—he must institute his own deeply unconscious helpless counterhate of his beloved object. In this way he enters the realm of the psychotic depressive or schizophrenic process of unreality.

In my own opinion, coronary heart failure due to coronary spasm may be the same process, except that "the mind holds—the heart breaks." Fortunately, in practice, the psychotic depression or schizophrenia is rare (though not unknown) in the course of an analysis. Usually we see with reference to the heart, instead the much more simple substitutive symptom of fear of "heart stopping."

Though the fear of heart stop is only a feature of the neurosis, its analysis throws a sharp light on the relationship of the image of the heart to the process of cybernesis-repression formation, because the fear of heart stop extends its roots deep beyond the "subsequential repression" into the "primal repression." Or, fear of heart stop shows us how and why the "superego forms."

CASE I. FEAR OF HEART STOP IN A PHYSICIAN

A physician in his forties, married, father of two children, comes to analysis because of impotence, fear of speaking in public, and—among other complaints—the irrational terror that his heart will stop when he gets into bed.

As a physician, he knows that it is not possible for him to anticipate cardiac standstill and that his heart is in no danger of stopping of its own accord, while he can breathe comfortably. Nevertheless, just after he retires, he sits in bed fingering his pulse waiting irrationally for his heart to stop.

In a few weeks therapy restores his potency. His obvious heart fear disappears.

At the height of this period of sexual potency, he has the following dream having to do with musical (sonic) instruments:

> My wife and I decide to get married and "make it legal" (though actually we've been legally married for several years). We enter a church and begin the wedding march. We need the music to go with it.

I see, off on one side, a church organ with church pipes and two curious spinette pianos, one on either side of the organ. All three instruments are curiously blended into the wall against which they are placed. I decide that I will play the wedding march (even though you can't play the wedding march and march to it at the same time).

I sit down at one piano on one side of the church organ, and as I start to play every key slides off the piano and falls to the floor . . . I turn to the other piano on the other side of the organ, and as I start to play *again* on the other side *every key slides off the piano and falls to the floor.*

I then turn to play the organ, *pumping at the pedals with both feet to get enough air into the pipes,* when my two feet *push through the pedals and into the wall of the organ and smash it. . . .* Behind me there stands a man who fixes these instruments as I break them.

His associations were, briefly, as follows:

"*To make it legal.*" This can refer not to the marriage which has existed legally for many years but only to the fact that the analytic work has restored his potency. It is the potency which is recent and which, in response to the pleasure principle, he wants made legal, i.e., made a permanent and unassailable law of his personality. He is clearly unsure that his superego will permit it; no one is there to "make music."

"*We enter the church.*" This is the building of authority, equipped with the power to "make it legal"—or to repress it—and make it "illegal," i.e., temporary and vulnerable. The superego must decide whether he is permitted to have an erectile, penetrating, sexual organ.

In order to make it legal, however, these organs of the church must be played as part of the ritual; no priests or ministers or organists are present. Therefore: "*I see off on one side a church organ* with church pipes and two curious spinette pianos, *one on either side of the central organ.*"

On closer examination, he corrected this. The "pipes" of the organ were hidden; they were *inside* the wall.

The organ is again the combined heart-genital image. He associated the "pumping" with his feet to "central pumper"—to "heart," and to "penis," as the pipes became quite obviously "lungs and voice box." He has retreated from the *wedding march* and has taken a sitting position at the two pianos, finally to "pump pedals" in an infantile position, as the pianist-organist. But the fragility of the church instruments with which he is to "make music" dominates everything.

"Every key slides off the piano and falls to the floor—and again, on the other side." To be sure his "usurpation" of church authority is punished, because of his masturbation (*playing* at the wedding march instead of *marching* to it). All his abilities to "make music" are denied to him, but more precisely, *the limbs of his sonic instruments are taken away from him.* The "keys" fall off; the "pedals" smash. . . . A man, the analyst obviously, "fixes" them as he breaks them.

Moreover, the dream insists on there being *two* pianos and his playing *two* "spinette" pianos one on each side of the central organ.

What is the meaning of this curious arrangement?

* * * * *

Remember that this man is a physician neurotically concerned with the irrational fear of "heart stop," and that no image in the dream is consciously seen by him as anything but a musical (sonic) instrument. The dream, moreover, occurs when his sexual potency has reached a new height, i.e., he has had *to repress* these tendencies shown in the dream to become and remain potent.

We know this man, as a physician, has dissected a human cadaver; he has dissected a human heart; he knows the inner appearance and anatomy of the human heart; yet he is dreaming about the heart and does not recognize it (until it is proven to him) because he is dreaming of it as a combined heart-genital-limb sonic instrument—as the sonic image of the heart becomes dyssynergic in relationship to the threat to his limbs and genital (keys fall off, pedals smash); and further, he *needs* to disguise the smashing of the heart (and penis) to stay asleep.

* * * * *

However, the actual arrangement of pianos and church organ in the church is a remarkable piece of precision in magical symbols of the structure and function of the heart in symbolic relation to the rest of the ego. The church organ associated instantly not only to genital but also to the heart which depends intensely on oxygen (pipes). The "organ" *organizes the two sides* (left and right auriculo-ventricular chambers) of the piano-heart. Even the "stringing" of the pianos found a parallel in the *chordae tendinae* (the chord strings of the valves on either side—cf. also the expression, "My heart strings"). And, as we know, in one sense the valves of the heart are its "keys"; they help make the various physiologic "music" and "murmurs" of the heart.

More pertinently, however, the "keys" are expressions of the limbs of the body; the arms, fingers and legs play the piano. The falling off of the keys represents then the piano (chamber of the heart) devoid of the limbs that can make the piano "beat." So too with the pedals which make the organ "go."

We are now finally prepared to see that in this dream, *the vital organs of the church authority are being smashed*. True, as soon as he breaks them, the analyst figure who stands behind him repairs them. *And because he is more interested in playing* (at) *the wedding march than marching to it, the entire and devastating "dismemberment" takes place*. He destroys, in brief, not only church authority but also his own manhood; he prevents the consummation of the wedding; he "stops the music."

His "superego" formation is clearly mirrored here. His early childhood "dismemberment" threats, in part caused by oedipal aggressions of his own against an ignorant father, were such that *in order to quiet his terror of dismemberment* (mainly genital castration anxiety, the "reflex" of a highly accentuated passive homosexuality) he had to *repress* his wishes to destroy *the sexual power and the heart* of his father.

With this *primal repression* operating, his "subsequential" repressions kept gravitating to this early level. *As he grew,* the heart aggression and heart fear were *completely* repressed; the genital inadequacy remained on the surface.

As can now be seen—and as stated before—*the heart fear now reappeared as a transvestite* influence; he saw himself as a "beautiful woman." He, at first, when the analysis began, considered himself a feminine type; he had no right to a man's place, etc. In the place of a normal masculine authoritative communicability, there was instead an enormous exhibitionism, any threat to which made him tremble with terror during public performance, no matter how well prepared he was; this symptom is very common in women doing public speaking.

The transvestite influence derived, then, from his heart fear; the contrary wish to perform in a masculine way brought to the surface therefore "heart stop"—really a stopping of all his nonperforming defenses against anxiety.

Needless to say, as would be expected in a physician, this fear of heart stop alternated with dread of a coronary attack.

CASE 2. FEAR OF "HEART STOP" IN A WOMAN
AFTER PREGNANCY

A woman who had enuresis in childhood developed the not infrequent hysteric displacement: "There must be something wrong with my mind." This in turn was defended periodically with the idea: "My mind is superb. It must earn me great fame."

Her hysteric terror of "going crazy" diminished, however; she became pregnant and was delivered of a normal child. During her pregnancy she particularly enjoyed the idea that there were *two* hearts beating in her—hers and her child's.

After delivery, though her fear of "going crazy" diminished markedly, in its place (or alongside its residuals) there appeared a new symptom—the fear that her heart would stop. This fear, accompanying a sense of faintness that used to come together with her fear of "going crazy," was particularly strong one day when she watched her baby being held by a close friend, a woman upon whom she had been very dependent emotionally.

Her associations were particularly illuminating.

The idea that she *had* to expel the baby (the "new heart")—and could not keep it in her—connected with the idea that she could not "keep" her urine in her either. Unconsciously—and soon consciously —she discovered that she equated "going crazy" not only with uncontrollable urination but also with uncontrollable defecation which she had never suffered but always feared.

In brief, to be a woman without a male sex organ meant that "everything fell out of you"—you could either not control yourself or else the sex organ of the male could force you to lose control—even force you to defecate as in pederasty. Around this idea had been built the defense of defiance; a psychic formation, the equivalent of an "illusory penis," covered over the humiliating idea that to be a woman was to "lose control and make a mess" (*go crazy*).

The pregnancy elevated her position as a woman. She had not believed herself capable of such an achievement. Particularly the process of childbirth helped, though this too was a process not entirely under her control. Yet the child was a tangible and acceptable substitute for the defiance against the "degrading position of women." As a result, *her ability and willingness* to control her rage and terror increased; the symptom of "going crazy" diminished in proportion; but by the same token—as the *necessity for the illusory penis vanished,* particularly in relation to the woman friend who held her baby for her—the symptom of fear of heart stop supervened; the *baby* now commanded the woman's affection.

Here again we see the formulation that the loss of a member—even an illusion may have a "member value" (illusory penis)—*directly produces a dyssynergic image of the heart, in this case in terms of fear of "heart stop" and "collapse."*

The same transition marks out clearly the epoch of superego formation in this woman, as it did in the physician above, with whose case we may compare it briefly.

In the physician the symptom of "heart stop" related to his aggression; it was in part *retaliation;* but it was more basically the echo of the *primary repression* as the superego formed in its developmental conservative function of *synergizing* the image of the heart and the rest of the ego; as Freud showed, anxiety causes repression, and therefore primary anxiety or a series of anxieties *must cause primary repression;* this, in turn, creates the fundamental architecture of character, because, as Freud stated, this primary repression has a *gravitational* effect upon *subsequential repression;* the original aggressions of childhood thus keep re-echoing and are always handled—without analysis —by the same repressive machinery. For this reason "character is destiny," and *change of character is change of destiny.*

However, the "fixed" nature of repression in any character must therefore flow from that dyssynergy—that apprehension which the child feels upon first sensing the disturbed sonic image of the heart in relation to a danger. *Primary* repression is brought about by the superego formation, then, and both are created by growth as part and parcel of the process. And, *the heart is in this way conserved, at whatever characterologic cost.*

To return now to the case of the woman to whom the *gain* of the living child—no longer a *beating heart* within her—is also in part the loss of an "illusory member." Incapable now of hostility to the much-beloved child who affirms her feminine value, she nevertheless must *rearrange* not only her external social values, attachments, etc., but also *an internal change* in her own superego or ego ideal must come about; it is this which—as in the physician—must recall the *original* deep dyssynergic image of the heart.

We know that this kind of enuretic child forges an ego ideal which is phallic; mother and so too herself *must* have potentially *different* organs from other women; in her childhood, she considered herself *defective;* her "water pipe" was broken and there was no controlling it; this is the illusion of the enuretic child; she is *perpetually blamed for her enuresis;* her only chance to quiet her anxiety is to create and to aspire to the position of a phallic woman with absolute control and, similarly, to dominate men; by thirteen years of age, as is common to certain groups of enuretic children, her enuresis is under control. She has now reached the point where she can identify with the phallic woman *sexually;* the residuals of her early anxiety, *the fear of being blamed* for lack of control are now converted. *She becomes the blamer,* and seeks out masochistic men who relish being blamed. Under these conditions there is no anxiety; anxiety returns only at those points where she may fail to please a more successfully phallic woman; her character and her destiny hinge on these critical areas. When certain developments take place which indicate to her that her fetishistic image of women must be changed, she at first breaks out into her old terror that she is "going crazy."

Her primal oversevere repression is being defended by this idea of "going crazy"; her real terror is quite simply that she will so lose control of herself as to submit to a man, become pregnant and accept femininity entirely; when she is helped to move in this direction, the "going crazy" symptom markedly diminishes; incidentally so too does *her fear of being blamed and her blaming;* at the same time new abilities to work—*to synergize*—appear.

However, one final and deepest piece of aggression, dyssynergy, anxiety, repression and oversevere superego formation remain to be analyzed—that which results in the fear of "heart stop" and "collapse."

It will be remembered that she enjoyed the feeling of "two hearts beating inside"—her own and particularly the child's; the child represented her father to her; she played with the terrifying idea—as is not uncommon during pregnancy in such women—that the child might be destroyed by her *not letting it out of her belly.* She might *stop its heart*—such was her "illusion"; this was swiftly denied—she would be superb in the delivery of the child. But this entire preoccupation was a displacement from her deep and violent resentment of her father; her envy that he had the penis that could control the mother; she blamed him and other men more powerful for her mother's neglect of her when she was a child *at an age when her nervous system was not yet myelinized,* when she could not control all her functions, and was blamed and shamed for her urinating. As a result, she denied her father's importance; her mother was all-powerful; and she too must one day become like this all-powerful mother.

Or, in other words, her fear of "going crazy" was the fear of the mother's rebuke; she would make a mess; but the fear of "heart stop" was the *retaliation* (and the loss of all repressive defenses) against her quite simple oedipal wish to destroy the father beginning with two to three years of age when the need for the mother is not yet compensated for by the love of the father.

Her first—*primal*—repression, then, in an entire series of heart-conserving repressions was to repress every approach to her father, every capacity to submit to him; her next repression—*still within the primal series*—was further to mitigate this aggression by denying that mother had no controllable "spiggot"; and finally, as a result, failing to have such an instrument of control, *she* must be defective, must be blamed, until such a time as she can become sexual herself and become therefore the dominating *blamer*.

Her subsequential repressions—to avoid the frightening heart image—had to gravitate in this direction to forge the *blaming-dominating character* of the once enuretic child.

Growth itself, by making possible neo-ego formations, thus conserves our heart by a quantitative series of repressions. We transform this quantitative series into those qualitative traits, good or bad, advantageous or disadvantageous, which we call "I."

This determines not only our personality; it determines our synergies to no small degree; it tells us to what degree we learn the eternal vigilance and perpetual mobilization of manhood—to what degree we submit to the eternal tenderness and perpetual child-love of femininity.

The conservative aspects of repression show the synergic principle of survival operating at its most basic aspects. In this way "I," the neo-ego of speech, defends the "self" from the archi-ego of that easy terror and suicidal flight which comes from the inability to repress that which should—or must—be repressed.

Chapter VII

THE PAROXYSMAL TACHYCARDIAS:
INTRODUCTION

Up to now, the paroxysmal tachycardias, particularly the auricular type, have been assumed to be of "functional origin," i.e., capable of being set off by various *physiologic* conditions, emotion being *one* of these "explosives." Up to now, also, paroxysmal *ventricular* tachycardia has been considered to be, and justly so in the vast majority of instances, much more *serious* than the auricular form of the paroxysmal attack. Paroxysmal ventricular tachycardia brings with it the danger of heart failure and other complications much more cogently than the auricular type and, by contrast, frequently results from organic disease.

Both disturbances require the attention of trained internists and cardiologists. Nevertheless, whatever cardiologic care is required once the attack has started, there is no doubt that a goodly number, if not the vast majority of paroxysmal auricular tachycardias, are of sheer neurotic origin. The evidence indicates that a certain number of even paroxysmal *ventricular* tachycardias have their origin in neurotic stress, as will be illustrated here.

In this chapter, several cases in both men and women are only very briefly described; each case might very well occupy a book by itself. The *auricular* cases outlined here have all undergone analysis with salutary results.

Nowhere is it so clear that *a sonic system of image control dominates the heart mechanism in ordinary waking life,* and that the sonic image of the heart plays a great role in the development of human character.

For every person who has had these attacks has found his life and personality profoundly distorted by them; these attacks produce withdrawal from life in a very intense and characteristic way; they may also precipitate severe and long-standing sexual impotence in men.

It is, finally, with respect to the tachycardias that the sonic aspect of a synergic psychoneurology must make its new impact upon psychoanalysis.

A. Short Paroxysms of Auricular Tachycardia
Example of an Attack

A man, aged thirty-five, married, with a small son, and having no serious financial or physical problems other than his major complaint, presented himself for analysis of the following symptom: in the past few months, he had begun to have episodes of "paroxysmal auricular tachycardia" ("runaway heart")—so diagnosed definitely by his physician. These "runaways" went at the usual rate of 180–250 per minute; they lasted varying lengths of time, rarely as long as an hour, more often 5–10 minutes during which he had to lie down, trembled in terror, felt he was dying, "scared to death."

He was now sure he would die young—though he was otherwise in splendid physical health. The attacks of "runaway heart" came "out of the blue" even when he seemed to be having a good time—without any particular anxiety. Very soon three other major aspects of his character hove into sight. He could never finish anything he started, whether this be school, a book, a course of any kind, and would break off any one of these projects with various kinds of contempt for the person in authority connected with them—the teacher, the author, the lecturer "was a phony anyhow." He had to "cover up" all these unfinished projects with various kinds of lies to pretend to his friends that he had actually "gone through the course"—or "the book"—or whatever. He lived in constant terror of the humiliation of being exposed.

Second, he longed for his vanished attractiveness as a young adolescent and his promise of great intellectual attainments which he now thought lost to him forever.

Third, he resorted to magical thinking without realizing the extent to which it was magical—though "nothing worked out right," it was the fault of "some stupid son-of-a-bitch" or "some phony" who had failed him.

As a result of the operation of these three characteristics, he was in a constant terror of exposure and humiliation compensated by his attack upon "phonies."

One day, he had an attack which could be fully studied:

He was pretending to play football with his small son and another boy. He passed the ball to his son (who was a very brilliant precocious child mentally) and challenged the boy to try to "break through" the father's guard. As his son, carrying the ball, came at him—and with sudden small-boy agility shifted, eluding the father's lunging body, and "broke through" to make a goal—the father fell to the ground, with an intense and terrifying feeling of rage and humiliation. He lay flat on the ground, seeing his son touch goal, then thought of getting up. At this point his heart "started a runaway."

He turned over on the ground, clutching his heart as though he were dying; his son ran up and supported the father's head; his wife who had been watching the game with amusement came running, very concerned. He said, in a dramatic pleading voice which he himself despised, that he was on the brink of death. He was aware that he was dramatizing his very real symptoms, alarming in themselves, but he had had a sufficient number of attacks to know they were of neurotic origin and that this attack too would pass. He was aware that in some way he was "getting even" with his son and reacting to his humiliating failure to prevent his son from "breaking through," *and to his idea of what he might in fantasy have done to his son had he tackled him and brought him down.*

In a few minutes, thus cradled by wife and son, his heart rate abruptly reverted to normal; he got up, brushed off his clothes, went into the house, had a huge dinner (he was fond of "gorging himself"), had wine, and felt wonderful, elated at his "escape from death."

*   *   *   *   *

As with all analytic cases, much has to be condensed in reporting and the interpretation given to the facts presented in what must seem an arbitrary way. Yet, this is the risk in all analytic writings. Suffice it to say that this case yielded readily to therapy. Its psychopathy was that of a severely hostile but intense identification with mother in which any image of emergence of self (as in birth) was fought with the greatest danger of dismemberment and even decapitation with a corresponding defensive rage, as in his son's "breaking through his guard."

B. Paroxysmal Auricular Tachycardia of 30 Years' Duration in a Case of Interauricular Septal Defect

Here is a second example in a man treated ten years ago—a man of extraordinary courage and ability who had attacks of paroxysmal auricular tachycardia for over thirty years. His history is important not only because he had a congenital heart defect which made him a highly sensitive reactor to those conditions which made for "runaway heart"—but also because his attitudes toward life contain, for those who can read, a part of the secret of long life. Told the usual tale that he *"should have died at birth,"* he is now in his sixties surprisingly youthful, dynamic, successful, sexually vigorous—and free of attacks.

At the age of eight, John E. discovered—in the midst of a harrowing childhood including the divorce of his parents—that because of his heart he was "different from other boys." His mother, a fanatically religious person of Catholic background, and his father a Protestant, had separated three years before when he was five, and John had elected to go with his father, who became, however successful, something of a philanderer. Before the separation of his parents, John had had an older brother who died of blood poisoning from an accidental wound. In some way, John held himself responsible; he had cautioned his brother to take care of the wound immediately but the brother had refused and the mother had been too immersed in her fanaticism to give his brother the proper care. John had therefore elected to go with his father who, for all his tendencies to philander, was a more liberal, progressive man. John felt his manhood depended on being near his father. He visited his mother regularly, however, and devoted himself to care of her, during his adolescence and later manhood, as long as she lived. He was determined to profit from his father's success but hated his father's philandering; at the same time he was intensely jealous of his father's overt affection for various mistresses; there were sexual scenes which he managed to witness and which excited him prematurely. Nevertheless he admired his father's drive to success; John himself chose the Protestant faith.

John was told he "could never be like other boys" because he had an "athlete's heart" or "musical heart"—that he would have to stop all sports and must never exert himself in any way, that he must stay in bed for a few months and obey all his parent's and all medical instructions. (This was not the correct diagnosis.) John understood, obeyed, but thought that all this had resulted from his masturbation, already excessively stimulated by the activity of his father and the father's mistresses. John had never before had any intimation that his heart was "different"—except perhaps that he could not run as fast as other boys.

From eight years of age on, John refrained from all strenuous sports, but for the rest he was determined to deny any abnormality of his heart—as far as letting it interfere with his plan for life. He never stayed away from routine calisthenics though he avoided trying out for the teams.

At sixteen years of age, again a gym teacher perceived John's white face in the calisthenic line, questioned John closely; John stoutly denied ever having anything wrong with his heart or ever *knowing* there was anything wrong with it.

"Well," the gym teacher said, "I know enough to know that you have an athlete's heart. If you feel uncomfortable during calisthenics, just drop out of the line."

John never dropped out, worked on the parallel bars and the trapeze.

In the years of young manhood during the entrance of America into World War I, John met a girl who attracted him and yet whom he feared, because of her peculiar suspiciousness. John himself had begun to fear that maybe "he was a homosexual"; he had had several experiences of masturbatory play in his childhood with a perverted male secretary of his father's. This "fear of being a homosexual" John kept to himself; it became his deep "secret." He was determined one day to marry and have a family nonetheless; at the same time something indefinably disturbing about the girl interfered with his attraction to her.

John married the girl nonetheless. He resolved to dedicate himself to helping her get over her obvious emotional disturbances, in spite of his father's objections and warning that this was a premature marriage, too full of extra responsibilities.

1. THE FIRST ATTACK

At twenty-four years of age, six months after his marriage, John lost his job. Worried, he was walking along the street looking for work—*his wife had just announced her pregnancy to him*—and he felt *acutely humiliated* by his father's prediction of economic disaster—when he felt his heart suddenly "flip" or "turn over like a motor turns over when you crank it." It "turned over" once, twice and a third time and it was "off to the races." It hammered away at a very fast but very regular rate; he felt very weak and sat down "like a child." He forced himself to stay calm, reasoning that this had something to do with his "musical heart"; he remained for two hours—his heart racing steadily. He saw a pile of lumber down the street; practically crawled to it; stretched out and lay there for three hours more until—after a total of five hours of runaway heart—it suddenly reverted to normal rhythm. He returned home, saw no doctor, faced his wife's tension and nagging and went to sleep.

"Looking back on it," he said, when he first recounted it, "after all the attacks I had for the next thirty years, I'm sure it had something to do with my wife's getting pregnant—though then I just felt humiliated being out of a job at a time like that. I sat on the curb just wishing to be a kid again."

2. THE SECOND ATTACK. THE CORRECT DIAGNOSIS

Three years later, at twenty-seven years of age, he had his second attack under suddenly tragic conditions. He had prospered; he had forced his wife—by "sheer will power" and patience to become more the woman he wanted—at least as far as her social appearance and manners were concerned; he had a child whom he adored.

The child died—after an overwhelming infection. The shock, his grief, the funeral brought him to the verge of breakdown. Nevertheless John forced himself back to work. Two days after the funeral, riding a bus, standing in the crowd holding on to a strap and trying to read the paper, he felt his knees sag and he found himself, fully conscious, slipping to the floor. In a flash of thought he saw himself dying and his body descending into his grave, as his child's body had descended; as he slid to the floor of the bus *the terror of the feeling* started another attack of paroxysmal auricular tachycardia. With his heart racing, he forced himself to get up, to get out at the next stop. He lay down on a bench in the subway for two hours; the attack continued; he forced himself to go home, with his heart racing and his head queer; said nothing to his wife, lay down for four hours more. With the attack still going, he got up to eat dinner; his wife noticed his pallor; he said it was nothing; he finally admitted he was having some kind of attack. A physician was called, a heart specialist.

The diagnosis of "paroxysmal auricular tachycardia" was made; but more than that—the so-called "musical heart" was correctly diagnosed for the first time; it was a heart with a "defect," a small "hole" between the two auricles—so that some of the blood in each heart would be intermixed with each contraction of the heart as already described in another case. The blood rushing through the hole—venous from the right heart, oxygenated from the left heart—made the musical sound that had been heard before. In other words, the auricles and ventricles were under extra burden; probably in this way his "heart pacer" was more sensitized than might otherwise have been the case.[1] And though one is *born* with this condition, *he never had an attack until twenty-four years of age when he had learned of his first impregnation of his wife*. This second attack had been started by what was obviously a hysteric terror of dying and "descending," as his child had just done. In the dim background was the memory of his brother's death and burial. There was, too, the opposite terror (and unconscious wish) of "giving birth."

The doctor was astonished at the patient's survival, cardiac com-

---

[1] An identical case in a somewhat younger man recently has been treated by me. This case had a normal heart.

pensation (achieved by John's persistent attention to calisthenics), and fine physique. "You're the kind of case," the doctor said, according to John, "who should have been dead at birth." The doctor, however, could not seem to stop the attack at once; he gave John some sedatives; the attack stopped during sleep, some ten hours after it had begun.

3. SUBSEQUENT ATTACKS. THE SICK CHILD

John went to work the next day and every day. He fought his way to the top of his field, his intelligence and daring, his capacity to "identify" with other people, study them, and figure out what they were thinking, won him wealth and reputation on a very wide scale.

They had another child. *When the child contracted scarlet fever,* John had his third attack. When a few months later *a neighbor's child contracted polio,* he had his fourth attack. By this time, John was determined to try to find out what started them by his own self-observation, since physicians could tell him only that "some cases of paroxysmal auricular tachycardia are of emotional origin."

He observed that, shortly after alarm about anything relating to a child, just before the attack, he would have "waves or fluttering of the stomach." Later, in the analysis, on the brink of an attack that was stopped by timely interpretation, he was able to admit that just before the waves or fluttering of the stomach, there were *waves and fluttering of the anus* (connected in his unconscious with "birth mutilation"). But by himself he never could get any further than the observation of the threat to a child and the "fluttering" in the stomach. On hundreds of anxiety-provoking occasions, his heart would "flip" or "turn over" once or twice but it would never become a true "runaway"—*unless the death of a child seemed imminent* (e.g., the first attack which reappeared as the wish to abort the child).

For many years John went on through his life, working hard, drinking cocktails, smoking—then he thought cigarettes might have something to do with it and gave up smoking. But his heart still "flipped" under anxiety. He went through a siege of pneumonia. Finally his child, grown up, went away to college.

4. THE "RUNAWAY HEART OF CAPITULATION"

John was alone with his wife. He was just fifty. He had always been faithful to her, had never philandered. He had struggled with her suspiciousness and peculiar social behavior over the years; then she entered the menopause. Her ever-present jealousy of his contacts with many important men and women of culture now began to mount with increasing violence. He faced every barrage of accusation; he loved her in spite of everything; he enjoyed her sexually. As these scenes with his wife grew more and more unbearable, he would try to calm himself by living on sedatives, which had become his mainstay in these trying days.

At this juncture, a new and powerful business combine arose and threatened his position in his field. He had one of two alternatives; to engage in a protracted battle with them for control or to merge with them and take a subsidiary but very lucrative administrative position within the new combine free of all care and secure for the rest of his life; he was too respected, feared, and powerful to exist as their rival.

All his impulses cried out for fight; but his strength was sapped by the emotional onslaughts of his wife—and by another rather unusual fact. He found himself very much attracted to one of the men in the combine—almost a physical attraction. It would be a close friendship—something to take the place of his lost brother or perhaps his son. His wife—in moments of seeming clarity—urged capitulation.

John capitulated.

As he told of this, John's anguish broke out all over again; he kicked his legs helplessly.

"I capitulated," he almost yelled. "I capitulated."

The moment he signed the documents that day, John began to feel something happening inside him, "eating him up"; the internal gnawing increased for hours then abruptly his heart "flipped" once, twice, and a third time and it was "off to a runaway." It "ran away" for twelve hours; none of the medications administered by a physician worked (quinidine, procaine amide hydrochloride). Finally a very greatly increased dose of phenobarbital and a mild dose of digitalis apparently made it revert to normal.

As John told me this portion of his history, I asked: "What does the word *capitulation* mean to you?"

He said: "Letting a man have his way with you—to surrender—give up."

For a while, John's tensions were lessened. He adjusted to his new role and was prepared to serve out his life as a subsidiary administrator. He was past fifty; his only child had made its own preparations for a life away from home. And John now faced the final epoch of his relationship with his wife.

She became literally frenzied in her accusations; one night, the distilled essence of her hatred for him burst out beyond all rational bounds. Her words came at him "like sledge hammer blows punching me in the belly." He could feel his stomach muscles tightening and getting painful with each one of her venomously phrased attacks. He sat there numbed and the waves of stomach pain ascended "higher toward the heart." Suddenly he was aware of the fluttering sensation in his rectum and stomach and then he was aware that "this was the end of something." She was insane; he could see now what he had always refused to believe, the actual extent of her repressed hatred for all men—and dimly he recognized something in himself was at an end —something that had been identified with her and was precious to him maybe even because of hate. At this moment, the attack began. It was the most violent of all.

He tried everything to stop it. Nothing helped. After many hours, he felt he was dying and he held up his arms with the sensation that his blood was draining out of him; with his last strength, almost losing consciousness, he staggered to the bathroom and forced himself to vomit—to vomit out everything—and to keep vomiting. That stopped the attack. "It was," he said to me, "as though I had to decide which one of us would live—inside me."

John's wife was indeed psychotic. She was now actively hallucinating and delusional. While preparations were made to commit her to a hospital, she committed suicide.

John never had another attack. He lived alone, continued to work, and eventually retired from all routine. He is now past sixty, admired as a leader in his field, and active only as a consultant. He is a remarkably youthful man, and in spite of his "interauricular defect" he gives every evidence of surviving for many years to come.

In our work together—at one point, John spontaneously described the following:

5. PREGNANCY FANTASY

"A funny thing, doctor, for the two years I was courting my wife— after every date with her, I would be sick to my stomach and I would come home and vomit. I don't know why. And that reminds me:

"The two times she was pregnant, and she had morning sickness, I had morning sickness right along with her. When her belly got bigger, I had the distinct feeling my belly was bigger. And when she felt life—it seemed to me, I felt something kicking inside my guts. Finally, when she went into labor, my belly would cramp up right along with hers."

John learned that his own neurosis contained a deep identification with his hated and loved mother—whose death he did not like to admit and whom he felt he had sinfully deserted; he learned that there were women, like his wife (who always seemed to him to be more child than woman) who have the capacity to attract the hidden neurotic forces within a man and out of hate and fear to make that man "pregnant" with the burden of a full-grown woman who does not ever wish to be a wife. John's life had been so arranged—together with the increase of unconscious ("defective") passive feelings about his heart which prevented him "from being like other boys"—that he was prepared by his neurosis to accept that "phantom pregnancy." John had remembered that once, for a masquerade ball, he had dressed like a woman and he resembled his mother so strikingly he had been mistaken for her. He never again dressed as a woman going to a ball.

*   *   *   *   *

With respect to the form of *breathing* that is associated with an attack, the following observation is of interest:

An internist had been examining a woman with malignant hypertension who had never before had paroxysmal tachycardia. He asked her to breathe to study her respiration, and, very tense, she began to hyperventilate (overbreathe). In a few seconds she developed a harmless but to her terrifying complication—namely, *the tetany* resulting from too rapid a loss of carbon dioxide, a condition in which the voluntary muscles particularly of fingers and toes stiffen "like a person dying" (tetanic contraction). Her face broke out into a sweat of terror and her eyes bulged. He commanded her sharply to hold her breath (the carbon dioxide is quickly restored and the tetanic stiffening resolves). The next second her heart began an abrupt paroxysmal auricular tachycardia and as abruptly stopped a few minutes later.

John E. reported precisely the same observation to me. He would be thinking of something and suddenly there would come a sensation of nameless terror—in a flash—and he would stop breathing. At that moment his heart would "flip" and "turn over" and "race away."

The *meaning* of this action is that of final culmination of the entire psychological process. John would have a fleeting vision of being his dead brother (or dead child) or wife whom he wished would die—and of himself lying in the coffin and the lid being closed down upon him. The similarity of this "last breath of life" to the "first breath," i.e., to birth, is obvious.

*   *   *   *   *

The very brief "thumbnail sketch" of a man's history just drawn to illustrate the psychic contours surrounding "runaway heart" can be deceptively "interpreted" in the usual way. This man, John E., was identified with his mother, had a hidden deep love for his father. His paroxysmal attacks can be said to be due to an abruptly released repression. The attack stops when the repression is re-established. Our ordinary interpretation might add with complete justice: the sudden release of repression would greatly stimulate the sympathetic nervous fibers and overcome the inhibiting parasympathetic nerve fibers to the heart, thus producing a paroxysm of tachycardia. When the repression is re-established the parasympathetic simply regains control. The treatment of such a man is precisely the treatment of an ego which contains a severely repressed hidden identification with a mother whom he distrusted, feared and hated on some scores, and loved on others. This increased his homosexual ego instincts and weakened his heterosexual ego instincts. His increased homosexual instincts were sublimated intellectually for purposes of control of his environment —and whenever this failed, the "attack" broke out.

But this type of interpretation will not do.

Observations in women will show that there is more here, but even in the case of John E. there are certain things which can only be explained by the deep psychic equivalence of the image of the heart with that of a child. The heart's beat, newly individuated at birth in relation to breathing and circulatory work, plays a particular, hitherto unrecognized role in establishing the foundations of the sense of reality— a sense which begins when the circulating blood of the child at birth "flows into" its first outline of itself as a real external ego who has just undergone a transition from the state of being "unreal," that is, an utterly dependent internal portion of the mother's body and circulation. Psychic reality begins when the umbilical circulation is cut and the full erotic pulsing tide of life courses through the newborn's body and brain, powered by its own heart. Psychic reality begins when, in the brain, the new heart beat etches the full circulatory outline of the new child. This brain-heart change is not the first, though it is perhaps the most obvious and visibly dramatic change. There were others all along the way; the first was the tremendous event when the rapidly growing cells of the embryo suddenly "created" the beat of the thickening arterial segments-to-be-hearts—the very pulse of life; the second was the long process by which these two segments joined, elongated, coiled, descended from the neck area of the embryo finally to become established as "the heart" within a chest cavity. At approximately six months of intrauterine life we say the foetus is "viable," i.e., could theoretically survive if prematurely born; and the third great brain-cardiac epoch is birth, three months later. It thus ought to be clear that we are not speaking of any "birth trauma"; that was Otto Rank's folly. We are speaking of an entire series of brain-heart events which prepares for the sonic heart image, the establishment of the pulse of life, the provision of *viability* in which the heart finally becomes the completed work machine, and the separation from the circulation of the mother when the new heart beat and heart rate and blood pressure mark out the new child. Since, furthermore, the "heart throb" presides over our erotic life—our pleasure and our pain in all our sexual erotic tissues—this series of brain-cardiac events belongs to all the implications of psychoanalytic theory; however, it enables that theory via the principle of synergy and the image of the heart to reach deeper into the structure of thinking and feeling than ever before.

The evidence of a tachycardia birth trauma is not hard to find.

Recently, paroxysmal auricular tachycardia in an infant has been described by Wilburn and Mack (1954). The attack began *in utero* just before birth, continuing for three and a half days after birth at a rate in excess of 280 per minute. After three and a half days and (appropriate treatment) the heart rate became 128 per minute. Twelve hours later, a second attack began; it lasted more than twelve hours and subsided once more. At six weeks of age, a third attack began, with a rate in excess of 312 per minute. A day and a half later the attack subsided. At fifteen months of age the child was apparently normal and free of attacks.

In 1943, Eideken gathered only seventeen cases of paroxysmal auricular tachycardia whose rate exceeded 300 per minute. Of these, twelve were infants. The most rapid rate was 365 per minute in an infant who died.

C. Episodes of Paroxysmal Auricular Tachycardia in Women

1. paroxysmal auricular tachycardia in pregnancy

A thirty-year-old woman in fine health, Sara G., who has had previous children and is now five months pregnant, walks up a hill one evening with her husband to attend a play in a summer theater. They are handed programs and find their seats. As the theater begins to darken, Sara G. sees on her program an actor's name which abruptly reminds her of a boy with whom she used to play sexual games when they were "next-door" children—games upon which her severe, dominating, overclean, masturbation-condemning mother poured moral damnation. At once, *upon seeing the name as the theater darkens,* she *feels uneasy.* In the play, one of the female actors comes out with a bow and makes a motion as though shooting an arrow at a boy. The motion of "shooting the arrow" begins her attack of tachycardia.

They left the theater, walked down the hill to a local doctor who said the attack came because of pregnancy and walking up the hill. He tried to stop the attack by "pressure on the vagus," which did not work. (*In another attack in another female patient, on the basis of the same theory, mecholyl, a powerful "parasympathetic* hormone," was injected with complete failure and very distressing and alarming symptoms of circulatory collapse to boot.) Sara G.'s first attack stopped spontaneously after about twenty minutes.

Sara G. went through her pregnancy and delivery of a normal child uneventfully; her obstetrician said he had seen many "paroxysmal tachycardias" begin in pregnancy and generally, as far as he knew, they disappeared after delivery. Such was not the course here. Instead the attacks came more frequently and while some were short attacks, others lasted as long as three to four hours. Her heart was completely normal in every form of physical examination. She began nevertheless to believe herself a cardiac invalid, convinced she would die.

During her pregnancy her physician had explained that this was due to the increased cardiac burden of pregnancy and presented her with the following facts, all true (from which she concluded her heart just could not stand pregnancy).

During her pregnancy the mother's heart work increases very slowly. This increase begins at the twelfth week and continues gradually to increase through the twenty-fourth week. From the twenty-fourth week until the thirty-sixth week the work of the mother's heart increases more sharply to reach a maximum of approximately 50 per cent above the normal output before pregnancy. The greatest maternal heart work takes place in the thirty-sixth week. But then, from the thirty-sixth to the fortieth week, in the last four weeks before delivery, the mother's heart burden is decreased by 25 per cent— as the heart of the child prepares to carry its own burden of individuality.

However, Sara G's first attack took place just at twenty-four weeks of pregnancy before the sharper increase in heart work.

After a number of years of worry and terror, Sara G. came for analysis. The analysis abolished the attacks completely and she is now able to take care of her house and family with energy for other work in addition.

Sara G. had been born the second daughter to a Jewish family in Canada. Her mother dominated the father completely, washed everything—including her children's genitals—incessantly, and in the fury of cleaning and managing the lives of everyone, managed also to convey to Sara that her father must have something wrong with his head and his testicles. The mother screamed at the father when he bought a second-hand car, predicted an accident, which happened when Sara at eight, against her mother's command, decided to venture out for a ride in the new car with father. Father became nervous and promptly ran the car into a ditch.

Then Sara's cousin died and someone took a picture of the little girl in her coffin and sent it to the family. Sara's mother put the picture on the piano. Sara developed a terror of dying and of being put in a coffin. Then a flu epidemic hit the small town. Her older, favored sister died, and her father was among the men detailed to load the corpses of flu victims onto trucks in the night for burial. Sara felt that everybody wished she should have died and her sister should have lived. She felt too that "she was more like father"; fortunately she had other female mother ideals in aunts and teachers and gradually covered over the past by determining to leave home, start a new life, get married and have her own children. Among the memories of her childhood was the little Christian boy with whom she had had sexual games to her mother's loud horrific dismay. Her husband was part Jewish, part Christian, a fact which made Sara always feel that her mother would never accept her husband or her children.

It was possible quickly to establish three facts. *The first* was that her fear of death and her horror of being buried (the photograph of the child in the coffin was to her a *sleeping* not a dead child) *came long before the attacks of paroxysmal tachycardia*. These attacks had in their turn brought them to the surface and had increased that fear; she could not recall a rapid heart in childhood, only a choking sensation; *she never could sleep in bed flat on her back stretched out with her hands at rest upon her body;* she had to alter something in that position—either her hands had to be flung out or her body twisted away from that position; *otherwise she would be the "dead sleeping child in the coffin." Second,* she felt that she should have died and her more brilliant and beloved older sister should have lived; this, she felt, would have been her mother's wish if the choice between them had to be made; *she, the baby of the family, had survived;* and at the time of her first attack of paroxysmal tachycardia, she knew that the child with whom she was pregnant *would also be the baby of her family—* she would have no more children; *she identified herself at that point very sharply with the baby within her.* At the same time, she had begun to dramatize the hostility of her own mother toward her husband. In other words, at the time of the first attack of "runaway heart" she was *dually* identified; unconsciously with the hideous aspect of mother who, she thought, would have preferred her to die in place of her sister and who thought there was something wrong with father's head and testicles; and more consciously with the child within her own belly. *Third, all her attacks took place thereafter only in the presence of her husband—or when he was within call or easy reach.*

In the theater, as the lights dimmed, she saw the name which reminded her of the Christian boy with whom she used to play tabooed sex games; and, on that afternoon, they had just come away from the home of a Jewish couple in whose presence the husband had been treated as "a leper"—with veiled contempt, she thought. It had "gnawed at her." She felt horribly humiliated—a failure. She should never have been born. She should have been dead, should have died in the place of her sister, and have lain dead sleeping in a coffin as in a photograph on the piano. She opened the program, saw the name of the taboo boy— as taboo as her husband—in her memory heard her mother's screaming; and, at the moment the arrow was shot out by the girl actor on stage, her heart "flipped."

*   *   *   *   *

Every experienced analyst (and deeply intuitive person) knows that neurotic heart acceleration in and of itself arises from fear and particularly sexual fear. But "automatic escape" of an organ so central, so vital as the heart is not to be explained so simply. Put teleologically for a moment, there is a wisdom to the operation of the marvelous mechanisms of the human body. The "escape" or "flight" of the heart serves an economic purpose. Something very deeply self-preserving is accomplished by paroxysmal tachycardia; it is of course not desirable that a human being should be driven to such desperate lengths and to such acute alarming discomfort to induce so automatic a defensive flight. But, at the same time, anyone who has ever seen a person with paroxysmal tachycardia lie full-length and immobilized with cardiac terror will soon realize that this immobilization serves a particular purpose, however primitive that service. (Men will not so easily lie down, they get up and walk around in a "terror of stopping.")

It cannot be explained by the usual well-known analytic mechanisms, as already stressed. It is neither due to "oral aggression" alone nor to "anal sadomasochism" nor to simple "rape fear" nor "castration anxiety," though it can be found in many subtle ways to *partake* of all these panics and guilt-making impulses arising out of the primitive depths of individual evolution.

For purposes of contrast, one might state a case of very great acceleration but not true paroxysmal tachycardia in a woman, Anna T., who had been actually raped when she was a very small girl of seven. After that she developed rheumatic heart disease from which she recovered, and thereafter her character was so changed that in her mother's words she "lived with death." She married, had children, but thereafter never went to bed to have sexual intercourse *without her heart going faster and pounding,* until the act, which she nevertheless enjoyed, was over. She never had paroxysmal tachycardia, but her heart symptoms were so pronounced that a diagnosis of "coronary disease" was made; however, pounding of this kind may, as we have noted before (the case of Martin O.), produce coronary symptoms of an alarming character.

2. PAROXYSMAL AURICULAR TACHYCARDIA AND RAPE FEAR

Contrast the case of Anna T. with that of Margaret R., who had a small daughter of nine. One day the daughter went visiting at a friend's home in an apartment building a block or two away. The mother in that home was an older more experienced woman to whom Margaret R. looked up, but whom she also resented because the older woman seemed to have won the affection of Margaret R.'s daughter. She suggested to Margaret that the daughter should be allowed to go home by herself to increase the child's sense of independence. Margaret had acquiesced. On the way out of the older woman's apartment building, the child was assaulted by the janitor but managed to escape unharmed. The child came home and in great fear reported what happened to her mother Margaret. Terrified, enraged, horrified, Margaret tried to reach the older woman on the phone—certain that the older woman did not know what had happened, did not know the janitor in her building was a psychopath, and yet had been mainly responsible for the child's lack of protection. The line was busy. Margaret R. developed a severe attack of paroxysmal tachycardia lasting several hours.

Observe, however, the point at which the attack begins in Margaret R. *It begins when she cannot reach the older woman upon* whom Margaret R. has depended and thus feels *humiliated and publicly to be condemned for having allowed her own protectiveness of the child to be suspended,* for having relied upon the older woman's suggestion. The "busy signal" of the older woman's phone is a "cut-off" of or "busy barrier" to Margaret R.'s *quick need to "connect with mother," to report and retaliate against the criminal man.* (Margaret R. had once in her life seen her father's sex organ by accident and had been shocked by the great size of it—the memory of it still shocking and reported to me with a subdued expression of shame.) The emotional mood is difficult to describe: humiliation, dread, condemnation, shame, rage that has no outlet, despair without comfort seem to appear at once—an abrupt sense of being cut off and being propelled out into a world of danger and bestiality. Not uncommon is the cry "I wish I had never been born" (a girl so to be attacked). Then she realized there was only the frightened child upon whom to visit anger that cannot be expressed because the child is after all guiltless. *All feminine sexuality and all its results*—and all retaliatory powers—*are cut off at the root,* the entire "sack of ego" is emptied and, denying the child just as it might be denied even if it still existed in the uterus, the heart automatically reverts to the ego's first awareness of life—just before it began to be an individual—toward the hiatus of birth. Not rape, then, but an assault on the entire beginning and meaning of individuality. The obverse of this would be, as it once would have been, to seize a weapon and kill the psychopathic rapist—parallel to the "shooting of a boy" by a girl, as in the case of Sara G. Such an attack includes rage against the penis and testicles and head of a man. A justified if hideous castrative aspect of dominating mothers exists in the characters of these women who are unable to retaliate and who suffer from "paroxysmal tachycardia of emotional origin."

Of interest, finally, in the childhood of Margaret R. is the fact that when she was eight, she and her cousin had very nearly been "taken for a ride" by a psychopathic torso-murderer of small girls. Only Margaret's memory of her mother's warning that there was such a man in the neighborhood saved her; she said, "I screamed at my cousin who nearly accepted the ride he offered us; I ran and she after me until I thought my heart would burst."

To have her own child actually assaulted years later was sufficient provocation for the paroxysmal attack.

3. PAROXYSMAL TACHYCARDIA AND "ACCIDENT FEAR"

Another example, a very short attack in a third woman, Teresa W., illustrates its swift oscillation in response to the strain of everyday living.

Teresa W., her mother and father, her husband and her two very small sons drive out on a crowded parkway in a large and powerful car. Her husband is at the wheel, her two small sons and herself in the front seat. In the back seat are Teresa's mother and father, the mother a quietly critical, severe, tense woman, the father an easy-going man. The back seat is also filled with packages and baggage so that everyone is rather tightly packed into the car.

Teresa's husband drives for awhile on the slower-moving inner lane and then finally pulls out into the faster-moving outside lane. At this moment Teresa looks back at her mother and notices the mother silently shaking her head against the move to the outside. Though her husband is an excellent driver and has never had an accident, Teresa becomes apprehensive and as tense as her mother in the back seat. As they begin to pass other cars, Teresa shudders at the "close shaves"—

the narrow distance between the inside and outside lane of moving cars, which she now watches compulsively, with a mounting sense of disaster. Suddenly she looks up at the front mirror and sees another car behind them, driven by a Negro apparently intent upon crowding either her husband or the man on the inside out of the way to push his way through in violation of all traffic rules. Teresa's husband looks up at the same moment; the Negro now maneuvers his car perilously close to both cars ahead of him—and Teresa breaks out into an attack of runaway heart.

She says nothing but is terrified; her husband catches a glimpse of her face and recognizes (as he tells her later) that she is probably having an attack—she has had so many he knows them now; he quickly maneuvers his car to block the Negro whose auto falls back out of sight.

Teresa's attack, lasting perhaps in all thirty seconds, stops as abruptly as it began. The journey continues uneventfully.

The next day, Teresa brings this episode into the analytic session. She knew by then that her apprehension of catastrophe was a chronic thing, particularly on a highway—*except when she was driving alone, her own hands on the wheel. By herself she was absolutely calm, confident, in complete control,* and had driven a car long distances on dangerous highways. Under these conditions, the chronic apprehension of catastrophe was completely absent. The moment she had to relinquish control of the wheel to anyone, husband or not, the sense of apprehension and catastrophe returned. If a stranger was at the wheel she suppressed her expressions of terror; if her husband drove, she constantly had to make all kinds of suggestions as to speed, lanes, nearness to other cars, etc. But with her mother, her quietly but severely critical mother shaking her head (compare with the case of Sara G. and her "accident" with her father)—then Teresa was "fit to be tied."

The sight of the Negro (taboo man) trying to "squeeze in" from behind is obvious in its meaning. The aggressive Negro, the inverse counterpart of the easy-going father, expresses Teresa's fearful hidden wish toward the easy-going father—and surely defines Teresa's conscious fear, that *if she and anything belonging to her are not precisely what her mother wants her and them to be*—in the mother's presence, particularly—then "catastrophe" will take place. *The more tightly packed things are in a small space, and something sexually taboo threatens to smash its way in*—with no room left for maneuver or escape—the greater is the tendency to paroxysmal tachycardia. Teresa's attack stops the moment she sees her husband—aware of her dilemma —block the Negro and get away into the clear, forcing the Negro "out of sight," i.e., repressing the taboo sexual impulse and fear. The *child* portion of the equation in this small crisis was of course projected as the terror of the mutilation death of her two small sons.

It is, therefore, in women that the concept of paroxysmal tachycardia as of psychologic origin—so clearly a manifestation of the dyssynergic image of the heart—can be secured as proven.

It is important to stress the fact again that, as the case of Teresa W. shows, it is not "rape fear" which is basic nor "castration of the woman's illusory penis" nor "hostility to a child" nor "anal attack" nor "homosexual panic." None of these will suffice by themselves.

It is rather a totally new concept that is required, the concept of the image of the heart as a root portion of the image of the ego.

4. PAROXYSMAL AURICULAR TACHYCARDIA AND "SEXUAL DISSOLUTION OF SELF"

The "final" attack in a woman, Rita N., under treatment will be of interest.

Her attacks changed their character as therapy progressed. They became brief, lasting only a few minutes, as Rita N. became more and more aware of the dyssynergic image of the heart and its projections into the outside world.

She had in particular equated—unconsciously—the ideas of death, birth, and the "sexual dissolution of self" which went together with complete orgasm, attributing to the power of the father's sexual organ the magical power "to create" her and "to destroy" her.

Just previous to the attack about to be described, Rita N. had two very brief paroxysms; one upon hearing of a "scandalous" sexual affair involving a woman she feared and hated, the other immediately upon learning about the pregnancy of a woman toward whom she had intense feelings of rivalry.

The final attack (final in the sense that it demonstrates the growing power of complete surveillance over the dyssynergic image of the heart as it is projected into the terrifying idea of the "sexual dissolution of self") came upon reading a lurid passage in a novel *The Outsider,* by the Negro novelist Richard Wright.

This was the passage ("He" is the Negro hero of the tale):

> He switched off the light and kissed her and she melted, letting her lips cling fully to his; he carried her to the bed and they slept together in their damp clothes, being too drunk to undress. It was the beginning of the unleashing of a mutual silent, and intense passion. During the following week, Cross had her in his bed, on the floor, standing up, in the bathroom. . . .

The last sentence particularly consciously repelled her—its treatment of a woman as "a stuffed dummy," and it *started the attack.* She instantly recognized that it had aroused an unconscious terror as well as a conscious repulsion. She immediately began slowly to reread the passage; when she reached the word "melted" and perceived its aggression against individuality also connected with the orgastic idea of "sexual dissolution of self" and its association of death (and birth) because of the power of the taboo father (Negro), the attack came swiftly to an end.

D. Attacks of Paroxysmal Ventricular Tachycardia

It is now known that even the more serious ventricular tachycardia can be produced paroxysmally by sheer psychologic stimuli. Recently a proven case was reported in a woman who had a paroxysm *while the electrocardiograph was running* (for another aspect of investigation of her problem.) The *ventricular* paroxysm occurred when a box of pills was opened with the design of having her take one for her physicians to study its effect upon her. *At the moment of her perceiving the pills,* an intense expression of terror registered on her face and the electrocardiograph registered a paroxysmal ventricular tachycardia, the *proven* result of sheer terror.

These cases are more common than is realized. And, to match the man (John E.) who had *paroxysmal auricular tachycardia for thirty years,* here is the case of a woman who had *paroxysmal ventricular tachycardia for over twenty-four years.*

It must be remembered that, while in paroxysmal *auricular* tachycardia organic disease as a cause is quite rare, on the contrary it has been thought that in paroxysmal *ventricular* tachycardia, well over 90 per cent show some organic cause. (Both quinidine and digitalis are capable of precipitating an attack of ventricular tachycardia.)

Our accent upon this case must avoid the detailed pharmacologic facts, disputes, and theories; we are concerned here with the psychic factors so far as we have been able to obtain them.

According to Schlachman and Bellin,[2] the patient was a fifty-four-year-old woman whose first attack occurred at the age of thirty years. These attacks lasted a few minutes and recurred once monthly. Her menopause began at the age of forty years and at this time the attacks were more frequent and of longer duration. On several occasions she had to be hospitalized. Twelve years ago, she had an attack which persisted without interruption for three days. An adenoma of the thyroid had been removed recently; it had been considered an exciting factor.

This time the patient, who had had nine pregnancies, had sustained a violent emotional shock. *A child next door, about four years old, a boy, had accidentally hung himself and strangled to death.*

This was immediately followed by her *paroxysmal ventricular tachycardia which lasted for twenty-three days, at a rate of 220 per minute.* (Schlachman reports that he finally succeeded in stopping the attack by an oral dose of digitoxin [0.8 mg.] repeated the next morning in spite of a pulse rise from 160/min. to 190/min., after all other measures had failed.)

This type of case—with its provocation by the *shocking death of a child*—is very similar to that of the case of John E.

And the more one studies paroxysmal tachycardias in general, the more one perceives that *the entire heart mechanism responds to* all the "branchings of thought and feeling" stemming from the sonic image of the heart.

Thus all the considerations we have thus far developed, show the

2 I am deeply indebted to Dr. Milton M. Schlachman and Dr. David E. Bellin for the case material.

118   The Sonic Image of the Heart

same "cross reference" between the ideas of "heart-limbs-memory-mind-anxiety." Particularly, any threat to the life of a child, in certain human beings, of both sexes, provokes paroxysmal tachycardia; but especially dismemberment-decapitation threats of all kinds from accidental hanging to the implications of rape, rape murder and torso dismemberment provoke the "runaway heart."

Of all of these ideas, birth is the prototype.

Chapter VIII

ANALYSIS OF EDGAR ALLAN POE'S
THE TELL-TALE HEART

No student of human psychology, in particular no hunter of the psychic forces behind heart disease, can afford not to know intimately and profoundly the life, work and greatness of Edgar Allan Poe.

For Poe's life is the life of child and man under continuous psychic and external attack upon his heart, his genital, his manhood. His literary achievement—the throbbing and rhyming leap of his incomparable musical speech—is child's and man's heart and psyche fighting back. Not only was his work a desperate rescue from the assault of a dinosaur's (disguised as human) world upon his very early childhood —from the moment of his naked, newborn entrance into this world to the moment of naked exit—but much more than that, chiselled into the stone pages of time is the track and travail of his heart for all of us to perceive its neurotic force as a warning.

Very few things, in this life, are as terrifying as the heart signs of an excruciatingly intense neurotic anxiety as in certain explosive forms of panic reactions. Who of even "normals" has not been alarmed, during high fever, by the crescendo sound of the heart beat in his own ears or by the sensation of the heart leaping "to the throat" in an accelerating palpitation? The "pressure to confess" is enormously heightened by this particular kind of *cardiac whipping* administered by the long arm of hideous psychic guilt; this is the basis of certain drugs used to induce signed confessions of crimes that may or may not have been committed.

There is a letter written by Poe as he was emerging from one of his

119

final "deliria" in the last, the fortieth, year of his life (July 7th, 1849) which contains this cryptic sentence: *"I was never really insane except upon occasions when my heart was touched"*—by which he means actually physically touched by his various breakdowns. By twenty-two years, after he left West Point, his complaints of "weak heart" and "nervous depressions" are constant and by thirty-five, he has had three severe "heart attacks." His horror of the exaggerated beating of his own heart during one such attack is contained in this verse from the famous poem *For Annie:*

> The moaning and groaning,
>   The sighing and sobbing,
> Are quieted now,
>   With that horrible throbbing
> At heart: ah that horrible,
>   Horrible throbbing.

*   *   *   *   *

Among his *Tales Psychological and Gruesome,* we find the subdivision *Tales of Insanity* which comprise two: *Berenice,* the story of a man who must pull the teeth from the corpse of his beloved (a sufferer from epilepsy) who is buried by mistake before she is really dead; and *The Tell-Tale Heart,* the shortest and stripped the most bare of any extraneous detail.

In *The Tell-Tale Heart,* a man obviously mad, but denying his madness as he talks and boasts of his superacute hearing, describes how he murdered an old man because of that old man's evil eye, on the eighth day of an intense nighttime rehearsal of his murderous plan, *and how the sound of the weirdly living heart beat of the old man* (dismembered and buried under the floor) *forced him to confess.* The madman says:

"Object there was none,"—except an obsessional thought:
"I think it was his eye! yes, it was this! One of his eyes resembled that of a vulture—a pale, blue eye, with a film over it. Whenever it fell upon me, my blood ran cold."

(This circulatory expression—*my blood ran cold*—is an important one to our present purpose. In human speech it has many more direct cardiac parallels such as "an icy hand gripped my heart," etc. Poe himself as a child used to fear what happens to the old man in this dream— being murdered, as he slept, by an icy hand upon his chest in the darkness.)

To go on: For seven long nights, the madman (like *The Shadow* of our current mysteries) rehearses the approach to the old man's room, opening the door just a little at a time with a shielded lamp and, after an hour of this cautious entrance, shining a slit of light upon the old man's sleeping face in the hope of catching the Evil Eye in the beam. But the Eye is always closed. (This is the reverse of a child's witnessing eye opening the door just a crack to look out into a lighted room *or that of a loving parent opening the door of a child's darkened room just a slit to see if the child is asleep*.)

During these seven days, he is very kind to the old man, comes into his room in the morning, greets him affectionately, asking him did he sleep well (*again as an affectionate parent might do to a beloved child, or a son to a beloved, respected father*).

The murder takes place on the eighth night; inadvertently he makes a noise in the pitch darkness; the old man wakes up frightened, shouting "Who's there?" The madman sits without stirring in the same pitch-black room near the old man's bed, knowing the old man is awake and frightened and unable to see his concealed visitor. Anyone who has ever had night terrors or ever questioned a child closely about "fear of the dark" can place the origin of this exactly. The frightened child (the "old man") hears a noise, sits up in bed, and sees a shadow in the room or imagines a shadow among shadows. Since it is silent, as a shadow, it says nothing, does nothing, but in the child's imagination waits for the child to cease his terrified vigilance. Thus "the old man" of the story is surely a terrified child—and the "filmed-over pale blue vulture eye" is the offending and endangered organ of the child's aggression. It is also important to remember that at birth many children appear as wrinkled as an "old man."

Then the madman (The Shadow) directs a beam of light upon the Evil Eye—counterpart of the child looking at the slit of light in the crack of the door—and, at this point, the madman whose hearing is so superacute reports that:

there came to my ears a low, dull, quick sound, such as a watch makes when enveloped in cotton. I know that sound well too. It was the beating of the old man's heart. It increased my fury, as the beating of a drum stimulates the soldier into courage.

One can now recognize the old man as the terrified child. "The Shadow"—and the child—hear the same heart beat. Notice, too, the *drum* as externalized source of *courage*. And so, up to this point, we have only the thinly disguised story of a child's night terror with the feared projected Shadow animated, made the insane murderer, and given a voice to tell the tale.

Now what the child (the "old man") fears is enacted, as the Shadow prepares to detach himself from the pitch-black room.

The beating [of the old man's heart] grew louder, louder! I thought the heart must burst.

The Shadow attacks! The old man is dragged to the floor and the heavy bed is dragged over him (simple counterpart of the terrified child *hiding* under the bed).

But for many minutes the heart beat on with a muffled sound . . . At length it ceased . . . I placed my hand upon the heart and held it there many minutes. There was no pulsation. He was stone dead. His eye would trouble me no more.

(Indeed what child, hiding in such terror under the bed, would not —if it were the only gruesome alternative—change places with the Shadow, as Poe does in this story, and, as in suicidal desperation, try to stifle his own loud heart. Poe did actually attempt suicide toward the end of his life.)

Now, the rest of the story is the future fate of the projected Shadow (the madman who tells the tale) and how he is forced to confess his crime. The Shadow madman dismembers the "old man's" corpse, catching the blood in a tub, and hides severed limbs, head and torso under the floor. Except for a shriek (a child's cry), the "old man" has left no trace of himself, but precisely this shriek induces neighbors to send three detectives. The Shadow madman lets the detectives in and confidently takes them up to the murder bedroom, giving them chairs *and himself sits down on a chair placed directly over the dismembered body,* "in the wild audacity of my perfect triumph." (This placement indicates again that the madman belongs—as a projected shadow—to the terrified, fictitiously dismembered child playing out his own fantasy, and is a visual projection of the sonic image of the heart.)

Now, it is the Shadow's turn to be terrified as the three detectives (magic three of the male genital reasserting itself over the castrative terror—therefore reassertion of the waking self) obstinately sit there and refuse to go.

The Shadow madman says:

> But, ere long, I felt myself getting pale . . . My head ached, and I fancied a ringing in my ears . . . The ringing became more distinct . . . Until, at length, I found that the noise was *not* within my ears [At this point the child reclaims the Shadow without the reader being told this—for *this is the art of interpretation in the great writer*], yet the sound increased. It was a low, dull, quick sound—much such a sound as a watch makes when *enveloped in cotton* . . . the noise steadily increased . . . louder—louder—*louder!* And still the men chatted pleasantly and smiled. Was it possible they heard not? Almighty God!—no, no! They heard.—they suspected!—they knew!—they were making a mockery of my horror! . . .

> "Villains!" I shrieked, "dissemble no more! I admit the deed!—tear up the planks! here! here! It is the beating of his hideous heart!"

This is one of the most remarkable stories in all literature. Note that the story starts with an attack upon the repulsive, vulture-like *Eye* of the "old man" but ends with the beating of his "hideous heart." The double irony of the poetic justice is beautifully done—for the "heart" which betrays the Shadow is also the "heart" which betrayed "the old man." At the same time, since "the old man" is dead, the Shadow is really hearing his own heart beat, just as the frightened child (Poe who conceived the story) hearing his own heart beat so loud, had to hide under the bed away from the Shadow he imagined to exist, and to whom he (Poe as child) gave substance and independent life in this tale. As such, the projected "Shadow" is really the child's own aggression, disowned in a castrative, dismembering fear of great helplessness—until the "magic three" appear (reappear) for vengeance and justice. The "Shadow" is thus the embodiment of the child's own hatred *attacking the child,* pushing him back into the uterus (beneath the planks in the floor—and a child not yet born has physiologically no *members*)—parallel to the expression "I am so terrified and humiliated by terror, I wish I had never been born." So too, the madman of the *Tell-Tale Heart* is a counterpart of Poe's *Raven,* the black bird, of Death, and of the "highborn Kinsmen" who take away the body of *Annabel Lee.* This story, then, gives us the clue to one whole facet of Poe's artistic method and its psychologic source.

But the entire story revolves around *The Tell-Tale hideous heart* and it describes to us *the continuous attack upon the heart of a human child so crushed by an unspeakably brutal childhood,* such as that of Edgar Allan Poe. For whenever a child is so poorly fed (it is said he and his sister were fed on alcohol soaked in gin to keep them quiet in his first three years), so much exposed to death and sickness (his father was an irresponsible eccentric alcoholic who disappeared before Poe was two, and his mother, an impoverished actress who died of tuberculosis before he was three) and subjected to further brutal restrictive treatment (he was adopted by the tender Frances Allan and her violently hostile husband in deference to her wishes)—that child will suffer *a continuous attack upon his heart.* His "blood will run cold," an "icy hand will grip his heart"—all phenomena having to do with elaborations of the sonic image of the heart.

Such a child will never admit its separation from the embodied identity with its mother's blood and belly.

And Poe said so:

> And neither the angels in heaven above,
> Nor the demons down under the sea,
> Can ever dissever my soul from the soul
> Of the beautiful Annabel Lee!

Annabel Lee was exquisitely symbolic of his mother who died of tuberculosis. Poe loved four women intensely, all of whom died from tuberculosis—his mother, Elizabeth Arnold; Mrs. Stanard; Frances Allan, his foster mother; and Virginia Clemm, his cousin and child-wife.

Poe remained practically impotent throughout his entire life. He could not reach out to sexuality at all. Never dissevered from the ego of his mother, he could only be a manic-depressive personality, elated when he believed he controlled the mother image, depressed when he perceived himself ejected and dejected from her actual body. His flight to drugs and alcohol were only attempts to stabilize a fundamentally unstable psychic equilibrium. His heart symptoms were present *before* he became seriously drug-addicted. He had three heart attacks by thirty-five; and, though he has been delirious at forty, he dies a cardiac, not a delirium, death—as his physicians, often fingering his irregular pulse, had predicted.

Edgar Allan Poe is then *the extreme example of the continuous attack upon the heart.* Could he ever have tolerated a rival child, could he have dared to create a living child? He had to "love" someone who stood for his mother and his sister, someone who would die as his mother died and someone whom he could "protect" from his desire to destroy that sister, that rival child.

His "fixation" upon mother was no accident. His "primary repression" had so powerful a gravitational effect on his life thereafter that the dyssynergic sonic image of his heart dominated his life. All his "subsequential repression" was so designed as to keep that dyssynergy operating in all the usually projective symbolization of the heart—small animals, rats, frog, pendulum, etc., in the truly cardiac "heart-stopping" imagery for which he is justly famed.

PART II

The Sonic Aspects of a Synergic Psychoneurology
Heart Image and Heart Mechanism
The Acoustic Echo Reflex

Chapter IX

THE SYNERGIC TRANSFORMATIONAL PREMISE OF BRAIN-BECOMING-MIND—THE BRAIN AS A TRANSDUCER

AT the outset, it should be stated, in order to deepen our understanding of the *sonic image* of the heart and the *electrochemical mechanism* of the heart, that from the point of view of sonics as a science in general the distinction between frequencies of vibration audible to the ear and those inaudible to the ear is arbitrary. *Sonics* encompasses all the various aspects of mechanical vibratory energy—and the *heart mechanism is a machine* that in one sense may be said to produce *a mechanical,* however physiologic, *pulse* which sets up waves of vibratory energy throughout the body. From this point of view, the entire body contains and emanates the vibratory energy generated by the contraction of the heart.

In engineering, sonics is the technology of vibratory mechanical energy as applied to problems of measurement, control and industrial processing; in psychoneurology the same energy may be utilized by the nervous system for that measurement and control we call *thinking* and for that sensori-motor "processing" we call *adaptation.* In brief, sonics has a wider application than its fortuitous relationship to the human ear, however much it is the special concern of that sense organ, in the audible range.

Sonic energy operates in structures and solutions comparable to that of the nervous system and its biochemical milieu. As the frequency of sound increases, the wave length correspondingly decreases and approaches the dimensions of atomic or molecular structure.

Thus the function of "sonic energy" has grown beyond what was and is meant by the audible range. It includes new developments in relation to electrochemistry. For example, an *electroacoustic transducer* has been developed in technical fields, in many forms, by which *sound generation and detection is brought about electronically*. There is thus a "transduction," a conversion, of one form of energy into another and back again. And the *synergy* of nervous action demands the "working together" of these two forms of energy transformation.

To a synergic psychoneurology these phenomena are of fundamental importance—in our premise of a nervous functioning whose basis is that of *brain-becoming-mind*. Or, in other words, the very foundation of a rational, synergic psychoneurology is that of a transducing of energy from one form—*electrochemical—into another, largely sonic*. For without the sonics of speech and hearing—and Helen Keller's case shows that the "sense of vibration" or vibrational acoustic energy itself in general can be thus used—man would have no "mind."

Hence, our long-standing interest in the *growth equations of the nervous system* which we developed years ago and described in the Monograph called *The Growth Concept of Nervous Action*, equations as applicable to vibratory as to electrical motion. In this way, in 1944, on the basis of an essentially electroacoustic (or piezoelectric) equation, we discovered the law for the growth of the brain and cord, and its relation to body shape, metabolism, etc., basing our work on the previous work of Wetzel. Its accuracy is indubitable, as the tables included in Chapter X indicate. For there is every reason to believe that *the nervous system is essentially a transducer system, operating piezoelectrically*—each nerve cell not unlike a transistor crystal—so that *the essentially* electrochemical brain becomes the sonic mind.[1]

For in this electroacoustic equation underlying the law for the

[1] This formulation obeys all the dynamic laws of processes in motion. Electrochemical phenomena deal with the motion of charged *particles*. Sonic or wave phenomena deal with the "space between" particles—with wave fronts of interspaces. Thus, "electrochemical" becomes converted into its "opposite" when it becomes *transduced* into sonic energy and a certain electrochemical *quantity* becomes converted into a sonic quality.

growth of the brain and cord, not only do we perceive the probability of the fundamental transducing mechanism but also the *establishment of equilibrium*. We have already named this the "tension-relaxation equilibrium." As will be seen, this equilibrium functions as a "metastable equilibrium." This balance of forces makes possible the *psychoneurologic phenomenon of repression*. Physiologically it may be equated to an "ultrasonic," (or asonic, inaudible, "unconscious") and therefore repressing set of psychoneurologic transformations.

The law for the growth of the brain and cord in relation to the body thus provides us with (1) evidence of the nervous system as an electroacoustic transducer, whereby the electrochemical brain becomes the sonic mind; and (2) the metastable equilibrium making possible the equivalent of "ultrasonic" transformation of "repression" (cf. Chapter XIV).

Let us take a simple analogy to illustrate why the transformational premise of *brain-becoming-mind* involves the transducing of energy from electrochemical to sonic and back again, and why this gives us a hitherto unseen picture of anxiety and the image of the heart in relation to mind and body.

To illustrate: a clock, once wound by hand and run by a spring, now runs by electricity. It has an "alarm" just as any ordinary hand-wound alarm clock may have, and *we*, outside the clock, may *set the alarm* for a certain time. When that time arrives, the electrical energy which runs the clock also makes possible the release of a clapper (the heart in palpitation) whose mechanical energy striking a bell (the ideational word-structured signaling system of anxiety) now creates acoustic energy which we call in this instance not "sound" but "alarm," or more precisely "the sounding of the alarm." If we stuff our ears with cotton so that we cannot hear, and yet the clock is on a surface contiguous with us, or touching our bodies (*or in our pocket*), then the *vibration* of the clapper and the associated disturbances of our tactile and thermal sensations will similarly, *by the acoustic energy of vibration,* alert us to the implications of the time set. The clock, now an electric-mechanical-acoustic transducer, having become internalized in our pocket, is a portion of our alarm system.

Now let us suppose that the alarm-setting mechanism has gone awry, and that the alarm in our pocket goes off at such frequent irregular intervals and so irrelevantly with respect to our needs in the outer world, that it both shocks and confuses us. It will not suffice now simply to stuff our ears with cotton; we must also prevent the clapper itself from moving and disturbing us by its "palpitation" of us.

A counterenergy must now be directed against the sheer mechanical action of the confusion clapper. (For many years, psychoanalysis has called this counterenergy the "countercathexis" with which the ego "defends itself" against the alarming "id." I have already suggested that "libido" may really be an expression of sonic forces.)

In our clock analogy, we cannot stuff the clock with cotton; its mechanism would be spoiled. The simplest thing to do is to have control of a "shut-off" which we can manipulate at each inappropriate alarm. *We cannot destroy the alarm system altogether* if we wish to have—and in order to survive, need—an alerting mechanism. Nor can we interefere with the "timing" mechanism; we have need of a sense of time which is also a sense of space (and spacing)—in brief, of reality, itself.

A portion of our attention, of ourself, must be delegated now out of the sheer necessity to "shut off," i.e., to *suppress,* the inappropriate alarm mechanism.

Or else, we must invent an automatic device which will not demand our constant, conscious vigilance but *will reconvert the acoustic energy back into electrical energy,* which is in this instance "silent."

To repeat: we cannot, if we wish to survive, destroy the alarm-setting mechanism. Nor can we have an inappropriate alarm system. We cannot interfere with the timing mechanism of reality. We cannot afford, in the interest of efficient adaptation, constantly to stand guard over the "alarm-button."

We have only two alternatives (short of stopping the clock or throwing it away—suicide or psychosis). One is to try to correct the inappropriate alarm system by "rewiring" or "rerouting" impulses. The other—and the more practical since life is full of various "dangers" (situations of alarm)—is to have a technique for the reconversion of acoustic into electrical energy; or, in brief, to establish a new relationship, a new *equilibrium* of forces and a new proportion between the audible-inaudible balances, between the sonic and "ultrasonic" forces.

Here the analogy with the internalized alarm clock comes to an end. For *the "bell" which is struck within us is our word and postural system of growth and development*—our signaling system of anxiety containing all the records of our "alarms," and all our "counter-energies" (the "countercathexes" of our ego defenses), and all the mechanisms of equilibration which make possible our repressions of energy and our countermobilizations of energy.

For, *each level of growth has its repressive sonic-electrochemical equilibrium, and that of infancy before myelinization—before the insulation of the nervous system—is vastly different from all the others.* This process of insulating the nervous system, so that the child begins to sit up, talk, walk, etc., is nearly complete by three years of age, and almost totally complete by six. *This three- to six-year period is the period of oedipal development*—the period *after* the helplessness of the uninsulated nervous system.

In other words, all the new relationships which come into view when one assumes an electro-acoustic transducing and transformational basis to human growth and mental function—all these new *sonic* factors fit perfectly to the valid data of psychoanalytic experience.

The definition that we have given (cf. Part I) of anxiety as a dys-synergy between the sonic image of the heart and the rest of the ego can be further refined. The sonic image of the heart includes the sensation resulting from that specific sonic-electrochemical equilibrium belonging to the period of birth, infancy and helplessness, *when the nervous system was unmyelinized*, i.e., not yet insulated. This experience is forgotten for many years, and no name can be attached to it by a child before three. Later we call it "anxiety." The pulse—the peripheral arterial image of the heart and the flow of blood itself

—must set up entirely different sensations in an uninsulated system. The sense of alarm is everywhere in severe acute anxiety as though sonic forces penetrated massively. The sense of dissolution which accompanies the "palpitation" of the heart, this sense of utter helplessness with its destructive excitation, these "waves of anxious fear" (so peculiarly intense that it has been called "libidinal excitation")—all these would be the consequences of a regressive retransformation from adult equilibrium to infantile equilibrium *in which the alarm —the sonic impact upon all the tissues of the body*—is overwhelming and floods the apparatus of sensation. As one person described his anxiety on hearing the keening of an air-raid siren: "I became so frightened that the sound whistled through my muscles."

The first step, then, in establishing a psychoneurology based upon the process of brain-becoming-mind is to demonstrate that the actual growth of brain and body is itself in all likelihood the growth of an electro-chemical-acoustic transducing system so that the electro-chemical brain becomes the sonic mind.

In Chapter X we shall illustrate that the law for the growth of the brain and body, although first developed from Joule's Law, can be derived equally well from the equations for a sonic oscillating system in which power surges from source (fertilization) to system (growing brain-body) until, with progressive "damping," an ultimate equilibrium is struck—with various states of metastable equilibrium along the way marking out the great repressive transitions of growth and development.

As a matter of fact, the original equations developed by Wetzel for the "motion of growth" are practically identical with those applied to sonic vibratory systems. The more one studies these phenomena of nervous growth and function including its control of the body, the more one becomes aware, in nervous tissue, of the theoretic probability of its action as a dynamic interplay between sonic wave fronts which operate in the interspaces of nervous matter and electrochemical energy of the charged particles which outline "the outer shell" and inner compartments of these interspaces of nervous substance. This dynamic interplay is, as stated, the essence of synergy.

Or, in summary, the nervous system is an electroacoustic transducer which, activated, is always—even for the nervous aspects of a single cell—the perpetual transformation of *brain-becoming-mind*. We can have but little interest in any organism—or in any universe —in which this is not true.

It follows, too, that the modern science of sonics, particularly in the field of transducers, is "imitating" as well as elucidating the essence of that transformation of brain-becoming-mind which we have postulated as the basic premise of a new and synergic psychoneurology.

From this point of view, not only psychodynamic but also neurodynamic phenomena come under re-examination. From the point of view of brain-becoming-mind, *the "reflex" can no longer be considered the basic unit of nervous action.* The "conditioned reflex"—a contradiction in terms—loses its meaning as a "physiologic" basis of psychology. Instead, what comes into sight, is a concept of a *unit of energy in transformation*—a sonic-electrochemical equivalent— which we tentatively name here *the synergic quantum in relation to synergic mechanism.* Such a disease, for example, as multiple sclerosis, will one day take on entirely different aspects when it will have been studied as a disturbance of synergy.

In this way, the concept of a synergic psychoneurology, in which the electro-chemical brain and nervous system become the sonic mind, opens up new possibilities of investigation in both psychodynamic and neurodynamic fields of scientific endeavor.

Chapter X

THE ELECTROCHEMICAL AND SONIC EQUATIONS UNDERLYING THE LAW FOR THE GROWTH OF THE BRAIN AND BODY

IN this chapter it will be demonstrated that the law for the growth of the brain and body points to nervous action as an electroacoustic transducer.

That growth of the body in general was the result of a process in motion analogous to that of any damped oscillating system, was first brilliantly shown by Wetzel (1937). And, as is known, the law for the "oscillation" of any "damped" vibrating system obeys all the laws of motion.

Our own contribution tried to build upon Wetzel's. The brain, we discovered, occupied the position of integrated force in the equation. In order to make this theoretical relationship real, we had, however, to show that the entire concept was applicable to *an electro-chemical system*—as well as thermodynamic—the brain's known characteristic. This meant that the Sherrington concepts of "reflex coordination" had to be abandoned; and the very first explorations in this path of thinking, therefore, indicated that the "reflex" itself would have to be discarded one day as "the unit" of neurodynamic action. Moreover, as far back as 1934, it became clear that the concept of a nerve cell as a "way station" alone was a primitive mechanical concept. It would be necessary as a beginning (Schneider, 1943) to construct an entirely different basis for a rational electrochemical and thermodynamic law of brain growth and function—one that must at the same time relate to the thermodynamics of growth, to potential and kinetic energy transactions, to heat production or "basal metabolism," *and to sonic energy transformation* in view of Jacques Loeb's concept of the nerve cell as a "relaxation-oscillator"— a fundamentally sonic idea developed by Loeb as early as 1900 but neglected.

A. Derivation of the Law for Brain-Body Growth on an Electrochemical and Sonic Basis

This was made possible by utilizing Loeb's rather than Sherrington's concept of nervous cellular function and integration. Hoagland demonstrated the validity of this concept electroencephalographically in 1936, thirty-six years after Loeb first announced it.

Briefly, Loeb's concept led one to conceive of the whole organism, from the moment of fertilization, to be under the impact of a growth *electromotive* force, and to think of the life process as a manifestation of the function of *irritability* which in the higher species received more and more tangible and complex mechanization in the organization of the nervous tissue. From this, it followed that all the transactions of the organism could be viewed, in accordance with thermodynamic law, as either potential or kinetic energy transactions, their sum total amounting to the thermodynamic work of growth. Wetzel (1937) had already confirmed Tangl's conception of a thermodynamic work of growth. Since these transactions could be none other than variations of irritability and growth electromotive force operating in and through irritability, then to the nervous system must accrue the forces of growth and to its lot must fall the task of integrating the potential and kinetic energy transactions of growth at any given time. Thus:

Thermodynamic Work = Potential Energy + Kinetic Energy (1)
Or:

$$Thermodynamic\ Work\ of\ Growth = PE\ of\ Growth\ + \\ KE\ of\ Growth \quad (2)$$

Put in another way, the organism, in growth and function, could be considered as an amalgamation of *tension processes* (determined by potential energy transactions) and *relaxation* processes (determined by kinetic energy transactions). This new way of phrasing the problem was already encouraging since medicine had only recently begun to describe under a definite heading, the *tension syndromes*, from vascular hypertension to ulcer, migrain, etc., not even excluding carcinoma so intricately bound up with the estrogenic tensors, which are sterol derivatives.

Next, since we could consider the entire organism as well as the neuraxis a conductor, Joule's Law was applied, or:

$$Heat = Work = i^2\,Rt \tag{3}$$

where i is the current intensity, R the resistance, and t the time of passage of current.

Since the heat of the organism at any time could be given by:

$$Heat = Mass \times \frac{heat}{mass} \tag{4}$$

then,

$$Heat = Mass \times \frac{heat}{mass} = i^2\,RT. \tag{5}$$

Since $i = \dfrac{E}{R}$

$$Heat = Mass \times \frac{heat}{mass} = i^2\,Rt = \left(\frac{E}{R}\right)^2.\,Rt = \frac{E^2}{R}\,t \tag{6}$$

Therefore,

$$Mass \times \frac{heat}{mass} \times R = E^2 t \tag{7}$$

Since Faraday's Law for electrolytic chemical systems permits the expression of mass as:

$$Mass = z \cdot i \cdot t \tag{8}$$

where m is mass, z is electrochemical equivalent, i is current intensity, and t is time, the formulation of Equation (7) now represents a system acting both electrochemically and as a conductor which fulfills two important known functions of animate organisms.

At this point we are able to make the distinction between growth heat and maintenance heat, thanks to the brilliant work of Wetzel (1937), whose whole concept however was inapplicable because his was a system dealing solely with the dimension of log_e mass or q, the quantity of growth, and furthermore took no account of the nervous system as a *determining* factor. [This, we believe, is responsible for the slight but significant deviation of Wetzel's theoretic heat curve, between the ages of two to five, as compared with the empiric data of Scammon (1930), Benedict (1920), and others.]

Nevertheless, students of growth are indebted to Wetzel for the neat dissection of heat production into these two component parts: the heat of growth, the dynamic component; and the heat of maintenance, the nondynamic component needed to maintain life. Or, in other words, the "circuit" in the living organism, as a conductor and as an electrochemical unit, is not made of durable copper but of organic conductive and operative material which has constantly to be refurbished in the "wear and tear" of sheer existence.

Thus, Equation (7) may be considered as taking two forms, accepting Wetzel's value for the heat of maintenance per unit mass as 25.3425 calories per kilo.

$$Mass \times \frac{Maintenance\ Heat}{mass} \times R_{(m)} = E^2_{(m)}t \tag{9}$$

and

$$Mass \times \frac{Growth\ Heat}{mass} \times R_{(g)} = E^x_{(g)}t \tag{10}$$

the subscripts (m) and (g) referring now to maintenance and growth respectively and x referring to the variable nature of $E_{(g)}$. Equation (10) was described as the "basic equation," thus:

Growth Heat $\times$ Growth Resistance = (Growth Electromotive Force)t

Since $R = \rho \frac{L}{A}$ where ρ is the specific resistivity of the conductor, L its length, and A its cross-sectional area, we now have accessible all the variables and need only the formulation of nervous mass as growth electromotive and sonic force.

There are two main dispositions of nervous mass anatomically: cord mass and brain mass. Functionally, however, we conceive of the growth electromotive force as operating in two main forms through nervous mass: the first, the so-called "decerebrate" organization encountered in the living organism under such conditions as sleep and coma in which the practical disappearance of the EEG wave indicated that the cord weight alone could represent (without too great an error) one organized disposition of force; the second, that of the waking state in which both brain and cord operate together, not simply additively, but as "transformers," i.e., exponential to each other.

Thus, growth electromotive force was represented as:

$$(E)^{x_1}{}_{(g)(1)} \, t \propto cord \, weight \tag{11}$$

and:

$$(E)^x{}_{(g)(2)} \, t \propto brain \, weight^{\log_e \, cord \, weight} \tag{12}$$

where the exponent takes the logarithmic form.

Equation (10) itself hence takes two forms corresponding to the two dispositions of growth force represented by Equations (11) and (12). Or:

$$(Mass)^x \left(\frac{Growth \, Heat}{mass} \times R_{(g)} \right)^y = brain \, weight^{\, \log_e \, cord \, weight} \tag{13}$$

$$(Mass)^x \left(\frac{Growth \, Heat}{mass} \times R_{(g)} \right)^{y_1} = cord \, weight \tag{14}$$

where x, y, x_1, and y_1 are exponents corresponding to the dimensions of $E^x{}_{(g)}t$ and $E^{x_1}{}_{(g)}t$ respectively.

There now remained only the necessity to distinguish between maintenance resistance, $R_{(m)}$, and growth resistance, $R_{(g)}$.

When growth has "ceased," i.e., when it has reached adult equilibrium, there are no further significant changes in length (until senility, when length may decrease slightly). A maintenance level will then have been achieved and resistance at this state will be given simply by $\rho \, \frac{L}{A}$ which, for all practical purposes, may be considered constant.

While growth is going on, there will be a change in the three directions, length, transverse diameter, and anterior-posterior diameter;

the changes in these directions will accompany any change in mass per unit time.

Thus for any increment in mass, say $\Delta(m)$, there will be a corresponding $\Delta(L)$, $\Delta(A_1)$, and $\Delta(A_2)$ where the subscripts refer to the two diameters of cross-sectional area. These data may be obtained from Meredith's (1935) excellent study.

For any increment of mass per unit time, the change in the dimensions of the resistance of the increment becomes:

$$\frac{\Delta(L)}{\Delta(A_1) \times \Delta(A_2)}$$

At the same time, while the change in the relationships of the increment is taking place, changes in the total length and the total area are also occurring so that during growth $\rho\,\dfrac{L}{A}$ is not constant. Furthermore, a significant alteration in resistance will take place only so long as the ratio

$$\frac{\dfrac{\Delta L}{\Delta(A_1) \times \Delta(A_2)}}{\rho\dfrac{L}{A}}$$

is not constant, since at maintenance the fraction

$$\frac{\Delta L}{\Delta(A_1) \times \Delta(A_2)}$$

will be unity and $\rho\dfrac{L}{A}$ will be constant.

Hence growth resistance can be adequately represented by:

$$\frac{\dfrac{\Delta(L)}{\Delta(A_1) \times \Delta(A_2)}}{\rho\dfrac{L}{A}} = R_{(g)} \tag{15}$$

Equations (13) and (14), expressed in natural logarithms, now become, letting H_g represent growth heat per unit mass:

$$x \log_e mass + y [\log_e H_{(g)} + \log_e R_{(g)}] + C =$$
$$(\log_e Br. Wt.) \ (\log_e Cd. Wt.) \tag{16}$$
$$x_1 \log_e mass + y_1 [\log_e H_{(g)} + \log_e R_{(g)}] + C_1 = \log_e Cd. Wt. \tag{17}$$

Since alpha frequency of the electroencephalogram follows the growth of the brain, it may be expressed as

$$_a Frequency = A \ (Brain \ Weight) + B \tag{18}$$

Or:

$$_a \frac{Frenqency - B}{A} = Brain \ Weight \tag{19}$$

Then, by dividing Equation (17) into Equation (16), we obtain:

$$\frac{x \log_e mass + y [\log_e H_{(g)} + \log_e R_{(g)}] + C}{x_1 \log_e mass + y_1 [\log_e H_{(g)} + \log_e R_{(g)}] + C_1} =$$

$$\log_e Br. Wt. = \log_e \left(\frac{_a F - B}{A} \right) \tag{20}$$

Equation (20) may now be tested from the empiric data. The exponents are derived by the method of expansion of determinants.

For the male values, using an average of various weight curves in the literature as our basic data, the constants are:

$$
\begin{aligned}
x &= 5.59175473 \\
x_1 &= 0.68545936 \\
y &= 0.43740094 \\
y_1 &= 0.04971345 \\
C &= -0.39333199 \\
C_1 &= 0.33581311
\end{aligned}
\qquad
\begin{aligned}
A &= 0.00836557 \\
B &= -1.39910521
\end{aligned}
$$

The heat values used here are, more correctly, lower than those utilized in the introductory paper. The present values are from Benedict's (1920) data for boys from one to thirteen years of age, and Bierring's (1931) data for weight and heat from 20 kilograms to 73 kilograms. The tables show the results, with two solutions for those values where Benedict's and Bierring's data overlap. The values from 63.5 kg. to 73 kg. represent various adult stages at which growth may reach equilibrium.

B. The Possibility of Derivation of the Law for Brain-Body Growth on a Sonic Basis

It is clear that using Loeb's concept of the nerve cell as a "relaxation-oscillator" also makes possible the application of laws of motion having to do with such oscillation of forces as they become transformed. A "relaxation-oscillator" even though in so physiologic a unit as a nerve cell must combine a linear "stiffness" force and an inertial force—a combination which is the basic requirement of a vibrating system.

Even the loss of energy which is always present due to "frictional" or "viscous" forces can be accounted for; in this way some of the vibrational energy is converted into heat energy (reflected in living organisms as part of "basal heat" or "basal metabolism"); this force is represented as "damping," and the damping force is proportional to the velocity.

As a result again an equation of motion—this time of vibratory motion—can be written in which the brain occupies the position of integrated force, of integrated vibratory force, i.e., of sonic force, just as in Section A it occupies the position of electromotive force.

An equation of this kind can be found in any textbook dealing with vibrating systems (cf. *Sonics* by Hueter and Bolt), e.g., the differential force equation:

$$X\frac{du}{dt} + Y_xu + K\smallint udt = F \qquad (21)$$

in which u, in a growing system, is the differential $\dfrac{du}{udt}$ so that the

integral of the first term becomes $Log_e\ u$ or $x\ log_e$ mass exactly as the first term of the electromotive equation in Section A in equations (16) and (17).

TABLE I

Age years	Mass kilos	Heat/mass* Cals./Kg./yr.	$\log_e R_{(g)}$	Brain wt. (grams)	Cord wt. (grams)**	Alpha freq./sec./yr.	Total heat Cals./yr.
Birth	3.25	(43.25) (50.71)	1.4800	(386.81) (400.68)	(3.90) (3.97)	1.95	(140.56) (164.80)
½	7.57	55.66	2.6370	816.38	7.57	5.43	421.15
1	10.06	54.44	2.9270	937.91	9.31	6.45	547.67
2	12.70	51.17	3.5943	1045.52	11.22	7.35	649.86
3	15.04	48.28	5.2483	1164.30	13.61	8.34	726.13
4	16.71	46.24	4.9094	1182.71	14.31	8.49	772.67
6	20.45	{ 42.60 / 46.94	3.7978	{ 1199.28 / 1207.59	{ 15.40 / 15.57	{ 8.63 / 8.70	{ 871.17 / 959.92
8	26.34	{ 39.05 / 41.64	3.6656	{ 1265.32 / 1271.52	{ 18.00 / 18.16	{ 9.19 / 9.24	{ 1027.58 / 1096.80
10	32.53	{ 35.99 / 37.83	3.4032	{ 1310.53 / 1316.18	{ 20.31 / 20.47	{ 9.56 / 9.61	{ 1170.75 / 1230.60
12	38.68	34.99	3.1106	1346.22	22.39	9.86	1353.41
14	48.62	31.40	2.9963	1389.86	25.45	10.23	1526.67
16	56.00	29.21	3.1156	1416.76	27.59	10.45	1635.76
18	63.00	27.78	1.4098	1377.12	26.85	10.12	1750.14

63.5	27.6378	1.2577	1372.33	26.71	10.08	1755
64.0	27.5000	1.2656	1372.60	26.78	10.08	1760
64.5	27.4109	1.2734	1373.56	26.87	10.09	1768
65.0	27.2615	1.2810	1373.42	26.93	10.09	1772
65.5	27.1756	1.2887	1374.25	27.02	10.09	1780
66.0	27.0606	1.2963	1374.38	27.08	10.09	1786
66.5	26.9474	1.3038	1373.56	27.14	10.09	1792
67.0	26.8657	1.3113	1374.93	27.22	10.10	1800
67.5	26.7556	1.3188	1374.79	27.27	10.10	1806
68.0	26.6176	1.3262	1373.56	27.28	10.09	1810
68.5	26.5401	1.3335	1373.42	27.34	10.09	1818
69.0	26.4058	1.3408	1372.05	27.32	10.08	1822
69.5	26.3165	1.3480	1370.96	27.35	10.07	1829
70.0	26.1857	1.3551	1368.22	27.28	10.04	1833
70.5	26.0993	1.3623	1367.53	27.29	10.04	1840
71.0	25.9859	1.3693	1364.25	27.22	10.01	1845
71.5	25.8741	1.3763	1360.14	27.10	9.98	1850
72.0	25.7639	1.3833	1354.73	26.93	9.93	1855
72.5	25.6552	1.3903	1347.16	26.66	9.87	1860
73.0	25.5479	1.3971	1335.47	26.24	9.77	1865

* To obtain growth heat per unit mass, subtract 25.3425 (Wetzel's constant) from heat per unit mass.
** Cord weights measured without nerve-roots attached.

So too, the second term of the vibratory equation (21) is a "resistance" component just as it is in equation (16) and (17).

The terms $Y_x u + K\int u\,dt$ when provision is made for "maintenance" as opposed to "growth" become identical with $Y(Log_e\,H_g + Log_e\,R_g)$ as applied to a system of changing cellular dimension.

The two equations are thus practically identical, and in *both* the displacement of mass can be measured along a scale that is fixed with respect to the ground, whether we speak of the height to which we grow or the force of gravity against which we learn to stand erect and walk.

In both equations the nervous system comes to be the expression of integrated *electrochemical and acoustic force,* a cogent piece of evidence that the transformational premise of brain-becoming-mind is based solidly upon the synergic psychoneurologic concept of the brain as an electroacoustic transducing apparatus.

It is clear that, if this is true, the science of psychoanalysis itself will have a new and modern view of what has for so long been called "the psychophysiologic apparatus"; instead of being based upon the physics of the nineteenth century, it will move into the twentieth century—and its terminology and techniques will change accordingly, in many ways that cannot now be foreseen.

But, to pursue our more immediate task of outlining some of the relationships of sonic heart image and electrochemical heart mechanism, it is now necessary to study the psychophysiology of sonic forces in general before proceeding to certain aspects of the heart mechanism itself.

With respect to the equations and forces just developed, it will be clear, however, that so basic a sonic machine as the heart will have played a definite role in each state of equilibrium. *As we know, heart rate goes down steadily* as brain mass and force increase to "level off" when adult full-grown equilibrium is reached. The same is true with regard to body temperature, blood pressure and metabolism.

Or, in other words, the equations just discussed indicate that *very large and powerful electrosonic forces exist between heart and brain,* and that in the disturbed synergies of the sonic and the electrochemical forces of heart and brain lie the answers to such a problem as vascular hypertension.[1] Thus, for example, the hydrostatic pressure elements of the circulation will be ascribable to sonic forces because of the oscillation of gravity and will have sonic effects in contrast to the electrochemical forces of diffusion through the terminal semipermeable membranes.

Indeed vascular hypertension from this point of view can be defined as an attempt on the part of the organism to make up, by sonic pressure effects, for an electrochemical and perhaps temperature failure. Or, in the old psychoanalytic terminology, the "libido" (sonic forces) must be devoted to circulatory pressure rather than to nervous relaxation.

[1] Farris, Yeakel, and Medoff (*Am. J. Physiol., 144*:331, 1945) were able to produce hypertension in emotional gray rats by auditory stimulation (air-blasting); this hypertension is apparently permanent.

Chapter XI

THE PSYCHOPHYSIOLOGY OF THE LABYRINTHINE-SONIC SYSTEM—ITS RELATIONSHIP TO HEART IMAGE AND HEART MECHANISM

HAVING tried to establish some evidence for the nervous system *in general* as an electroacoustic transducer, we must now pay some attention to the *special acoustic or sonic system* which we usually identify with the word "sonic" though we mean specifically the quality and range of *audibility,* i.e., of the sense of hearing. This sense of hearing is, together with our speech, a portion of the high evolutionary achievement of man. The special "word area" of the brain—the Island of Reil—is connected both to the hearing and the speaking mechanism, though our hearing and speaking apparatus can perceive sounds and make sounds not directly related to words at all.

In neurodynamics the word "acoustic" has always meant the sense of hearing whose end organ is the cochlea, and it will be quite a task to change our thinking to recognize that there are general underlying acoustic forces in *all* nervous action—forces of which hearing and speaking are only the most highly developed specialized manifestation.

Yet, we have known for centuries that the hearing organ itself was integrated with the *organ of balance*—the labyrinth—in the same mechanism, and that because the labyrinth gives us in addition to equilibrium, *direction in space, and orientation of our bodies to the force of gravity* as well, there was an entire labyrinthine-sonic system to reckon with; this labyrinthine-sonic system has a long history, existing in many previous forms of life, always with essentially the same functions however rudimentary.

The relationship of this labyrinthine-sonic system both to the heart image and to the heart mechanism is equally striking and the facts are well known though they never before have been marshalled along the lines of synergic psychoneurology, except in my previous monograph (1949).

For example, with respect to heart mechanism, strong objective *vertigo*—"the room spins"—is one of the prominent prodromal symptoms of severe coronary artery closure; it is not a vertigo due simply and solely to fall of blood pressure which in and of itself would produce mainly fainting.

Conversely, increase of labyrinthine pressure will produce *slow pulse* through its effect upon the cardiac vagus. Labyrinthine attacks will produce not only "vertigo, vomiting, and slow pulse" but, with respect to the image of the heart, they produce, as in Ménière's disease, a sense of terrific anxiety—impending death and dissolution of the ego.

The simple explanation here is the one already given in Part I: the relationship of the limbs ("memberment") to the body is disturbed; the underlying relationship of arteries to heart is similarly disturbed, or, in other words, the root image of the heart is *guarded*—in its synergy with the rest of the ego—by *labyrinthine integrity;* a mutual relationship obtains. *Coronary closure produces vertigo; labyrinthine attacks produce a terror of death,* of dissolution of the arterial and limb support of heart and body. Just as the torso "branches" into its limbs and must be equilibrated in space with reference to the force of gravity, so too does the heart in the torso send its arteries branching into these limbs. We have already seen in Part I of this book how closely *heart-anxiety-members* relate to each other in psychodynamic structure; here too we find, at the neurodynamic level, that the *labyrinthine-sonic system bears a peculiar relationship to the heart.* To find then that the entire specialized *acoustic organ* and system (the cochlea and its pathways) are integrated with the primitive labyrinthine-sonic system of man and that this in turn bears a special relationship to anxiety, coronary closure, heart rate and blood pressure, is to become aware of a curious underlying sonic principle—*not merely an exercise in semantic translation* from one scientific field to another.

Strangely enough, however, it was difficult to elucidate those relationships neurodynamically because the taste mechanism of man seemed to lie athwart the areas (the tractus solitarius) which would integrate all these mechanisms centrally.

For this reason, it was long ago suspected by me that taste was not really a special sense—it itself bore evidence of being instead a sonometric function. The following study was, as a result instituted some years ago, and is here reproduced as a link in the chain of considerations of this part of our work. Needless to say, the problems of the special labyrinthine-sonic system relate not only to heart mechanism, hearing, speech and mind, but also to neurodynamic problems of deafness.

THE PSYCHOPHYSIOLOGY OF THE SONIC SYSTEM

THE INTEGRATIVE SONIC-ULTRASONIC BARRIER

Poincaré once pointed out that there were two kinds of facts: those which are simply things to know—and do not necessarily lead anywhere—and those which, to paraphrase him, like keys, open up locked doors, perhaps even define doorways where none were suspected to exist in the confines of old and well trampled precincts of established knowledge. It is the latter sort of liberating fact for which a scientist really searches to experience new freedoms, to create fresh vistas, and to construct more powerful instruments for the benefit and progress of man.

The concept of an unsuspected *dual* hearing system—one portion primitive and ultrasonic,[1] the other recent and sonic—both ordinarily operating *fused* as a unit but in disease *dissociating* and competing— one the more primitive portion silently "listening" to the essentially narcissistic wishes of the archaic depths of man's body, the other the more recent portion hearing the demands of the external real world, both integrated by a physiologic sonic-ultrasonic barrier, such a con-

[1] Throughout this discussion, it must be recognized that the word "ultrasonic" is interchangeable at higher frequencies with the term "belonging to metastable equilibrium" —an equilibrium which functions chemically as well as physically. Growth itself provides these equilibria of repression.

cept might open up new doorways if its validity can be established firmly.

Toward that end, from 1945 to 1949, this writer attempted to forge a new and *genetic* concept of nervous action to go hand in hand with genetic psychology. This new concept depended in part upon a reevaluation of the so-called "taste tracts and area" of the hindbrain and upon a re-examination of taste as a "special sense," i.e., as having four distinct kinds of fibers to subserve the apparently four distinct modalities of taste: bitter, salt, sour, and sweet. For this area of the brain and these tracts gave every sign, neurophysiologically, neuropathologically, and clinically of being an area essential to the integration of the ego, something difficult to reconcile with the idea of its being primarily and purely a "taste area."

Many facts suggested that its function was basically integrative. The "taste region"—the region of the solitary tract and nucleus and its associated nucleus commissuralis (close by the labyrinthine and auditory nuclei)—was severely hit in all the organic drug psychoses, particularly in that encephalopathic form of alcoholic paranoid hallucinosis most closely resembling schizophrenia (L. Bender and Schilder, 1933). At the same time, as is well known to every experienced neuropsychiatrist, *hallucinations of taste are extermely rare,* if indeed they ever really occur, except as the general idea of "being poisoned," as compared with hallucinations of the other special cranial senses: of vision, of hearing and of smell. The taste area was thus "silent" when one would have expected it to be most eloquent. In this silence it was indeed comparable to the "higher silences" of the archipallial caudate nucleus subserving emotional integration and of the neopallic frontal lobe subserving syntactical, ideational, and intellectual integration. It was as though there were a continuous system of "silent areas" each operating at its own distinct qualitative and quantitative level. What was the nature and meaning of this "silence"?

Moreover, the facts of taste physiology itself denied that the region of the solitary nucleus and tract could possibly be a "pure" taste area. It had been known for almost a century that the sensory component parts of the solitary tract—the chorda tympani (seventh cranial nerve) to the anterior two thirds of the tongue and the glossopharyngeal (ninth) to the posterior one third of the tongue and the vagus (tenth) to the pharynx and larynx were *mixed motor-sensory* nerves carrying the great parasympathetic outflow to the head and neck. The sensory components of the seventh, ninth, and tenth (the solitary tract) moreover transmitted touch and pain as well as taste. It was thus impossible, despite the persistent and antique myth, that this could be primarily or "purely" a taste tract.

To summarize past and current work recently leading to certain psychosurgical perspectives (Schneider, 1952), three major concepts may be described as follows:

(1) Taste is not a "special sense" having four different kinds of fibers for four distinct modalities of taste; it is really basically a cholinergic (parasympathetic) phenomenon combined with other sensations upon the tongue to produce "bitter, salt, sour" (oral *unpleasure*), and "sweet" (oral *pleasure*).

(2) Within the so-called "taste tracts" (including the tympanic plexus) there existed a *primitive equilibratory-sonic system*—once external and now *internalized*—derivatives of the old lateral-line organs of acquatic anamniotes. The lateral-line organs were motional, equilibratory-sonic, chemical-detecting, and sexual-sensing organs. In man these residual *nerve elements* were still joined to the labyrinth as they had been ages before, though the labyrinth had become much more highly evolved in relationship to the new cochlea. The peripheral juncture is made by the tympanic plexus (seventh and ninth) which innervates the newer ossicle system and supplies the oval and round windows, by a branch of the nervus intermedius (seventh) which passes through the internal auditory canal to merge with the labyrinthine division of the eighth nerve; and centrally the juncture is made by the seventh and ninth nerve nuclei themselves which are almost buried within the labyrinthine and auditory nuclei, close by the solitary nucleus and solitary tract. *The older sonic system and the newer sonic system were thus tied together in a definite and intense way.*[2]

---

[2] Recently Rosen (1951) has tried to justify his procedure of sectioning the chorda tympani by the use of my theory. He claims that section of the chorda tympani is an operation "to preserve the labyrinth" and justifies this by describing the seventh and ninth nerve components as though they alone comprise the old, now internal, sonic system. This is a theoretic error, leading to inconclusive therapeutic results.

(3) The area of the hindbrain to which the seventh, ninth, and tenth nerves ascended could not be a "taste area" solely; it was still a motion-sensing, equilibratory-sonic system precisely as it had been in lower forms; and, as with the chemical-detecting function of the lateral-line organs, it served taste only incidentally. *The main function of the solitary nucleus was to integrate these various attributes in relationship to incoming sympathetic-excitor impulses and to outgoing parasympathetic-inhibitor impulses of the entire body.* Its secondary (higher) fibers ran with the dorsal spinocerebellar tracts (Allen, 1922–23) in which the afferent sympathetics of the trunk terminate; its sensory fibers, as has been stressed above, carried the great parasympathetic outflow. It connected *with visual motion* through the labyrinth and the posterior longitudinal bundle. It was thus in a position to integrate vegetative equilibria with the most primitive qualities of hearing and seeing; and, of these two latter functions, hearing was by far the more important to the lower species. (Thus the traditionally "blind bat" flies by a sonic —actually ultrasonic—"radar" system; it utters shrill cries and guides itself by the sonic and ultrasonic echo of sound vibrations reflected back against its own wings and equilibratory-sonic mechanism; the grasshopper has its "ears" in its knees; its hop integrated with its sound perception.)

In its "silence" and its position then, the solitary nucleus (and its associated commissural nucleus) appeared to be the "frontal lobe" of the primitive vegetative-sonic system. In this system the ganglia of the primitive equilibratory-sonic apparatus—the sphenopalatine, the otic, and the geniculate ganglia—played a predominant role. In the lower

It is important to know that the first labyrinthine semicircular canal forms from an infolding of the lateral-line organ of the head area and that two of the other lateral-line organs become the first crista ampullaris. Thus the labyrinth is, strictly speaking, a portion of the old sonic system, especially in its earliest formation and basic functions. The duality of the two sonic systems is not encompassed simply by nerve elements on one side and labyrinth and cochlea on the other; the labyrinth itself partakes of the duality —in its basic attributes primitive, in its newer relationship, to the emergent cochlea, more highly evolved.

The fact that vertigo and tinnitus can be cured by destruction of the labyrinth (in many but not all cases) is thus in keeping with our view of a primitive internal sonic system. Because the chorda tympani is a derivative of this system this does not mean that its section can cure a diseased labyrinth; it is highly doubtful that section of the chorda tympani can in and of itself have any lasting effect on labyrinthine function.

aquatic vertebrates the predominant ganglion of the head is the geniculate, the center of sensory seventh nerve function; the semilunar ganglion of the fifth cranial nerve is small in comparison, the reverse of the proportions in higher mammals. *This same apparatus enabled the lizard to respond to sonic stimuli of 80,000 vibrations per second* (Guggenheim, 1948). It was, in comparison with man's sonic range of audibility, truly "ultrasonic." It was therefore in man "silent."

The solitary nucleus, and its various interconnections at a very basic level of nervous integration, could operate with the other "silent" areas: the caudate nucleus of the archipallium and the frontal lobe of the neopallium, in a total ultrasonic mechanism. At the same time it had a most intimate, indeed inseparable, connection with the newer *sonic* auditory structures. It bore a dynamic relationship to speech and emotional expression; the seventh cranial nerve innervates emotional facial expression, the ninth and tenth innervate speech and respiration; it could not help but have access, however "silent" it itself might be, to the newer *phonic* activity of man, and so to the formation of words and emotions and ideas. The sonic-ultrasonic aspect of the concealed duality of the hearing mechanism of man (and of higher vertebrates) thus was a neurologic basis for the establishment of the sense of reality. The primitive sonic system listened to the body and its insistent, however archaic and narcissistic, impulses; the newer sonic system listened to the outer world, assessing sound, space, direction; their fusion of the narcissistic and the objective made the *seemingly unitary* sense of reality, in psychic terms. Having a psychophysiologic basis for the fact of their fusion, we now also had a psychophysiologic basis for their *dissociation*. The sense of reality must depend upon the intactness of *an integrative sonic-ultrasonic barrier*.

Subjected to psychodynamic consideration, this concept fitted with surprising accuracy the requirements of Freud's *postulates for an integrative barrier* which, in the interests of the sense of reality, regulated narcissistic impulses and at the same time legislated the psychosomatic syndromes; it thus had to participate in dream formation and had to have access to the repressed, because as a barrier it had to function to suppress impermissible narcissistic impulses which would reappear visualized in the dream.

In *Beyond the Pleasure Principle,* Freud (1920) pointed out that in this manner explicit conscious and preconscious pain could be converted into unconscious—because repressed—psychic *tension* and "deflected" to the body and its organs. He showed that this mechanism could not reside in the cortex, even though its existence could be clearly deduced from the sheer psychoanalytic manifestations of the psychosomatic syndromes, the traumatic neuroses, and the psychoses. This mechanism—for which he sought incessantly—betrayed the operation of a new, more basic, more powerful principle than the pleasure principle; hence his title: *Beyond the Pleasure Principle.*

As Freud predicted, this mechanism now provides a physiologic basis for auditory and visual hallucination. The sonic-ultrasonic integrative barrier *dissociates.* Now the ultrasonic *becomes sonic* under special conditions, regressing to its archaic function as an independent primitive hearing system also connected with visual motion and vision. The older sonic system listens to itself without the integrated impact of outer reality and the derivatives of that outer reality. The instinctual (sympathetic-excitor) narcissistic impulses now are free to portray their wishes in "voices and visions" precisely as in a dream, except that now—in the state of dissociation—*it is a waking dream,* no longer rendered harmless to the sense of reality, no longer presided over by the dream censor which guards sleep. This dissociation of the integrative ultrasonic-sonic barrier is the narcissistic neurosis.

Not only the auditory and visual hallucination, but the process of dreaming and repression itself indicate that *the principle of the integrative sonic-ultrasonic barrier supersedes the pleasure principle in psychodynamics.*

For example, everyone knows the peculiar quality of *dream speech.* Words "spoken and heard" in dreams are not of the same character as actual speech and hearing. They have a strange quality between hearing, seeing, and articulating the word image and yet actually partaking of none of these qualities precisely. That these are ultrasonic phenomena, in all probability, on the brink of becoming audible, is indicated by the common experience that we all know: when, in a dream, the words spoken become audible as clearly as in real life, *we wake up;* the transformation from the ultrasonic to the sonic moves us into reality. In a later study, in this series, a number of such dreams will be presented in detail; here they can be mentioned only in passing.

The facts of repression produce an even more striking proof of the theory of an integrative sonic-ultrasonic barrier. As Freud (1923) pointed out in *The Ego and the Id*, repression can take place only when preconscious linkages—syntactical processes of the fronto-temporal cortex—are broken. Thought components now become "unhinged" and are drawn into the unconscious, as opposed to suppression in which the syntactical links remain on the edge of consciousness *still available to the ego because still audible to the ego*. The preconscious is connected with speech readily and is thus the area of *sonic suppression;* the unconscious is not so readily connected with speech; it is thus the area of *ultrasonic repression*.

Repression then must be redefined for the first time in neurophysiologic terms. *Repression is ultrasonic transformation of originally sonic word linkages; in becoming ultrasonic the word linkages automatically lose their syntax because they come under the domination of the totally "silent" and totally primitive ultrasonic apparatus* which begins at the solitary nucleus (the "vegetative-sonic frontal lobe") and ends with the "silent" frontal lobes of the cerebral cortex. The repressed thus is under the control of the primitive sonic apparatus which is not "audible" and can not deal with syntax. It can, however, register the accompanying feeling tone, as Freud pointed out, which is essentially nonverbal.

When, in the narcissistic neurosis (psychosis), the integrative sonic-ultrasonic barrier dissociates, we then see clinically the "return of the repressed," the "fracture of the sense of reality," the "voices and visions"—all regressive phenomena in which the primitive sonic system becomes "articulate" in its own prehistoric way; at the same time it loses its selective and discriminating function in relationship to the newer sonic system. It now permits its excitor impulses, however narcissistic and unreal, full sonic and visual expression in the waking state. The primitive sonic system is thus the "ultrasonic repression-subsidiary" of the nervous system's major industry, ordinarily a "monopoly," of establishing and maintaining the sense of reality above all other things in life.

The connection between repression and psychic *pain,* between psychic tension and drug addiction (in which the region of the solitary nucleus is profoundly hit pathologically) becomes clear. Ordinarily, by virtue of ultrasonic transformation, painful psychic experiences are broken up and stored, i.e., repressed. This—without analysis—can only increase psychic tension which is handed down, so to speak, to the great parasympathetic outflow also controlled and carried by the solitary nucleus and tract. The "tension," originally psychic pain, is now deflected to the body organs themselves (the psychosomatic syndromes) or, if the body cannot take it—or amoral opportunity presents itself—drugs can be supplied where "the taste for the stuff" plays its concomitant role in "relaxation," as in marihuana poisoning (Bromberg, 1934) where reality, time, space, direction, and even the law of gravity are distorted and alienated, and sexual erotic feelings and images abound in magical style.

The secret of drug habituation, then, would lie in the ability of the drug to "key" the integrative sonic-ultrasonic barrier to a new level and to a new and more easily endurable proportion between sonic and ultrasonic energy transactions. (Every practicing psychotherapist knows how susceptible *musicians* in particular are to these drugs which literally "send" them, attractive particularly for the ease with which they convert psychic pain and tension into erotic pleasure.) Here it can be seen how the principle of the integrative sonic-ultrasonic barrier goes "beyond the pleasure principle." The theoretically grounded psychiatrist will at once perceive the distinct relationship between the integrative sonic-ultrasonic barrier and psychosexual energy transactions. The greater the degree of ultrasonic regression, i.e., the greater the barrage or "unbinding" of "bound sexual investment," the more the anxiety of "free-floating" sexual dissolution psychically. Sexual stability, then, depends directly on an intact sonic-ultrasonic integrative barrier.

It is clear then that this concept fits the phenomena of dreams, repression, drug addiction, and the psychosomatic syndromes, three examples of which may now be presented briefly in this light.

(a) Strongin and Hinsie (1938) showed that the parotid secretory rate invariably increases in schizophrenia. This phenomenon is not explicable ordinarily except as a "cortical release," something not consistent with the schizophrenic process. However, our present concept says that this is to be expected, not as a "release" but *as a dissociation*. The solitary nucleus controls and the solitary tract carries the parasympathetic outflow. When the primitive sonic system dissociates, *it takes the parasympathetic with it*. The parotid is accordingly stimulated to a "wild" degree with a resultant increase in secretory rate.

(b) It is well known (e.g., the Smithwick operation) how important a role the total sympathetic integration plays in circulatory hypertension and how resultant renal vasoconstriction (Goldblatt, 1941) elevates arterial blood pressure. Conversely the carotid sinus produces an arterial hypotension and syncope the aura of which may include tinnitus, vertigo, etc. Removal of the carotid sinus and the aortic depressor nerves in animals results in arterial hypertension. The carotid sinus is supplied by the two most important visceral branches of the solitary tract, namely the glossopharyngeal (ninth) and the vagus (tenth). In other words, the solitary tract and its nucleus play a role in the various "psychosomatic" tension-relaxation equilibria. Every practicing psychotherapist knows how the development of certain anxieties may result either in sinal syncope or in the elevation of arterial tension. Of importance here is the fact that hypertensives have exceptionally good hearing generally and are easily *sonically startled*. Hypertensives also show great anxiety as stimuli approach the ultrasonic level. Conversely Ménière's syndrome shows a consistently arterial hypotension. *The distinction between hypertension and Ménière's syndrome is then exquisitely sonic, with hypersensitivity to sonic stimuli characteristic of hypertension and Ménière's syndrome insensitive or hyposensitive to sonic stimuli.* This distinction is not solely founded on the activity of the carotid sinus but rather on the total vegetative-sonic integration mediated in the hindbrain; in this mediation the carotid sinus is a peripheral instrument of the integrative sonic-ultrasonic barrier.[3]

---

[3] It is important to recall the importance of sound to the human infant and how pervious it is to *sonic startling*. This writer has gathered evidence that the "alarm reaction" which Selye makes basic to his concept of psychosomatic relationships includes an unrecognized sonic factor. The traumatic neurosis shows definite relationships between un-

(c) The phenomenon of *tinnitus* in Ménière's syndrome and in otosclerosis has already been described by this writer, though not in precisely these terms, as *ultrasonic collapse,* affecting specifically the auditory appartus itself. In tinnitus, "the inaudible becomes audible." There is a specific lowering—as opposed to schizophrenic dissociation—of the ultrasonic level. This is why tinnitus is usually, though not necessarily noticed and reported as such, the first harbinger of deafness with or without labyrinthine attacks. The tinnitus becomes "invasive" and wipes out progressively the external sound perception in the higher frequencies or it may operate suddenly and catastrophically. This writer recently observed a case in a musician in whom the sudden onset of high-pitched "steamy" tinnitus resulted in total "nerve deafness" in three days without any signs of vertigo or labyrinthitis but with evidence of what must temporarily be called "exhaustion of the ultrasonic system" in its relationship to the auditory apparatus itself.

These three examples will suffice to show merely that various clinical and physiologic data can be reinterpreted in the light of the concept of an integrative sonic-ultrasonic barrier. Separate studies, to follow, will present these problems more fully. For the present, however, it is clear that the various conditions of the integrative sonic-ultrasonic barrier become of prime importance. In schizophrenia, the barrier becomes disintegrative; the sonic and ultrasonic dissociate with all the consequences that have already been briefly outlined. In Ménière's disease the proportions of sonic to ultrasonic become altered in the direction of diminished sonic activity and pathologic change in the ultrasonic (e.g., the normally inaudible becomes abnormally audible). The associated hypotension, characteristic of the syndromes of deafness, tinnitus, and vertigo, seems to indicate that *heart work* varies with the integrative sonic-ultrasonic barrier, being diminished in Ménière's as judged by low blood pressure and bradycardia. Contrariwise, in hypertension, the sonic range seems to increase with increased sonic sensibility; deafness is extremely rare, and *heart*

---

expected sonic stimuli and the convulsion. The traumatic neurosis is most apt to occur when the individual has not mobilized himself against unexpected startling, particularly sonic though also visual.

work increases. In both hypotension and hypertension, the circulation and the activity of the heart seem to bear a direct relationship then to the integrative sonic-ultrasonic barrier. Certain studies of my own indicate that, in the normal condition, the barrier goes through a normal daily variability, varying with fatigue and exertion, with tension and emotion. This is to be expected if the barrier is mediated by the solitary nucleus which appears to be the integrator of the vegetative-sonic equilibria.

But, interesting as this theoretic approach may be, it cannot be entertained at all, and has no validity whatever, if the solitary nucleus and the solitary tract are "pure taste areas." A re-examination of the facts concerning taste is thus immediately indicated.

Summary

1. An integrative sonic-ultrasonic barrier is theoretically described as existing in the human nervous system, basically mediated by the solitary nucleus and solitary tract and their various connections to the brain and to the body.

2. The various "silent areas" of the human brain—the solitary nucleus, the caudate nucleus, and the frontal lobes—represent the various quantitative and qualitative levels of ultrasonic transformations.

3. The integrative sonic-ultrasonic barrier is created by the unsuspected existence of a *dual* hearing system in man—a primitive sonic system, now ultrasonic—and the more recent sonic system created by the later development of the labyrinth in relationship to the emergent cochlea.

4. The integrative sonic-ultrasonic barrier, when dissociating, is capable of producing all the phenomena of schizophrenia. Hence the appearance of schizophrenic syndromes in various toxic diseases, i.e., drug addictions, affecting the region of the solitary nucleus, labyrinthine and auditory nuclei, caudate nuclei, and the frontal lobes.

5. The phenomena of hallucinations, dreams, repression, and the various psychosomatic syndromes are all explicable as the result of the dissociation or repressive operation of the integrative sonic-ultrasonic barrier.

6. The integrative sonic-ultrasonic barrier, as predicted by Freud, operates as a psychodynamic principle that goes beyond the pleasure principle.

7. This demands a re-evaluation of the age-old concept of taste, a task to which the following section is devoted.

II. TASTE AS A BASICALLY CHOLINERGIC PHENOMENON

Stated most concisely, these are the facts which have been established concerning taste, not one of which in any way, so far as this writer can determine, substantiates the age-old myth of four separate taste fibers for four separate modalities of taste: bitter, salt, sour, and sweet.

In this review these facts have been arranged anatomically, histologically, chemically, physiologically, pathologically, numerically, developmentally, and adaptively.

A. *Anatomic and Histologic Data*

1. The taste cells, which are hair cells like those in the cochlea are modified epithelial cells. They degenerate when their nerves are cut and regenerate when their nerves are restored. No other special cranial sense cells ever regenerate once degenerated, i.e., the other special cranial senses show a much higher degree of irreversible delicacy and specialization.

2. Taste upon the tongue is supplied by two *different* nerves, the chorda tympani (seventh) for the anterior two thirds, and the ninth for the posterior one third. Taste buds in the pharynx and larynx are supplied by the third nerve of the tractus solitarius, namely by the vagus (tenth). No other special cranial sense is thus innervated in so multiple a manner.

3. Histologically, the chorda tympani has been shown (recently by Costen, Clare, and Bishop, 1951) to be a mixed motor-sensory nerve containing parasympathetic motor fibers, both myelinated and unmyelinated, general nerves of somesthetic supply to the tongue: pain, touch, temperature—all myelinated, and unmyelinated sensory fibers as well. No other special cranial sense is supplied by such a nerve containing so many different varieties of fibers, of mixed motor and

sensory attributes. *The tractus solitarius is thus proved not to be a "pure" taste tract.*

4. Costen, Clare, and Bishop (1951) have shown conclusively that the "taste fibers" must run in the temperature fiber-range (2-4 μ) but that not all of the fibers of that range could possibly be devoted to taste. No other special cranial sense has its specific nerve fibers running in an envelope of fibers devoted to other senses.

5. Costen, Clare, and Bishop (1951) state that all opinions on the actual size of taste fibers are *inferential,* i.e., they are inferred from the results of threshold relationships of responses induced by direct electrical stimulation of the chorda tympani. *No one, in brief, has ever seen an actual, indisputably proved taste fiber or determined its size by direct inspection and direct measurement.* No other special cranial sense is fraught with such "inferential necessities"; their fibers in all characteristics are known directly.

6. "Taste fibers" to the anterior two thirds of the tongue may rarely, but definitely, take an aberrant course, going by way of the greater superficial petrosal via the otic ganglion to the tongue (Schwartz and Weddell, 1938) with no noticeable thickening of the greater superficial petrosal nerve reported in the instances of aberration. No other special cranial nerve fibers take aberrant courses; they may be congenitally absent or malformed but are never aberrant in this manner, without producing noticeable distortion.

7. The tongue is innervated *on the papillae* by the fifth cranial nerve (lingual) which however carries only somesthetic sensibility, not taste, as proven by Cushing (1903). Yet, if the fifth nerve supply is cut away, as Cushing showed, it takes sixteen to thirty-seven days for "taste" to reappear. Cushing explained this delay by a "physiologic edema" postoperatively blocking the seventh nerve taste fibers. No other special cranial sense is so overlaid in its end-organ distribution by another cranial nerve, nor would any other special cranial sense be thus "blocked" for so long a time by operative interference on an unessential nearby nerve pathway, an operation which did not touch those special sense fibers in any way.

Comment: These seven essentially anatomic and histologic facts *prove that the tractus solitarius is not a "pure" taste tract.* They show that *no one has ever seen a taste fiber.* They illustrate all the wide divergencies of structure and distribution of the taste mechanism as compared with all other special cranial senses. The "taste sense" by these seven facts alone *can be compared only with the sense of "touch"* which we now know to be a *composite sense* made up of pressure, temperature, kinesthetic sensibility, etc.

B. *Nerve-Stimulation Data*

1. Electrical and other stimulation of the trunk of the chorda tympani in the human being has never produced the "sweet" response. Electrical stimulation (cf. Costen, Clare, and Bishop, 1951) produces *only "bitter" or unpleasurable variants* such as "metallic" or "bitter-metallic-sour." No one, has ever found on *stimulation in the human being any* "bitter, sweet, salt, or sour" individual fibers that can be stimulated with selective responses correlated specifically to such isolated fibers. No *neoplasm* or any other *histologic* abnormality has ever developed anywhere in the taste pathways, from tongue to hindbrain, involving stimulation or ablation of these hypothetic "bitter, salt, sweet, and sour" fibers. No other special cranial nerve has ever remained so "hypothetical" either in stimulation experiments or in pathologic formation or information.

2. Costen, Clare and Bishop (1951) stimulated the chorda tympani (in an unsedated, conscious human being with normal taste on the tongue) at three points in its intratympanic course. Only at two points, A and B, nearer to the autonomic synapse at the geniculate ganglion were they able to elicit "bitter" or "bitter-metallic-sour" at thresholds higher than that necessary to elicit pain. At the third point of stimulation, C, further toward the periphery, *they could not elicit taste under any conditions of stimulation,* no matter how high their voltage nor how repetitive their stimulation, *with normal taste on the tongue.* No other special cranial sense is thus refractory to stimulation at a normal point in an uninjured nerve trunk.

3. Costen, Clare, and Bishop (1951) report "auditory buzzing" and vertigo on stimulation of the chorda tympani which they cannot explain adequately, in spite of the fact that Costen himself described the Costen syndrome: tinnitus due to compressional irritation of the

chorda tympani. *In brief, sonic and vertiginous responses in an unsedated, conscious patient are obtained on stimulation of a "taste
nerve" which will not yield a "taste response" under any conditions
at one point in its course and at other points will yield taste only under conditions as suggestive of autonomic stimulation as of sensory
stimulation.*

Comment: The electrical stimulation data of the most recent and
carefully controlled valuable study by Costen, Clare, and Bishop
(1951) elicits only one modality essentially "bitter" and sonic and vertiginous responses. The threshold relationships furthermore are such
as to suggest autonomic stimulation in view of the inconsistent sensory response. Our first ten facts, anatomic, histologic, and electro-
physiologic, militate strongly against any consistent evidence of primary taste fibers and they disprove that the tractus solitarius can be a
"pure taste tract."

C. *Chemical Tongue-Stimulation Data*

1. The stimulation of individual papillae, in two different series,
reflects a peculiar diffusion of the *hypothetical* four sets of taste fibers
"bitter, sweet, sour, salt." First, there is a most *peculiar numerical* distribution, less than half of 125 papillae in one series (60 papillae)
equipped to react to three modalities, (the Oehrwall, 1891, series);
and in the remainder (smaller series—Kiesow, 1896): 39 papillae—
there is again a "scatter" *with no individual papilla reacting to bitter
alone.* These are the two series:

OEHRWALL SERIES

Of 125 Papillae	Sweet	Bitter	Acid
27	0	0	0
60	+	+	+
4	+	+	0
7	0	+	+
12	+	0	+
12	0	0	+
3	+	0	0
Total 125	79	71	91

It will be observed that the individual responses summate.

This will be illustrated again in the Kiesow series below, where again no papilla is found to react to bitter alone.

KIESOW SERIES

Of 39 Papillae	Salt	Acid	Sweet	Bitter
3	+	0	0	0
3	0	+	0	0
7	0	0	+	0
26	+	+	+	+
39	29	29	33	26

These two series illustrate a strange "scatter" for a primary "special sense" with individual fibers for each of the modalities. A little more than half in one smaller series, in a larger series a little less than half of the papillae are fully equipped. No papilla reacts to bitter alone, though all the other modalities can be found exclusively occupying individual papillae.

Comment: Any theory of taste which will be valid must explain the peculiar distribution and the absence of the exclusively "bitter" papilla, just as it must explain the absence of "sweet" on direct stimulation of the chorda trunk. Our theory has no difficulty here; "sweet" is missing from the chorda trunk because "sweet" exists only as a specific peripheral chemical result in relation to "bitter" on the tongue; there is no "sweet" fiber; "sweet" is a reciprocal relation, chemically and physiologically to "bitter." Any fiber or combination of fibers that carry "bitter" will therefore carry "sweet." Similarly no papilla can react to "bitter" alone because "bitter" is the physiologic "fundamental" (to use a sonic concept). Upon "bitter" the other qualities are built by always present physiologic hydrogen-ion concentration (sour) by differentially mobile anions (salt), by a specific chemical transformation (sweet). Since these "physiologic overtones" are always present in the tissue fluids, "bitter" must constantly be modified. The summating totals of the above series show that any given stimulus on the tongue merely alters a composite reaction, and shows how the illusion of "equally" reacting modalities is built up numerically in the summation. Furthermore, the *variability* of distribution is as characteristic of *vegetative innervation* as it is uncharacteristic of specific fibers of special sense going to highly specialized end organs.

2. The injection of mecholyl, a parasympathetic stimulant, into the blood stream produces "bitter," which is also produced by parasympathetic stimulation as a concomitant of the nausea, vomiting, and vertigo of pregnancy in which strange taste perversions occur. Similarly, diabetes with high blood sugar produces sweet. No other special cranial sense is so obviously at the mercy of the cholinergic and the blood level of metabolites. In schizophrenia where parasympathetic stimulation is so "wild" and the parotid secretory rate goes up so markedly, there is no hallucination of taste (except rarely and questionably) but instead the delusion of being poisoned, underneath which is the intense "bitter" sensation, the total disruption of the normal oral pattern.

3. Certain substances taste "sweet" on the tip of the tongue and "bitter" on the back of the tongue. No other special cranial sense shows such an inversion of a definitive modality theoretically mediated by supposedly definite fibers such as "bitter" and "sweet."

4. Gymnemic acid paralyzes the tongue selectively to "bitter" and to "sweet"; "salt" and "sour" are left unaffected, again indicating the reciprocal chemical relationship between "bitter" and "sweet."

5. "Sour" is definitely determined by hydrogen-ion dissociation of *weak acids on the tongue*. Should the acid be stronger and the hydrogen-ion dissociation more intense, *then pain results*. In other words, "sour" is the qualitative expression of a quantitative reaction in the pain series. This fits with the fact that "bitter" and "sour" are both apt to be orally inhibitory, in contrast to "salt" and "sweet" which are apt to be orally excitatory, i.e., "bitter" and "sour" represent, from the standpoint of our theory, oral inhibition and oral pain, while "sweet" and "salt" are orally excitatory and in all likelihood are products of sympathetic opposition to parasympathetic synthesizing influence.

6. "Salt" is directly proportional to the relative mobility of the anion of the salt, the greater the mobility, the greater the "saltiness." (Of interest in this connection is the fact that electronic sonometers

to determine the viscosity of a solution are based on the ultrasonic vibrations set up by the differential speeds of ions as these move across the tip of an electrode, the supersonic vibrations being then electronically calculated.)

D. *Some Pathologic Data*

1. Many years ago Hunt (1909) described the preservation of taste in a case of encephalitic geniculate ganglionitis and practically complete destruction of the *sensory* fibers of the nervus intermedius. He therefore concluded, as did Gowers (1888), that taste ran up the fifth cranial nerve. But, in such ascending sensory degeneration, the motor autonomic fibers are spared. Taste is thus again indicated as a basic cholinergic phenomenon.

2. Gowers (1888) believed in the fifth nerve route for taste because he had seen severely compressive lesions of the seventh, ninth, and tenth nerve roots (the tractus solitarius) which did not result in any loss of taste. Such compressive lesions rarely abolish autonomic function.

3. Furlow sectioned the nervus intermedius intracranially for tic douloureux of the ear, cutting *both* motor and sensory fibers. Taste disappeared in the anterior two thirds of the tongue on that side as theoretically expected because of autonomic motor section as well as sensory. Put together with Hunt's observation, this would seem conclusively to prove that taste depends on the autonomic motor fibers.[4] No one has ever done a differential section of the seventh and ninth nerves in the human being, but if Hunt's observation is correct, as it appears to be, then section of the autonomic would abolish taste while section of the sensory elements would not. Even, however, if section of the sensory elements were to abolish taste, this would still not prove that taste is not a basic cholinergic phenomenon; it would prove only that both elements are necessary for a complete synthesis, the cholinergic and the sensory.

---

[4] Rosen (1951), stimulating the chorda tympani in patients under Demerol is at a loss to explain the absence of taste responses. The drug Demerol is a piperidene derivative. Piperidine paralyzes the motor-autonomic fibers.

E. *The Developmental Data*

1. The taste buds show a specific growth relationship numerically. They are much more numerous in early infancy and adolescence, the periods of sexual efflorescence. By maturity they begin sharply to diminish and decrease precipitously by old age. No other special cranial sense shows so sharp a relationship to sexual functions; even though they all decrease in acuity as time goes on.

2. Finally there are the integrative data. These show fluctuations from one year to the next and thus are included here under the developmental. In addition, taste varies from subject to subject with physiologic condition, emotional states, time of day, inhibition, and excitement, etc.

Comment. All the evidence so far fails to reveal one single fact in support of any "primary taste fibers." Instead all the evidence shows a total synthesis in which the basic cholinergic elements—the motor parasympathetic—appear to be basic. It must be recognized that normally all the requirements for each of the specific tastes are present all the time in the body. Thus there is always acetylcholine at the autonomic synapse; there is always physiologic sodium and salt; there is always blood sugar; there is always a definite hydrogen-ion concentration. It seems as though the stimulus-response "bitter" is that response which comes when the physiologic synthesis is thrown to that side. This is true also in diabetes; when the blood sugar becomes abnormally elevated and the total synthesis is thrown to the opposite side, then the reaction is "sweet." Spontaneous sourness can also exist as in the term *sour eructation.*

Certain data which ordinarily would have been included in the above groups have been withheld to be used in relationship to the numerical study which follows and which seems to show that it is mathematically impossible for the modalities of taste to be supplied by four separate primary types of fibers.

F. *The Numerical Data*

In this study we are heavily indebted to the work of Foley (1945) on the cat and to the excellent histologic study of the human chorda tympani by Costen, Clare, and Bishop (1951). The data on the cat and dog are sufficiently similar to that of man to be valid for a numerical evaluation.

These are Foley's data for the cat and the dog on the numerical composition of chorda fibers together with the taste bud count for the cat (Hayes and Elliot, 1943) and for the dog (Halliday, 1940).

Fiber Group	Cat	Dog
Total sensory	1157	2205
Total motor (autonom.)	798	1142
Unmyelinated sensory	208	507
Unmyelinated motor	231	132
Myelinated sensory	949	1698
Taste buds (ant. 2/3)	575	887

In relationship to the above data we must recognize two alternatives—the old theory of four primary fibers and the present theory of a total synthesis. In either case, we must have myelinated temperature, pain, and touch fibers, particularly temperature fibers in the chorda tympani. The presence of temperature fibers has been shown by Costen, Clare, and Bishop (1951) who also infer that their electric stimulation data can be interpreted as having the sensory impulses run in fibers of the temperature size (2-4 μ). Other investigators have obtained similar evidence of a relatively small range and size of the taste responding fiber. In addition to this physiologic evidence for a fiber of the temperature range group, there are all the distinctive facts about taste and temperature. Each modality of taste has its own distinctive relationship to temperature. Temperature has a typically different effect on each of the four modalities but not all stimuli for any quality are affected in the same way. For "bitter" and "salt" the threshold is raised by temperature. For "sweet" the threshold is lowered by temperature. For "sour"—that which we interpret as belonging to the pain series—temperature has relatively little effect on threshold. Furthermore, taste can be appreciated with any degree of acuity only between 0-30 degrees C. Below or above this scale taste is not reliable and pain reactions set in. For these reasons we must recognize that each of the four modalities must have pain, temperature, and touch fibers *in the chorda tympani*. This is logically necessary because of Cushing's proof that the chorda tympani alone can carry taste.

Now according to the old theory, if there are four sets of taste fibers, one for each modality and three sets of fibers one for each of touch, pain, and temperature to each taste bud, there would be on a 1:1 basis, 7×575 or 4025 fibers of the myelinated sensory variety in the chorda tympani of the cat. We may divide these by 2, because there is some evidence on direct histologic study that there may be a branching of the subepithelial plexus so that the same fiber occasionally supplies two taste buds. There is no evidence of a greater degree of branching. 4025 divided by 2 is approximately 2013 fibers of the myelinated sensory variety. *But the chorda tympani of the cat has only 949 myelinated fibers, of the sensory variety.* There do not appear to be sufficient numbers of fibers in the chorda tympani to satisfy the numerical requirements of the old theory of taste.

(At this point another fact about taste may be interpolated. "Bitter" on the tongue according to the physiologic studies of Howell, and since repeated with some, but not significant, variation by others, is 10,000 times as sensitive as "sweet," 140 times as sensitive as "salt," and 70 times as sensitive as "sour." If we relate this sensitivity to the above numerical relationships we can find no evidence of any especially rich nerve supply for the quality "bitter.")

Or, if we wish to leave touch and pain out of consideration, and in order to support the old theory deal only with the temperature range fibers 2-4 μ in which Costen, Clare, and Bishop (1951) believe the primary taste fibers run, we are at no better vantage point. Costen, Clare, and Bishop state that although taste fibers run in the temperature range group, not all the fibers in this group serve taste. At least 80 per cent of the chorda's myelinated fibers are of this range or approximately 760 fibers. Of these, in view of the temperature necessities, there must be at least one half of 575, or 288, temperature fibers branching at 1:2 relationship to the 575 taste buds; 472 fibers thus remain to serve taste on the theory of primary taste fibers.

Of the 472, 118 must be devoted to each of the four modalities, bitter, salt, sweet, and sour. But this would mean that there must be practically a 1:5 branching in the taste bud. This is histologically unbelievable.

We have no such difficulty numerically with the concept of a total synthesis. First, we assign a portion of the motor autonomic fibers, myelinated and unmyelinated to each taste bud. There are now available 1157 sensory fibers for the cat and 2205 sensory fibers for the dog. This gives us a reverse proportion of 2:1 or 3:1 taste fibers of synthetic activity for each taste bud. There is now sufficient provision for all the taste eventualities.[5]

There are other correlations besides these so far as clinical and experimental data go. These may be enumerated as follows:

1. *The Adaptation Studies.* Adaptation refers to the raising of threshold to one substance when preceded on the taste bud by a similarly tasting substance. Thus it was found (cf. review by Pfaffman, 1951) that twenty-four different salts such as NaCl, NaBr, KCl, etc., showed no adaptation for any other salt. It is not reasonable, nor indeed is there any evidence, to assume that there are twenty-four different salt receptors in the taste bud. The number of fibers needed for such a taste bud on the basis of a primary fiber for salt would make the chorda tympani one of the largest nerves in the body. The adaptation study with respect to salt thus almost in itself disproves the possibility of there being four different sets of taste fibers. "Sour" on the other hand shows adaptation for all weak acids. This likewise fits the theory of a synthesis since "sour" belongs in all likelihood to the painpleasure element of taste, and as is known pain-pleasure stimuli always show adaptation phenomena.

2. *The Aberrant Taste Pathway.* As noted above, Schwartz and Weddell (1938) have definitely shown that occasionally, though rarely, taste fibers take an aberrant course through the greater superficial petrosal nerve, traveling via the otic ganglia to the tongue. The numerical relationships studied above indicate that the aberrant taste fibers would make the greater superficial petrosal nerve an abnor-

[5] The most constant numerical relationship is the ratio between total autonomic *motor* fibers and the taste bud, e.g. in the cat 1.39 and the dog 1.29.

mally large nerve. No such increment of size was reported. If, however, we need only to consider a shift of at most 200 to 300 autonomic fibers, we have no difficulty in recognizing that the greater superficial petrosal nerve could thus carry the basic elements of reactivity, namely, the parasympathetic fibers, without any noticeable increment in size.

In concluding this review of the evidence it must be stated that there are a great many other facts which similarly support the view of a basic cholinergic synthesis. However, these are so voluminous that they cannot be included here.

One final question must be briefly discussed; this is the relationship between taste as a basic cholinergic phenomenon and the integrative sonic-ultrasonic barrier.

If taste is not a special sense, what is its precise character and how does it express the activity and meaning of the integrative sonic-supersonic barrier?

Taste is a basic psychophysiologic synthesis. What appear to be its definite modalities, "bitter, sweet, salt, and sour," are the expressions of distinct *shifts* in the total synthesis, each serving a distinct psychophysiologic purpose. Its psychophysiologic purpose is *the expression of oral-erotic sensation in relation to the ingestion of food and in relation to psychic states.* This orientation immediately gives us a clearer picture of the two great divisions of the autonomic system which is divided into the *craniosacral* and the *thoracolumbar* divisions.

We are now in a position to understand the definite character of the craniosacral organization, in contrast to the definite character of the thoracolumbar. The craniosacral division of the autonomic has precisely *the same fundamental purpose throughout: namely, the mechanism of erotic, sexual pleasure-pain.* Just as the sacral division has to do with evacuation and erection and orgasm, so the cranial division has to do with oral and olfactory and visual intake and satisfaction. *The cholinergic fibers of both the cranial and the sacral division have to do with the synthesis of erotic sensation* into the psychic patterns "oral," "anal," and "genital." (Perhaps we may now call such sensations simply cranial-sacral eroticism.) We could not see this unity of functioning as long as we considered taste a "special sense."

Thus the function of the *thoracolumbar system* is to express the autonomic *mobilization* corresponding to *fright and flight;* the *cranio-sacral* division expresses the autonomic *inhibition* corresponding to *pain and pleasure.* Thus we can see the integration of taste and salivation in connection with parasympathetic stimulation. The parasympathetic *stimulates the salivary glands* because it is functioning in relationship to *the pain-pleasure of taste.* Here we have finally the complete reason why the "inhibitory" cranial parasympathetic "excites" salivation; its action is *not* paradoxic; its action is, on the contrary, precisely what pain-pleasure *orally and lingually* dictates, just as the action of the thoracolumbar division is what fright and flight dictate—and we include in "flight" the flight toward as well as the flight away from an object. Again we find complete verification of the fundamental physiologic characteristics of psychodynamics. For the flight "toward" an object is the definition of *a narcissistic wish.*

Taste is thus the expression of the vegetative-sonic integration of the solitary nucleus and its associated structures; taste as a total synthesis cholinergically determined travels up paths which (electrical stimulation shows us) are *sonic,* in the primitive sense, or *ultrasonic* in the human and higher mammalian sense, i.e., inaudible unless there is some peripheral disease of the old labyrinthine-sonic system in which case we get tinnitus, vertigo, and deafness—together with taste disturbances in the acute attacks. And if the disease is central and disintegrative, then we get another malformation of hearing, namely *dissociative hearing* (with its associated visualization), namely schizophrenia together with excess parotid stimulation and the underlying "bitterness" of "being poisoned."

In brief, at one and the same time, by changing the character of our concept concerning taste, we establish the validity of the concept of the integrative sonic-ultrasonic barrier as Freud predicted; we find finally a complete physiologic concept of the mechanism of erotic sensation, and we perceive that—as has been mentioned before—the ultrasonic appears to be a great portion of the psychosexual energy transaction, perhaps its essence. Hence the phenomena of dreams, hallucinations, repression, psychosomatic syndromes, and traumatic neurosis can now be reinterpreted in terms of the activity of the integrative sonic-ultrasonic barrier. This orientation has been erected upon the concept of a hitherto undiscovered *dual* hearing system in man with all the consequences that must inescapably follow.

If the theoretic considerations presented in this paper will prove to have the validity they promise, a new door will have been opened through which we can pass to confront new problems and perhaps to more effective solution of old problems.

Summary

1. It would appear that the dictum of antiquity must go by the board: there are not "five special senses." Taste is not a "special sense." It seems mathematically proved, if the chorda tympani carries temperature fibers and if the histologic branching is no greater than a 1:2 ratio for nerve fiber to taste bud, that there are not four special sets of fibers carrying the four qualities "bitter, salt, sweet, and sour."

2. Taste appears to be a specific, unrecognized, basically cholinergic synthesis of essentially erotic sensation with definite qualities of pain-pleasure affect to which are attached—semantically—designation differently repellent ("bitter") at one pole and attractive ("sweet") at the other pole of the synthesis.

3. This brings into harmony the relationship between taste and salivation, both under cholinergic domination basically. During schizophrenic dissociation of the integrative sonic-ultrasonic barrier, in which the "parasympathetic goes wild," there is increased parotid salivation and extreme "bitterness" underlying the delusion of "being poisoned." This dissociation in the somatic sphere accompanies, therefore, the dissociation of the ultrasonic from the sonic in the physiologic and mental spheres with the resulting "voices and visions," as already described in Section I. Taste appears to be the expression of the activity of the integrative sonic-ultrasonic barrier, since the fibers carrying taste are evolved primitive equilibratory-sonic fibers.

4. The craniosacral division of the autonomic creates the "oral, anal, genital" eroticism postulated by psychoanalytic theory, a physiologic quantity and quality which may now be called broadly speaking *craniosacral erotic autonomic organization.* Thus the craniosacral division of the autonomic is inhibitory because it subserves the appreciation of pain-pleasure while the thoracolumbar division mobilizes

the reserves of the body in its most primitive implications of fright and flight.

5. The solitary nucleus and its associated structures again emerges as the "frontal lobe" of the vegetative-sonic system of primitive life and its silence—as witness the rarity of the hallucination of taste—is really not silence at all but a part of that ultrasonic transformation which appears to be the activity of all the "silent" areas of the brain.

Chapter XII

THE "ACOUSTIC REFLEX" OF ECHOLALIA. THE MANIFESTATION OF A SPECIAL ACOUSTIC PRINCIPLE IN THE FORMATION OF THE HUMAN MIND. THE CLINICAL SYN- DROMES OF ECHOLALIA, ECHO- PRAXIA, GRASPING AND SUCKING

FROM 1934–1939, I observed at Bellevue Psychiatric Hospital a num- ber of cases of the so-called "acoustic reflex"—as Kussmaul had orig- inally called the symptom of "echolalia." This phenomenon alone— on sheer clinical grounds—ought long ago to have aroused interest in the mind as based specifically upon the unique *sonic* transformation of electrochemical brain processes.

As with the "echo reflex" or "acoustic reflex" so too with echo- praxia, which might be called a "gesture reflex." In the "gesture re- flex" of echopraxia, the significance is still that of language—a sign language.

In order to present all the case material and the exhaustive study of the literature I made seventeen years ago, I have reproduced the original articles in this chapter particularly because of the tetrad which I then described. The fact that these "acoustic reflexes" are so frequently associated with grasping and sucking reflexes, with grasp- ing reactions, and occur in the course of psychoses, in organic vascu- lar disease and in brain deterioration show that (1) these "acoustic re- flexes" obey a very fundamental law, and (2) belong to very early levels of mental growth—e.g., in their reappearance among the re-birth phenomena of the convulsive state, whether alcoholic or eclamptic in nature.

The case material and the discussion of seventeen years ago follow:

The Clinical Syndromes of Echolalia, Echopraxia, Grasping and Sucking—Their Significance in the Disorganization of the Personality

Echolalia and echopraxia have long been known as associated symptoms in both neurological and psychiatric conditions. Grasping and sucking movements also have been studied experimentally and clinically. However, so far as the writer has been able to learn, these four symptoms have never been presented as a coherent tetrad of pathological manifestations. It is the aim of this report to point out their neurophysiologic coherence, and, on the basis of an extensive review of the literature, correlate the data with the clinical material presented here. Inasmuch as a complete post-mortem examination has not been available in any of the cases in this report, final conclusions cannot be drawn; however, a summary of those post-mortem data already in the literature permits several inferences.

The history of our knowledge of each of these symptoms may be briefly summarized as follows: Echolalia was first described by Itard in 1825 in an epileptic in whom it was associated with coprolalia. Romberg in 1842 designated it as the "echo sign" in a case of cerebral softening. Echeverria noted it as evidence of "will perversion" or of impaired or defective inhibition. Von Kraft Ebbing described it. In 1870 Bateman, in a monograph *On Aphasia* noted it in one of his patients and mentions a case of echoing in writing which he saw with McKelvie. He points out that Winslow described it under the heading of "Morbid Imitation Movements of Articulation." Kussmaul studied the phenomenon and considered it an "acoustic reflex." In 1884 Charcot noted it in epilepsy. In 1885 Giles de la Tourette described it in connection with coprolalia and palmus (*tic convulsif*). In 1888 Raymond presented a case with significant post-mortem findings which will be discussed later in this report. Noir in 1893 and later

Landon Carter Gray and Reginald Langdom Down noted it as occurring rarely in idiots and imbeciles, in Down's series in 4 per cent of imbeciles under his care. In 1898 Barr noted it in 2 cases out of a total of 1525 mental defectives. Tuke considered echolalia a symptom of general paresis and noted that it may be associated with many other nervous disorders. Pick in 1902 presented a case of transitory echolalia in a case of luetic vascular disease. It was Pick who pointed out that it could not be considered merely a symptom of cerebral softening, as Romberg had done, since it occurred in cases of "stupor," in severe infections like typhus with high fever, in postepileptic confusions, in "hemicrania concomitata," and in cases emerging from deep morphine sedation. Pick described the symptom also in degenerative brain disease. Cases with degenerative brain disease presenting echolalia were described by Liepmann (1900), Bischoff, Stranski, Quensel and recently in 1934 by Grasse. In 1908 Hobohm presented a case of echolalia in a postpartum psychosis. (Echolalia has long been noted in psychosis. It is described by Meschede in 1897 in a case of phrenolepsie.)

In 1916 Kurt Goldstein's monograph on the so-called "Transcortical Aphasias" included a treatment of echolalia. He points out that the original concept of a transcortical aphasia was put forth by Lichtheim who considered that the defect lay in an interruption of the pathways from the concept-building center to the final motor outflow. Goldstein insisted, on psychologic as well as anatomic grounds, that the critical lesion was in the frontal lobe on the left side, in addition to the diffuse left-sided and to a lesser extent right-sided cerebral atrophy. He described echolalia as having three peculiarities: (1) The exact grammatically correct syntax, (2) absence of inhibition and relative independence from the will of the patient, and (3) failure in complete understanding. He further postulated that two physiologic conditions have to be fulfilled: (1) The presence of an intact promptly functioning speech apparatus, and (2) an isolation of the speech area from the rest of the concept-building field. He emphasized the lack of spontaneous speech in these cases. He notes finally that echolalia occurs very rarely in lesions of the right (subdominant) cerebral hemisphere. According to Dejerine, transcortical aphasia is a highly hypothetical concept; he regards it as only a stage of amelioration in the cortical motor aphasia of Broca. In 1916 Pick again took up the question, differing from Goldstein's views. Earlier, in 1902, Pick had said that the echolalia was due to a lesion in the receptive portion of the speech area, in the region of the gyrus angularis and the contiguous area of the temporal lobe. He explained the impaired writing capacity in some of these cases where the echolalia improved by assuming that the cortex of the angular gyrus was more fully restored than the tract from the angular gyrus to the motor center of the hand. In 1916 Pick stressed the role of intelligent repetition in the normal function of language. In people who were weakened by various nervous diseases, he considered that repetition of a question was already possessed of a degree of automatism. He considered that injury to the brain produced a kind of regression and localized the disease process to the temporal lobe, citing in this connection a case of echolalia in mongoloid idiocy as a sign of defective temporal lobe development, not permitting the normal elaboration of language. He quotes Wyczoikowska (1913) to the effect that one does not "completely understand the word that is spoken to him until it is repeated by one's own organ of speech in a more simple way." Pick emphasizes the agreement of his concept, namely, that echolalia is due to a removal of inhibition which in the speech-learning process develops as types of conditioned reflexes, with the work of Pavlov and Kalischer. To support his contention Pick discusses those cases of echolalia developing in patients who have learned more than one language, and who become echolalic to the last learned language or to languages not yet learned or understood while apparently not comprehending anything of the earlier or mother tongues. In this connection it is important to note Fröschels (1917) case in a five-year-old boy with echolalia and little spontaneous speech who was readily taught to read. Fröschels reported this case as one of transcortical sensory aphasia. One of Barr's cases of mental defect could imitate in nine different languages with perfect inflection and enunciation. Since 1916 little has been added to these concepts although case reports are to be found notably by Hollingworth in 1917 in three cases of echolalia in mental defectives, in 1922 by Guillain, Lechelle and Alajouanine in a psychotic with echolalia and echopraxia (Bleuler mentions such cases in his textbook), in 1934 by Grasse in a case of degenerative disease. Thus we may summarize the facts about echolalia by saying that it occurs in various conditions in various types of disintegration or maldevelopment of the personality, namely, in mental defectives, in toxic and twilight states, in psychoses, in degenerative disease, in vascular disease especially of the dominant hemisphere, in postepileptic states and indeed in various stages of each of these conditions. Furthermore, we may summarize the main concepts about this phenomenon by saying that Pick considered it a kind of "Echoreflex" produced by removal of temporal lobe inhibition, while Goldstein considers it a disturbance of concept-building in which a lesion of the frontal lobe in addition to widespread atrophy or injury more marked on the left is the critical disturbance.

The history of echopraxia parallels that of echolalia with which it is frequently but not invariably associated. Dromand in 1905 made a detailed study of echopraxia and defined it as "the impulsive or automatic imitation of gestures of another person realizing itself immediately with the brusqueness and promptness of reflex actions." It is obvious, therefore, that in clouded states echopraxia is not so likely to be present and its frequency will vary with the degree of clearness of the patient's perception of the model to be imitated. It is not reported commonly in mental defectives. It was first described by Armanque in a discussion of mysticism. Charcot named it *échokinesie* and described it in degenerative disease, especially in patients with tics and in psychoses. Pierre Marie discussed it under the name of *échomatisme* and studied it in hypnotic somnambulism. Morel thought it a specific character of degenerative disease. Brettman in his thesis in 1888 cited numerous examples. Dromand attributed it to a disorganization of the personality and to an incapacity of the higher voluntary centers to inhibit this reflex action. Sérieux and his students Séglas, Demez and Roy regarded echopraxia as a secondary sign of dementia praecox, especially in the catatonic type. Leroy and Genil Perrin noted that patients after emerging from catatonic stupor imitated with an air of mockery. Lwoff and Targowla described a patient who imitated gestures, attitudes and words, even imitated animals. Serin who summarized this literature and presented a case of her own in

1922 considered her case one of voluntary imitation. Her patient was echopractic (and echolalic) only to one person as in one of the cases to be presented in this report. Goldstein did not discuss echopraxia; the possible relation of this phenomenon to injury of the frontal lobe has, so far as the writer is aware, never been postulated. Neither did Pick offer any explanation, but the idea of Dromand coincides with the parallel concept of Pick's: that these phenomena are "Echoreflexes."

As for grasping and sucking movements, more pertinent data concerning their relation to imitative movements will be presented in the discussion following the presentation of cases. Of grasping, groping, sucking and pointing, Bender and Schilder (1933) in a study of alcoholic encephalopathy say: ". . . there appear to be special apparatus, destruction of which brings grasping and groping to the surface. The same is true of the sucking reflex, first described by Wagner-Jauregg in advanced dementia paralytica. Betlheim has shown that it may also occur when there is a lesion of the gyrus supramarginalis, associated with an apraxia of the face. Thus, it appears that grasping, groping and pointing and sucking have a neurologic apparatus at various levels. The findings of Gamper show that there must be at least medullar and midbrain centers for these activities. Striopallidal influences are also acting, and there are probably cortical centers in the frontal lobe as well as in the supramarginal region. These are in addition to general cortical influences which may or may not be working on the level of psychophysiologic integration."

In 1926 the association of grasping and sucking movments was presented by Schuster and Pineas, following up the former's observations that, in a case of right hemiplegia and apraxia of the left hand, the grasping occurred in the eupractic right paretic hand. They presented the association of grasping and sucking in a variety of conditions, including cerebral vascular disease, and postencephalitic conditions. In 1924 Betlheim had already described the sucking reflex in a case of apraxia of the mouth and described snapping movements in this patient. Betlheim notes that Stransky described increased mouth opening and searching (or groping) with the lips, and that Dobrschansky described snapping movements also. In the routine examination of 289 patients with neuropsychiatric disease, Dobrschansky found the sucking reflex in eleven cases, including nine general paretics, one catatonic and one dementia. Fulton in 1934, working with primates, included in the syndrome of the premotor area of the frontal lobes an impairment of skilled movements without gross loss of motor power, spasticity and increased tendon reflexes, forced grasping and vasomotor disturbances of all the contralateral extremities. Richter and Hines (1932) had previously reported that removal of Area 6 of Brodmann was alone capable of producing forced grasping consistently. These findings go toward supporting Herrick's (1926) concept that the premotor areas determine which excitable areas of the motor cortex will be stimulated and in which sequence. The premotor cortex according to Herrick's concept and as substantiated by Richter and Hines, and Fulton, becomes an area in which all impulses toward movement converge, according to established (or "conditioned") patterns and then traverse the pyramidal tracts to express themselves finally in the movement and behavior of the personality. Recently Bieber (1936), in a paper read before the New York Neurological Society, has stressed the relation between grasping and sucking, pointed out that the grasp may be reenforced by sucking or facilitated by first bringing out the sucking movement and that this occurred pathologically in diffuse cerebral and localized frontal lobe (premotor[?]) lesions, and normally in newborns at feeding times.

No one, so far as the writer is aware, has been able to prove to what localized lesion the sucking movement is to be attributed nor, as stated above, has the writer been able to find the presentation of the echolalic and echopraxic movements in association with grasping and sucking movements. Inasmuch as the eleven cases presented in this paper include this tetrad in varying degrees and under widely varying conditions of disorganization of the personality, the writer considers this material as an opportunity to begin the exploration of the relationship of disturbances of the fine movements of the hand and mouth not only in so far as their primitive mechanisms of prehension reappear but also in their disorganization of the function of speech and down to infantile and primitive mechanisms of imitation. And here finally the writer wishes to point out certain anthropologic correlations. Echolalia and echopraxia have long been known to occur among primitive peoples and are recognized by them under various names, such as the designation *Latah* among the Malayans. Furthermore, Darwin (1890) points out in his *Descent of Man:* "The principle of imitation is strong in man, and especially as I have myself observed, with savages. In certain morbid states of the brain this tendency is exaggerated to an extraordinary degree; some hemiplegic patients and others, at the commencement of inflammatory softening of the brain, unconsciously imitate every word which is uttered, whether in their own or in a foreign language, and every gesture or action which is performed near them. Desor has remarked that no animal voluntarily imitates an action performed by man, until in the ascending scale we come to the monkeys, which are well known to be ridiculous mockers." Thus the imitation of man by animals occurs only in that animal which has also developed an organ of prehension closest to ours and (except for us) is capable of finer movements of the hand than the rest of the animal kingdom.

Eleven cases of the syndrome are presented. These include a variety of pathologic processes: cerebral vascular disease, degenerative disease, toxi-infective conditions, postepileptic states, and psychoses. The pertinent literature is briefly summarized in relation to each case.

GROUP I.—CASES WITH CEREBRAL VASCULAR DISEASE

Case 1.—Old right hemiplegia with contracture of the right hand. Echolalia. Echopraxia. Sucking. Lack of spontaneous speech. Personality well preserved.

Female. White. Age 76. Was admitted to Bellevue Hospital three times over a period of eight months. Relatives gave a history of long-standing hypertension and sudden hemiplegia of right extremities eighteen months previous to the first admission.

Positive physical findings included bilateral cataract formation, blood pressure of 234/134, marked peripheral and central arteriosclerosis.

Positive neurologic findings included an old right hemiplegia with a claw-like contracture of the right hand. The right deep reflexes were increased with abdominals absent on the right and a positive right

Babinski. The patient showed slight hypersensitivity to pain. She had always been right-handed. *Aphasic status* revealed that there was practically no spontaneous speech, although neither was there any anomia. Very occasionally she made mistakes, however, in color perception calling gray "cinnamon color." She identified objects and pictures accurately. Her enunciation was perfect. She was able to read. On her last admission she showed definite perseveration. Mentally she was oriented, quiet, cooperative, and usually amiable although at times irritable. She gave no evidence of pathologic trends.

Echolalia.—This symptom was markedly automatic and constant. It was modified only as a result of particular kinds of stimuli.

1. When an *impersonal* stimulus was given, no matter how absurd or illogical, the patient repeated with no other modification than a questioning, incredulous tone in her voice.

2. When the stimulus was *personally* derogatory or accusing there were constant attempts on her part to modify, thus:

Examiner: "You murdered your mother!"

Patient: "Oh, oh! You murdered your mother. No! No!"

3. When the stimulus contained long words or was complicated she would repeat only the tail end of the stimulus.

4. To obscene word stimuli she would usually repeat but showed her deep disapproval by an expression of disgust.

5. She knew German songs and could sing them after the examiner. Although she knew no French words she repeated them perfectly.

Echopraxia.—She would imitate all gestures as well as she could with her left arm. She refused to imitate obscene gestures. She was able to resist her echopractic impulses easier than her echolalic.

Grasping could not be elicited. As stated above, the patient had a claw-like contracture of the right hand. Writing could not be tested.

Sucking.—On the first admission, only increased mouth opening was present. She would open her mouth as many as fifteen times in a row when any object, including even a watch, was thrust toward her lips. Occasionally "kissing" movements of the lips could be elicited by touching the lips with a flashlight. On the first three admissions these were inconstant. On the fourth admission, months later, she had a definite and constant sucking-pouting movement when the juncture of the lips was touched. She did not search with the mouth or extend the tongue.

Similar Cases in the Literature.—Cases of echolalia with various degrees of motor and sensory aphasia have been reported in the literature following hemiplegia occurring from a lesion in the dominant hemisphere. The earliest similar case the writer has been able to find is that of Raymond published in 1888. Raymond's patient was 74 years old, had a sudden right hemiplegia with motor and sensory aphasia following embolization from rheumatic valvular vegetations to the artery of Sylvius. He does not record echopraxia, grasping or sucking. The aphasia remained almost complete in both motor and sensory spheres except for the appearance of a startlingly automatic echolalia for even the most complex and esoteric words. Following a second vascular insult the patient died and post-mortem examination revealed lesions in the following locations:

(1) At the level of the foot of the third left frontal convolution there was a depressed softened yellowish-brown area about the size of an almond.

(2) In the anterior part of the third temporal convolution on the same side there was another area of softening of similar size which was exposed by lifting back the posterior lip of the fissure of Sylvius.

Raymond is unable to explain why, since the area of Broca is destroyed by the lesion, the patient nevertheless recovers the ability to use words.

Case 2.—Left hemiplegia of unknown duration. Faint right-sided pyramidal tract signs. Echolalia. Sucking. Bilateral grasp. No echopraxia. Some anomia with motor aphasia. Apraxia of the right hand. Emotional lability, with tendency to exaggerated laughter.

Male. White. Age 50. He had apparently had hypertension of long standing with cardiovascular disease. A reliable history could not be obtained. He had been found in a shack by strangers who noted that his left side was paralyzed and that he did not seem to know what was going on around him.

Positive physical findings included a blood pressure of 180/105, a left scrotal hernia and an old fracture of the left tibia.

Neurologic examination revealed that the right pupil was greater than the left and somewhat sluggish to light. There was a left hemiplegia with left hyperreflexia and a left Babinski. There was a questionable right Babinski. He was mentally clear, quiet and cooperative with no evidence of pathologic trends. His aphasia was predominantly motor and there were definite disturbances in praxis of the right hand. A right hemianopsia was suspected but could never be definitely established.

Echolalia.—On admission he showed definite echolalia, sometimes repeating the response in a palilalic way, thus:

Examiner: "How old are you?"

Patient: "How old are you? How old are you?" Sometimes he would attempt to modify the response, thus:

Examiner: "What do you call this?"

Patient: "I don't know—what do you call this?" Or thus:

Examiner: "Are you happy?"

Patient: "Are I you happy? Sure—happy."

Furthermore, he showed the same automaticity to impersonal absurd stimuli and the same modification of personally derogatory stimuli as Case I. Thus:

Examiner (holding up a flashlight): "This is a piano."

Patient (laughing heartily): "This is a piano." Or:

Examiner: "Your penis is all black."

Patient: "No! No!" He laughed, continuing to protest vigorously. He responded to threatening stimuli also by laughter.

Echopraxia.—The patient showed no echopraxia. When gestures were made in front of him, he scrutinized them but never imitated. At times it appeared as though he was on the verge of imitating.

Grasping.—Although grasping was not noted on admission, it could be easily elicited bilaterally, more markedly on the left side. It was reinforced by elicitation simultaneously with that of the sucking movement.

Sucking was constant.

The only other noteworthy features were a pain asymbolia greater on the right than on the left, and a tendency to count backward when asked to count forward.

Comment.—It is interesting to note that Case 2, who showed apraxia of the right hand, was apparently incapable of echopraxia in contrast to Case 1 who showed marked echopraxia and absolutely no evidence of apraxia in the sound limb.

Similar Cases in the Literature.—Another type of vascular cerebral disease producing the symptom of echolalia in a setting of marked mental and motor involvement is that of Romberg's reported in 1842. His patient was a female, aged 49, with sudden bilateral spastic paralysis who was able to raise her left arm with her right. Even the right arm movements were effected with some difficulty (apraxia [?]). A month later after venesection with some improvement she suddenly began to show marked mental excitement, spasmodic twitching of the muscles of the face, restless movement of the arms with marked diminution in mental power, difficulty in collecting her thoughts, speech hesitant. She uttered loud screams and began to talk wildly. Echolalia then began to manifest itself. Delirium continued for another month with intervals of quiet days. The paralysis advanced especially in the left arm and right leg. She had a tendency to fall forward. Her paraplegia became complete. Shortly before her death, she became calm, memory and clear consciousness returned and then she developed pulmonary paralysis. Necropsy revealed lesions of "inflammatory softening" in both hemispheres of cerebrum and cerebellum, in both optic thalami and corpora striata.

Schuster and Pineas who in 1926 presented a study of grasping and sucking reflex movements state that Schuster's earlier studies included a case of right hemiparesis with grasping in the partially paralyzed limb where there was no evidence of apraxia while the left hand showed definite apraxia. In this patient a lesion was found in the subcortex not far from the left frontal convolutions with involvement of the corpus callosum. The first case in their 1926 series was a 65-year-old man with a right hemiplegia, grasping in the right hand, and a slowing of speech with frequent iteration of productions resembling palilalia. After a new insult during which catalepsy was noted, the patient died and post-mortem revealed a lesion in the left paracentral lobule going over to the median surface of the hemisphere and destroying part of the gyrus cingulus. The left gyrus fornicatus was destroyed and the entire middle and most of the posterior part of the left corpus callosum was thinned and pulled apart. There were areas of softening in the basal ganglia which probably accounted for his easy laughter.

In 1924 Betlheim presented a case study of a 62-year-old female with a left-sided hemiparesis, aphasia and, at first, no spontaneous speech. Although he does not note it as such, as his patient began to recover the power of speech, she showed definite palilalic fragments. Thus: (Was fehlt Ihnen?) "Ach ein, einen, einen Schlaganfall hab i gehabt." He notes that in succeeding days repetition of sentences improved slower than the spontaneous speech which remained with a marked motor aphasic defect. There was in addition high grade apraxia of the musculature of the mouth, apraxia of the right upper extremity, agraphia, alexia and dysnomia. The patient showed a marked snapping at all objects with her mouth. The personality of Betlheim's patient was otherwise well preserved.

Case 3.—Frontotemporal left subdural hematoma with subarachnoid hemorrhage following trauma in a 61-year-old arteriosclerotic. Faint right-sided pyramidal tract signs. Fragmentary and inconstant echolalia. Marked initial palilalia. Bilateral grasp. Sucking. Apraxia of the mouth. Marked anomia.

Female. White. Age 61. This patient was injured by an automobile which threw her to the ground causing a hematoma of the right side of the scalp in the parietal region. She answered all questions with, "I don't know." After two day she was up and about but so confused and restless that she had to be brought to Bellevue Hospital. The previous history was negative.

Physical examination revealed a blood pressure of 150/74. Otherwise except for mild peripheral and central arteriosclerosis, examination was negative.

Neurologic examination showed a right hyperreflexia of slight but definite degree. There was a slight right facial weakness and at times a right Babinski. Spinal tap showed clear xanthochromic fluid. There were no marked paretic signs. A diagnosis of possible left subdural hematoma was entertained but the patient's general condition did not justify operative intervention.

Mentally the patient was disoriented and restless. She ran around on the ward in constant activity making peculiar gestures toward her mouth. She would stand at the door holding her lips apart and motioning energetically toward her gums. She blamed her difficulty in speech apparently on the fact that her false teeth were taken from her. She misidentified people, mistaking the examiner for an old neighbor of hers. She showed constant flight of ideas, talking at great length and revealing motor aphasia, anomia, perseveration, palilalia, and fragmentary echolalia.

Palilalia and Echolalia.—On admission the patient's palilalia was very marked; thus, she said spontaneously:

"You are going to have these and these. They are going to have—they are going to have and here they are going to have—are going to have pain—they are going to have. And they are going to going to both the both of these are going to."

Examiner: "What is your name?"

Patient: "My name is what is it. My name. Well my name is like they are going to have a dark—a don't."

Examiner: "Pick up your hand."

Patient: "You feel the dark and I feel the dark here." (Pointing to gum of the lower jaw on the right.)

The next day she kept asking for her teeth, thus: "I want the teeth. I want the teeth. I got the upper and lower teeth."

Examiner: "What happened to you?"

Patient: "Well it is because you keep my teeth and you take my teeth."

Examiner: "Are you all right?"

Patient: "No, I am all right." She was very euphoric at times and showed a tendency to imitate gestures which was designated as *hypermimia* but was not considered sufficiently constant or automatic enough to be called definite echopraxia, although her imitation was frequently spontaneous.

Grasping.—The patient showed bilateral grasping more marked on the right.

Sucking.—The grasp was best reinforced during the sucking act which was prompt to the stimulus. As a matter of fact, the best way to to stop her incessant talking was to put an object in her mouth whereupon she at once began to suck.

After a few days the patient's speech showed signs of improvement but she developed a bronchopneumonia and after a short febrile course she died.

Post-mortem examination was incomplete, having been performed by a medical examiner who did not cut the brain. The surface findings revealed a left pachymeningitis interna which did not compress the brain. It was frontotemporal in location and there was in addition an adhesion to the under and outer surface of the left temporal lobe.

Comment.—In view of the incomplete post-mortem no definite statements about the extent of injury can be made. However, the case is included in this series as an example of the various gradations in iteration and reiteration which are possible. That aphasics in general make use of sign language is an old observation. Perseveration of ordinary aphasia may be regarded as a mild phase of palilalia with this difference, however, that ordinary perseveration occurs after stimuli are shown and relates the reiteration to the previous dissimilar stimulus. It is important to note that *palilalia* occurs here with increased spontaneous speech as compared to the lack of spontaneous speech seen in Case 1 who had *echolalia*.

Palilalia has been known as the "uncontrolled repetition of normally articulated words, phrases or sentences" since Souques described it in 1908 in a woman of 59 with left hemiplegia and mental deterioration. A similar case with palilalia and paligraphia in addition to echolalia has been more recently, in 1934, described by Grasse in a woman of 63 with diffuse atrophy of the brain especially in the left cerebral hemisphere and with especially marked destruction of the substantia nigra. Palilalia has also been described in various postencephalitic syndromes in which the characteristic acceleration of delivery is best seen. In this report no postencephalitic syndrome is included. Since we deal here with echolalia rather than palilalia, it is not pertinent at this point to do more than mention the cases of palilalia described in oculogyric spasms by van Bogaert (1934) and together with the linguo-salivary syndrome by Sterling (1932). However, it should be stressed that characteristic palilalia occurs not only in postencephalitic syndromes but also in cerebral arteriosclerotic mostly in pseudobulbar syndromes, as recently reviewed in a case study by Oliver (1934). It will be remembered that the case of Schuster and Pineas (1926) quoted above in connection with Case 2 showed palilalia, grasping and sucking together with apraxia of the uninvolved extremity. Their patient falls into the pseudobulbar type also.

GROUP II.—CASES WITH TOXI-INFECTIVE DISEASE

In this group of cases are included those with either diffuse parenchymatous disease as in general paresis, febrile episodes and diffuse toxic disturbances such as the case quoted by Pick as showing echolalia when emerging from deep morphine sedation. The two cases presented here are: (1) Exposure to carbon monoxide fumes in a patient with signs of cerebral and general arteriosclerosis, and (2) a general paretic.

Case 4.—Exposure to carbon monoxide fumes. Signs of general and cerebral arteriosclerosis. Bilateral marked pyramidal tract signs with bilateral Babinski more marked on the right. Semistupor terminating in coma and death. Bilateral grasping and sucking. Fragmentary echolalia. No echopraxia.

Female. Age 74. White. Relatives were unable to say whether she had had a "stroke" and had fallen after forgetting to turn off the gas jet or whether she had attempted suicide. She was admitted to Bellevue Hospital in semistupor from which she never fully recovered. This gradually deepened into coma and she died.

Physical examination was essentially negative except for marked bilateral arcus senilis and thickened radial arteries.

Neurologically, she showed bilateral pyramidal tract signs more marked on the right with bilateral Babinski. She also had shortening and lengthening reactions. There was a prompt pouting-sucking movement on stimulation of the outer surface of the upper lip and a more vigorous reaction on stimulation of the juncture of the lips. There was no searching or groping movement of the lips, mouth or tongue. She usually would not respond to questions. When spoken to, she occasionally echoed the last part of the phrase or sentence said in her presence. She would do the same thing if a series of numbers were counted out in her presence. She was never clear enough for any echopractic phenomenon to be elicited.

Comment.—Here as in Case 1 the movement of the lips is more of a pouting type of response. Here too as in Case 1 there were pronounced pyramidal tract signs.

Case 5.—General paresis. Progressive aphasia finally ending in complete mutism. Perioral tremors. Marked grasping reflex in the right hand. None in the left. Sucking-pouting movement. Pseudobulbar emotionality. Echopraxia. No echolalia.

Female. Age 60. History of fall with concussion two years previously. For the past three months sudden cessation in speech with progressive inability to understand the spoken word was noted by her husband who pointed out also that she had had severe crying spells and became excitable, throwing furniture around the house. She had also had right-sided "spasms" especially at night. On admission it was noted that the patient did not seem able to talk or express herself except by gestures and smiles. She said "yes" or "no" but appeared confused and disoriented. She had a broad-based gait with the tendon reflexes hyperactive in the upper extremities and depressed in the lowers with the ankle jerks completely unobtainable. It was noted that the patient very often made pointing movements with the left arm while the grasp was present only in the right hand. There were bilateral Mayer reflexes. She had a marked perioral tremor. A Parkinsonian-like tremor of the right upper extremity was noted. To the examiner, but not to people to whom she was unaccustomed, she would imitate his every gesture. At one time she almost formed the word "name" in reply to the examiner's question, "What is your name?" The blood and spinal fluid serology was positive and there was a definite paretic curve. She remained confused, disoriented and inaccessible. She was finally transferred to a State Hospital.

Comment.—The well-known predilection in paresis for the fissures and the especial predilection for the parietal, temporal and frontal convolutions to be atrophied particularly around the Sylvian fissure, makes one suspect that in cases like the above, the perioral tremor and sucking-pouting movement are determined by the same process that determines the aphasia and mutism, namely, a disorganization of the fine movements necessary for speech and facial expression.

GROUP III.—CASES WITH DEGENERATIVE DISEASE

Case 6.—Progressive deterioration of the personality. Transitory delusions and hallucinations. Automatic echolalia. Fragmentary and inconstant echopraxia. Grasping bilaterally and sucking. Snapping movements of the mouth. Perseveration. Jargon speech.

Female. White. Age 55. The patient's husband gave the history of onset as occurring three and a half years previously with changes in behavior, forgetfulness and episodes of depression. She subsequently became confused and euphoric while her forgetfulness increased. She was admitted to a hospital complaining of headaches and dizziness. The gold curve was 1111000000. Serology was otherwise negative and a diagnosis of degenerative disease of the brain was made. It could not be verified whether or not she actively hallucinated although she was noted to have "illusions."

Two months later she was admitted to a psychiatric institution where the additional fact was elicited that she had had severe tertian malaria in her youth. Her recent memory in the interval of two months had become progressively impaired. She could do a few very simple calculations but her judgment was exceedingly poor. She began to decline, became incontinent. Her English became poorer and poorer and finally her irrelevant speech was confined to her native tongue, Swedish. At that time the blood pressure was noted at 142/86. Two months later an encephalogram showed the lateral ventricles symmetrical but slightly larger than normal. A large amount of air was congregated over the frontal lobe, indicating a marked degree of atrophy in this region. There was marked widening of the sulci in the temporoparietal region but not as marked as in the frontal lobe. Encephalogram was not repeated due to vasomotor collapse which took place during the procedure. The patient was discharged to Bellevue Hospital after fourteen months of hospitalization. The case was considered one of Pick's disease.

On admission to Bellevue Psychiatric Hospital she was noted to be laughing all the time, following each attempted response with hilarious laughter. Neurologic and physical examination was essentially negative.

Aphasic Status.—She showed aphasia, perseveration, spoke usually in a jargon which was not even intelligible Swedish, she stuttered, she could identify some objects.

Echolalia.—She was *automatically echolalic* to English word stimuli. On all occasions the echolalia was followed by gales of laughter, a peculiarly stereotyped thalamic type of laughter.

Echopraxia.—On rare instances and more in response to physicians than nurses she would mimic their actions and gestures.

Grasping.—Grasping was very definitely and constantly elicited and if the cooperation of the patient could be obtained, *sucking,* preceded by increased mouth opening or snapping and biting movements would occur.

The patient was finally committed to a State Hospital.

Comment.—The complete automaticity of the echolalic response is worth emphasis. Together with this the fragmentary and inconstant echopraxia is significant of the inability even to use sign language to identify herself with her environment. The striking stereotypy of emotional responses, namely explosively empty hilarious laughter of a thalamic type, jibes with the concept that destruction of frontal radiations produces a thalamic animal and that hence, those most delicately acquired skilled movements, namely emotional expressions, become deteriorated and finally lost. The appearance of grasping and sucking movements of a "forced" nature is to be attributed to a similar incapacity to modify the fine movements of the hand and mouth. *The fact that the patient is echolalic in English, the language she learned last, and yet is able to repeat English words perfectly has been brought out by other writers, namely Pick who has described and discussed similar reactions in Béhier's and Bateman's cases, both of whom had learned more than one language and became, during the disease process, echolalic in the most recently learned tongue, yet unresponsive to the earlier learned tongues. Pick quotes this fact as justification for his concept that organic echolalia is a kind of reflex: an "Echoreflex,"* and that its appearance is due to a loss of inhibition permitting the more primitive form of learning response to reappear in a fashion comparable to the normal echoing of the child first learning to speak.

Similar Cases in the Literature.—Cases of degenerative disease as the underlying pathologic process in cases of echolalia and echopraxia, have been frequently reported in the foreign literature. These may be summarized briefly as follows: In 1900 Liepmann reported a case of degenerative disease of the brain which showed a severe atrophy of the temporal lobe with mild but generalized atrophy of the entire brain, more marked in the left cerebral hemisphere. This occurred in a 74-year-old woman who showed over a period of four years, a change in personality, forgetfulness, a transitory psychotic state with negativism, hallucinations and delusions with tremulousness of the hands and tongue, a broad unsteady gait and echolalia which became progressively automatic and was modified only when the patient was accused of being a prostitute. He compares his case with two similar cases previously reported by Pick both of which showed generalized brain atrophy, more marked in the left cerebral hemisphere and especially in the left temporal lobe. One of Pick's cases showed atrophy especially marked "in zweiter Linie" of Broca's convolution. Liepmann noted that the first and second left temporal convolutions were especially atrophic. Overlying the atrophic areas was a fluid-filled sac covered by pia. Liepmann also mentions a similar case described by Bischoff. Bischoff's case had in addition small areas of softening near the posterior horns. Clinically Liepmann's case showed echopraxia as well as echolalia.

Case 7.—*Echolalia and Echopraxia (especially in imitation of daughter). Biting and snapping movements of the mouth. Grasping and hoarding activities. Neologisms. Transitory hallucinosis.*

Female, age 47. Her daughter and cousin described her as an exceptionally neat and clean woman who had always been very bright but always a little nervous. Her husband had died six months previously, and she had been quite prostrated. She began to show menstrual irregularities, menstruating as often as three times a month. For many years she had had a tremor of both hands and arms, more on the left. She had always had a slight hirsutus of the chin and a bilateral divergent external strabismus. A month previous to admission she became very religious, thought she saw the Virgin Mary in the skies, and began going out into the streets to gather all sorts of rubbish, odds and ends which she called "orders" and which she said had great value for her daughter C. The first thing she took was a handkerchief from her daughter's boy friend and to their amazement rubbed her head with it. She then began to go into stores and order all sorts of things, stopped people on the street and asked for money. She would not pay for any of the things she ordered and would not let her daughter out of her sight. She became exceedingly obstinate and difficult to control, showed marked agitation at being constrained from her acquisitive tendencies and finally was admitted to the Bellevue Psychiatric Hospital.

On admission the patient was orientated but began immediately to pester the doctor for "orders for C." She showed perseveration and paraphasia of a mild degree. The grasping seemed more of a purposive type than the so-called forced grasping. Once she had hold of any object it was only with great difficulty that she could be persuaded or forced to loosen her grip. She showed bilateral intention tremor more marked on the left where also pseudoathetoid postures and adiadochokinesis was noted. Perseveration became marked. She coined such words as "supermentry orders" and "charter tickets." A key to her was a "key order."

Echolalia.—Echolalia was elicited in only one way with any degree of constancy—by using the daughter as an intermediary for the stimulus. When the daughter imitated the examiner, the patient imitated at once. In this way the patient became conditioned to the examiner's stimuli and would repeat what he said. But this echolalia was not automatic.

Echopraxia.—Exactly the same relationship held in the imitation of gestures. The moment C. imitated, the patient would imitate.

While the patient would repeat anything that C. would do, she would not repeat absurd calculations in the correction of which she showed remarkable accuracy. She could make relatively difficult calculations with great ease. After a few days she became sufficiently conditioned so that she would occasionally repeat the absurd calculation and then correct it.

Grasping.—As noted above, this was more of a purposive type although the patient showed no discrimination in the type of object to which she clung with such tenacity. Once she fastened on the examiner's ring and it was only with great difficulty that her grasp could be broken. She would not clutch the finger of anyone but her daughter C. Otherwise her grasp clung to anything she could carry.

Sucking.—There were no reflex sucking movements but if an object was held in front of her mouth and her hands restrained she would snap and bite at the object and become extremely agitated when prevented from securing it in any way.

Encephalogram revealed that the lateral ventricles were slightly dilated. Otherwise there were no suggestive findings.

Comment.—The writer has not succeeded in finding a parallel case in the literature although snapping and biting movements and grasping-to-hoard activities have been separately described for many years in various types of insanity. The etiology in this case is probably that of an organic process. Transitory hallucinosis occurs in these cases, as in the preceding case, but these seem to be relatively inconstant and to disappear as the more profound organic signs make their appearance. The relation of the psychologic transference and imitation to the daughter which could be conditioned toward the examiner is of great interest in considering the relation of these processes to the psychoanalytic concept of "regression." This problem of transference and imitation on a psychologically selective level comes out strikingly in cases of echolalia and echopraxia as they occur in psychoses. The next case is an example.

GROUP IV.—CASES WITH PSYCHOSES

Case 8.—Schizophrenia. Echolalia and echopraxia to a fellow patient and to a lesser extent to the examiner. Grasping and sucking movements.

Male. Age 30. White. Found in the Grand Central Station in the winter time wearing a straw hat and carrying a banjo. He had apparently come up from Tennessee. On the ward his behavior was bizarre, he hallucinated actively and was deluded. He was seclusive and manneristic and acted in a dazed, bewildered way. He picked out one of the patients whose every movement he imitated. He regarded this patient as "God the Father." The examiner got the patient to imitate in echolalia and echopraxia by using the "God" patient as an intermediary. The echolalic patient would occasionally repeat the examiner's productions but with less exactness and would frequently correct the examiner in an absurd or illogical calculation. He clung to the examiner as though for support and if a tongue depressor was put in his mouth he showed increasing sucking activity.

Comment.—Here the echolalic, echopractic, grasping and sucking movements relate to the problem of selective imitation and identification with the "God" which the patient has chosen and who appears as omnipotent. When this occurs a "transference" mechanism is in evidence. The syndrome in the psychotic patient is qualitatively and quantitatively different from that in the organic vascular type where the personality is fairly well preserved and where the automaticity of the responses may be modified. In the deteriorating organic patient the automaticity tends to become absolute though the evidence of organic origin remains inherent in the type of movement. The significance of the imitation is better appreciated by the organic vascular case, is altered in the psychotic case and disappears altogether in the deteriorating organic case, as in Case 4.

Case 9.—Postpartum psychotic episode with febrile onset. Echolalia and echopraxia at times automatic, at times absent. Marked grasping and biting with reinforcement of the grasping by the biting. Hallucinations. Delusions. Facetiousness. Markedly excited periods. Misidentification, including confusion of her own name and identity with that of her sister's.

Female. Age 35. Married nine years. Maternal grandmother had also had a postpartum psychosis when the patient's mother was born. The husband stated that they had been happily married and that this had been her first pregnancy. They had both wanted a child, especially the patient. The child was a normal female born after induced labor. Four days after delivery, the patient showed negativism and waxy flexibility. The next day visual and auditory hallucinations appeared and she subsequently refused to eat. She developed some temperature and on the day of her admission to Bellevue Hospital it was 104. The next day it dropped to 102 and was subsequently normal. At Bellevue the patient had to be fed by Levine tube, was at the time semistuporous and dazed, hallucinated and was delusional. On the second day of admission it was noted that the patient showed echolalia and as she became less stuporous she showed echopraxia also. She imitated everything the nurses and doctors said and even words that she heard in the hall outside her room. She would show almost constant grasping, the thumb turning inward in the infantile position. The grasping was much more pronounced during periods of wild excitement during which the patient misidentified herself as her sister and misidentified others around her. The grasping continued even though she was told not to grasp. When a tongue depressor was put into her mouth she bit on it tenaciously and continued to talk through her clenched teeth, asking, "Why do I bite on this?" She would try to avoid the tongue depressor but once it was put in her mouth she bit on it so vigorously that it was very difficult to remove. During these episodes of marked biting the grasping of the hands was strikingly reinforced so that the examiner was unable to loosen her grip which was so strong that the patient's hands blanched. She remained facetious and playful, sometimes shouting agitatedly and keeping up a constant movement of the fingers of the right hand.

Comment.—The most striking thing in this patient is the reinforcement of the grasp by the biting, a phenomenon paralleling and almost indistinguishable from that in the organic case, except of course as described by Bieber (1936), the organic cases show sucking rather than biting. The echolalia and echopraxia are less selective in character than that described in the previous case. This patient mimicked everything she heard and saw during her imitative periods. There was no direct relationship to the extent of the temperature since the imitation persisted as the temperature dropped. However, the clearer state of consciousness permitted more echopractic movement. Her misidentification of herself, her uncertainty as to what her own name was is a symptom which will be seen also in the next case.

Similar Cases in the Literature.—In 1908 Hobohm reported a strikingly similar case in a postpartum psychosis, aged 27, married two years, para 1, and who developed severe eclamptic convulsions previous to the delivery of a stillborn child. At first her sensorium was cloudy, she was febrile, and she talked at great length but her echolalia was so marked that she begged for simpler words to be used more slowly so that she could repeat them. She showed great insistence later in her course on designating her limbs as right and left whenever the examiner touched them. She was deluded and hallucinated. The echolalia continued for five weeks and then disappeared gradually. Hobohm does not record echopraxia, grasping or biting. This is the only case the writer has been able to find occurring in a postpartum psychosis. The fact that the patient had convulsions previous to delivery raises the question whether or not this was a postepileptic state. Without going into the question here, the fact that epilepsy has been considered by some to be a psychotic manifestation is important. Nevertheless the case in this series shows that epilepsy need not be present to provoke the syndrome postpartum. The appearance of the syndrome postepileptic is well illustrated in our next case.

Case 10.—Psychosis accompanying the convulsive state. Severe alcoholism. Coprolalia. Palilalia. Echolalia. Identified the examiner as himself and addressed various other people by his own name, reviling them. Echopraxia. Pain hypersymbolia. Mouth opening and biting. Groping with the mouth. Grasping inconstant and increasing during periods of excitement. Aphasia on fifth admission with perioral tremors.

Male. Age 30. Negro. Friends gave a history of epileptic attacks for eight months previous to his first admission to the hospital. These were preceded by generalized tremor followed by fall and loss of consciousness, biting of the tongue and a dazed condition afterward. The tremor lasted about fifteen to twenty minutes before the attack. There was a history of antiluetic therapy seven years previously. He admitted severe alcoholism for which he had been admitted twice before. On admission the third time he was confused and apprehensive with disorientation in time. His fourth admission occurred a month later, and friends stated that his attacks had been coming more frequently and that he became violent after them. His blood and spinal serology were consistently negative, and his blood pressure normal.

Echolalia.—On his fourth admission he kept repeating the phrase:

"You son of a bitch." The ambulance nurse noted that he repeated also everything that he heard. The admitting physician noted that he talked in a loud stentorian voice, in short ejaculatory phrases which he repeated over and over, and that it was no use asking him questions since he just returned them in a loud voice with some repetitions. Just previous to his admission, according to the abstract from the previous hospital, he had claimed that he had killed a man and woman and that he himself had died. The next morning on the ward he showed marked echolalia to whatever was said or asked of him, no matter how absurd. Frequently, however, he would modify the repetition by prefixing it with, "I said." His language was exceedingly obscene. He called the examiner by his own name and then proceeded to revile the thus identified examiner.

He repeated that he had killed a man and a woman and two boys and expressed ideas of remorseful rebellion. He asked to have his head cut off. He showed a marked pain hypersymbolia. Thus, when the abdomen was stroked with a pin he began yelling loudly that we were cutting his belly open and repeated the phrase several times. When, far across the room, at a distance of five yards the examiner raised his arm threateningly, the patient shrank into himself in abject fear. He shouted that he was being killed and being put in the electric chair when his feet were stroked with a pin or touched with the tuning fork. His gait was ataxic but there were no other neurologic signs. He showed also echopraxia.

Grasping.—The grasp was not constant and there were changing rigidities but it was noted that when the patient talked very excitedly and was echolalic the grasping in the left hand became very marked and sustained.

Biting and Mouth Opening.—He showed groping for the object with his mouth, and would also bite down on the object.

Gradually in about three days' time all these signs disappeared and the patient began to show insight into his delirious episode. He said he did not know why he had repeated everything that was being said to him. Admitted that he had thought he was being killed and being put into the electric chair for his imagined murder. He was elated and showed immoderate laughter. He was discharged perfectly clear six days after admission.

He was readmitted seven months later following a convulsion. He was dazed, confused, extremely euphoric and disoriented. He gave either no responses or disconnected, irrelevant and incoherent phrases; he frequently replied by giving his own name over and over. He showed almost complete motor and sensory aphasia, but with no other neurologic signs. There was a mild bilateral hyperreflexia but no Babinski. As he began to recover his speech he showed an inability to name or point out the parts of his body. He showed the same pain hypersymbolia and the same apprehension. There were marked oral tremors. Blood and spinal serology were negative and he was committed to a state hospital.

Comment.—This patient is very typical of those cases with epilepsy which have been described not only with echolalia but with coprolalia. As such it is similar to the first case described by Itard in 1825. In addition, however, there are several features worth emphasis. First, the identification of the examiner with the patient's own personality, a projection of the patient's own individuality into others whom he then proceeds to revile. Secondly, the marked pain and threat hypersymbolia, his crouching when threatened by the examiner standing across the room. His fear and apprehension and his delusions that he is being electrocuted for a murder he has committed thus are associated with a disturbance in the appreciation of distance and an exaggeration of pain. In Head's terms, we might say the relations of the postural model are disturbed in so far as accessibility is concerned. A similar mechanism takes place in the ordinary delusional patient who believes that an electric motor, for example, behind the wall of her room hits her in the small of the back, and intereferes with her sexual organs. Furthermore when the patient repeats what the examiner says but prefixes the "I said" he is doing nothing but again identifying the examiner with himself.

There is, however, another phase of the disturbance in epilepsy that is worth consideration. The electroencephalographic studies by Gibbs et al. (1935) show that just preceding the epileptic attack a very definite change in the rhythm of the electroencephalographic

motion takes place. If one couples this with the fact that during convulsions grasping comes out very plainly in the hand of the convuls-
ing side, and that this is due to a disturbance in premotor function,
the suspicion may at least be entertained that grasping is due to a
quantitative and qualitative disturbance in the rhythm of electrochemical motion of the brain during which the vector function of the
premotor area must be markedly disturbed in accordance with the
known laws of physical motion.

A very similar case but with interesting and important differences
is next described.

*Case 11.—Alcoholic psychosis initiated by convulsive episode which
is followed by automatic echolalia and echopraxia, bilateral "forced"
grasping and groping, sucking with searching. Threat hypersymbolia.
Acute and vivid hallucinosis. Color inversion. Monocular multiplopia.
Confabulation. Excitement.*

Male. Age 38. White. Machinist by occupation. Relatives said he
had been drinking heavily for years but had never had a convulsion
before. While at work he suddenly fell, convulsed, biting his tongue,
completely unconscious. On the way to the hospital in the ambulance,
he roused and began confusedly to take his shoes off and to get up.
The ambulance interne asked him, "Where are you going?" The patient replied, "Where are you going?" The interne asked, "Are you
cold?" and the patient responded, "Are you cold?" The ambulance
interne thought "the patient was kidding."

In the admitting office the patient echoed automatically whatever
was said. When the examiner alone raised his arm in a gesture, the
patient did not imitate but when all three people present, the ambulance driver, the interne and the examiner raised their arms in the
same gesture, the patient imitated automatically. When threatened
by a raised fist at a distance of several yards, the patient winced. He
showed, in addition, marked grasping, on the right especially with
groping. When a tongue depressor was held several inches from his
mouth he pursued it with his very tremulous lips and tongue, and in
spite of all commands *not* to grasp or suck, he did both vigorously
after saying in an infantile petulant way: "Give it to me! Give it to
me!" There was no aphasia, at first although some paraphasia later

appeared. There were no Babinskis at any time although there was bilateral hyperreflexia and generalized tremor especially on intention. Between stimuli the patient sat compulsively picking his nose.

The patient was admitted to the ward and after an hour the echolalia, echopraxia, grasping and sucking had disappeared. About six hours later the patient was hallucinating actively in both auditory and visual spheres. He showed marked monocular multiplopia. His affect was euphoric and facetious. He inverted all his colors—white becoming black, green becoming brown, etc. The next day he became wildly excited and had to be transferred to the disturbed ward where he was in active delirium and wandered around trying to get out of the doors. He confabulated intensively.

Physical and neurologic examination was essentially negative except for a marked hyperesthesia and hyperalgesia of the lower extremities, especially of the soles and calves. At the time of writing the patient is still hallucinating and in delirium.

Comment.—Here there is a definite sequence of events which may be briefly ordered thus: (1) severe and prolonged alcoholism; (2) sudden convulsion; (3) automatic responses producing the tetrad with threat hypersymbolia as in Case 10; (4) acute vivid hallucinosis with inversion of colors, confabulation and delirium; and (5) ending probably in return to clarity.

Considering grasping and sucking as our most primitive movements and echolalia and echopraxia as our early speech and action learning phenomena, we are able to discern a progressive disorganization of the fine movements involved in human speech and handedness. The acute hallucinosis, confabulation and excitement, the writer believes, is the result of the toxic disorganization of the records of fine movements which result in thinking and feeling. The threat hypersymbolia develops into acute paranoid reactions.

In addition to these eleven cases, the writer wishes briefly to mention that the syndrome has also been recently observed on the wards of this hospital in schizophrenic patients who are being treated with insulin shock therapy. Two of these patients developed convulsions and aphasia with right spastic hemiparesis but with *no Babinski* sign. As the aphasia and the hemiparesis resolved, sucking, grasping and echolalia were noted. These symptoms lasted a few minutes and then the patients returned again to their pre-shock hallucinosis. The *transitoriness* of the syndrome is thus seen to be characteristic of the resolution of disturbances producing convulsions, aphasia, and hemiparesis followed by hallucinosis.

DISCUSSION

Any study of disturbances in the function of speech and handedness ought logically to start from a survey of man's peculiar evolution. Darwin had already pointed this out in 1890 in his *Descent of Man*. There he said: "For many actions it is indispensable that the arms and whole upper part of the body should be free; and [man] must for this end stand finally on his feet. To gain this great advantage the feet have been rendered flat; and the great toe has been peculiarly modified though this has entailed the almost complete loss of its power of prehension. It accords with the principle of the division of physiological labor prevailing through the animal kingdom that as the hands became perfected for prehension, the feet should have become perfected for support and locomotion." Darwin emphasizes, "that man could not have attained his dominant position in the world without the use of his hands" . . . and that furthermore . . . "the structure of the hands in this respect [in the use of tools and the development of manual skill] may be compared with that of the vocal organs which in the apes are used for uttering various signal cries, or as in one genus, musical cadences; but in man the closely similar vocal organs have become adapted through the inherited effects of use for the utterance of articulate language."

Whenever therefore we find in various pathologic states the reappearance of primitive anthropomorphic or savage responses we must consider this as a disturbance of the conditions of the organization of those fine movements of the vocal organs and the hands, of which man alone is capable as a result of the development of the erect posture and its concomitant physiological attributes. Thinking and feeling are resultants of this evolutionary leap forward; we are a dominant biologic species because we can make finer and finer movements of greater and greater complexity. And, in accordance with the known mathematical laws of motion, the possibilities of our progress as a thinking civilization, given peace by the bridling of destructive forces, are infinite. Our sonic synergies are of the essence.

The writer does not believe that the phenomena can be localized. Even in brain tumors of such important locations as the frontal lobes and temporal lobes recent studies by Strauss and Keschner (1935) and by Keschner, Bender, and Strauss (1936) have shown that there is no appreciable difference in the incidence of mental symptoms. These writers stress the importance of increased intracranial pressure as one of the factors interfering with brain integrative functions.

As an example of the possible relation of the syndrome to the disturbances in brain integration, the occurrence in those postconvulsive and aphasic states following insulin shock therapy in schizophrenics is of interest. Damashek and Meyerson (1935) have recently shown that in insulin shock, there is evidence of a lowered oxygen consumption in the brain. If this be true the transitory appearance of the syndrome as the patient emerges from the convulsion or aphasia produced by the shock would indicate that it is a clinical sign indicative of a fairly definite lowered rate of energy exchange. From the point of view of the organization of cerebral dominance, it should be mentioned if they do develop paralysis these cases of insulin shock with aphasia usually develop a *right* (dominant) hemiparesis with or without the Babinski sign, confirmatory of the view that the structures subserving handedness and speech, the last to be developed in the evolutionary scale, are the most likely to suffer in diminished metabolic exchange.

As for that group of more isolated disease processes resulting from vascular lesions which interrupt *pathways* and do not interfere with processes of conduction and integration as such, there the personality is relatively preserved, as in our Case 1 who was able clearly enough to indicate her disgust or horror at obscene or personally derogatory stimuli which she had nevertheless to repeat. Here the interruption of a *pathway* is a relatively minor *subtraction* from brain integration as compared to the malignant *geometric* implications of disturbances in conduction which finally result in diffuse degeneration. Of those disturbances in conduction the electroencephalogram is beginning to give us some information.

Nevertheless, recognizing these qualifications, the question still remains: What pathway, when disturbed, is most likely to produce a subtraction from brain integrative function which will result in grasping, sucking, echolalia and echopraxia even when the personality remains more or less preserved? While final answers cannot be given, there is some experimental and clinical evidence bearing on these questions; we shall discuss the data pertinent to each symptom, seriatim.

1. *Grasping.*—The discovery in 1932 that grasping movements in the contralateral hand can be consistently produced by a lesion of the premotor area was first made by Richter and Hines, and subsequently substantiated by Fulton (1934) who has gone even further by postulating the existence of a premotor syndrome including impairment of skilled movements, spasticity and increased tendon reflexes, forced grasping, and vasomotor disturbances of all the contralateral extremities, on the basis of his work in primates. Here it must be emphasized that the results in primates cannot be transferred without qualification to the conditions in man. Nor, must it be assumed that lesions of the premotor area alone produce grasping, except unilaterally, for, as Cramer (1936) has recently reported, tumors of the corpus callosum which do not impinge on the frontal lobes may produce bilateral forced grasping. Again we see that disturbances of structures subserving the function of the organization of cerebral dominance may force the individual to revert to primitive responses. That lesions of the pyramidal tracts are not essential in the production of this phenomenon is not only shown by Fulton's work but can also be seen clinically in our cases, especially Case 11. Thus we may briefly state that grasping[1] is most likely to appear as the result of localized lesions of pathways when the premotor areas or their commissural or subcortical radiations are involved.

[1] Walshe and Robertson (1933) have already correlated the quantitative and qualitative changes of the grasping movement with various states of consciousness in organic disease. The writer does not wish to enter into the question of the relationship of the grasping movement to tonic innervation, nor to designate what should be considered a grasping "reflex" and what a grasping "movement."

2. *Sucking.*—So far as the writer has been able to determine, there is no definitely proven clinical or experimental data localizing the disturbance of a pathway or area capable of producing sucking. Nevertheless the association of sucking with aphasia and with apraxia of the mouth as in Betlheim's case, and in our Case 3, and the frequent association of sucking with aphasias with or without pyramidal tract signs leads the writer to believe it probable that the premotor area 8 governs the organization of the skilled movements of the mouth similarly to the manner in which the area 6 of Brodmann controls the organization of manual skilled movements. Richter and Hines (1934) showed that in apes when premotor area 8 was removed in addition to premotor area 6 that the hanging time was prolonged and the grasp intensified. Bieber's recent demonstration of the reinforcement and facilitation of the grasp by the sucking movement in man normally in infancy and pathologically in various states tends to support this belief; the reinforcement occurs in aphasics also and may be due, the writer believes, to involvement of both area 8 and area 6. It is interesting to note that Flechsig demonstrated that both of these secondary association areas become myelinated at the same time in the early months of infancy.

3. *Echopraxia.*—There are apparently no experimental data on this phenomenon. However, the fact that it was absent only in Case 2, where there was a definite *apraxia,* leads one to suspect that this function of the hand in the use of sign language is likewise dependent on the organization of skilled movements. That echopraxia should accompany the grasping phenomenon and compensate for disturbances in speech thus logically follows. It is absent not only where there is apraxia (in a patient with clear consciousness) but is consistently absent or diminished in the weaker limb even where this be comparatively endowed with considerable residual power as in our Case 5, and even when the other limb is echopractic.

4. *Echolalia.*—There are insufficient data to make more than a suggestion as to what possible isolated lesion or lesions might be responsible for this phenomenon. The only case the writer has been able to find where there was echolalia with fairly isolated lesions is that of Raymond reported in 1888 and indicated in the table. Here the lesion

may have involved 6 b of Brodmann and also perhaps a portion of 8 gamma. In addition there was a lesion of the anterior portion of the third temporal convolution perhaps involving the auditory cortex. It is probable that such a combination of sensory and motor involvement is prerequisite for the appearance of this phenomenon. Such a concept would reconcile the divergent opinions of those who claim echolalia a motor "transcortical aphasia" as opposed to those who consider it a sensory. It would also tend to reconcile the divergent concepts of Pick who claimed that echolalia was due to a weakening of the inhibitory function of the temporal lobe with that of Goldstein who considered a lesion of the frontal lobe as critical. The entire temporofrontal region is also hard hit in such atrophic brains as that reported by Liepmann.

If a correlation be asked on the basis of these considerations, one might say that grasping and sucking may be produced by a single lesion of a critical pathway but that to produce echolalia a double involvement of motor outflow and sensory intake is necessary. Such a correlation must wait for more precise pathologic data ere it be confirmed.

The problem of imitation, whether by speech, gesture, attitude or action, is of great importance in the normal development of the child, and has certain psychoanalytic implications. From the stage of crawling, sucking and grasping, the infant passes into the period of standing, walking, imitating and talking. As early as the fifth month, the infant begins to reach out for objects with the hand, which is to become dominant and begins to imitate parental phrases and gestures. These are attended by parental indifference, reward, or punishment, as the case may be. Freud (1932), in his *New Introductory Lectures*, points out that "since the process of recognizing a thing as a separate entity involves giving it a name of its own," he designates this function of the ego as forming part of the superego. He points out how this same process which involves recognition and naming is also (by imitation) the basis of identification. He says: "The basis of the process [of the development of parental, moralistic, and authoritative functions of the superego] is what we call an identification, that is to say, that one ego becomes like another . . . it *imitates* [my italics] and as it were, takes it into itself. This identification has not been inappropriately compared with the oral cannibalistic incorporation of another person."

In the cases presented there is the opportunity to see some of the relationships of naming to identification and imitation. Case 1 would imitate more readily to people whom she liked although her echolalia and echopraxia were almost "reflex" in character. Case 3 with palilalia showed marked flight of ideas and *misidentification*. Case 7 imitated constantly only her daughter with whom she identified herself and for whom all objects were grasped and hoarded. Case 8, the schizophrenic, imitated just that one patient who appeared as the omnipotent Father-God. Case 9, the postpartum, imitated everything she heard and saw and constantly had difficulty in separating her own identity from that of her sister with whom she kept repeating she "had crossed wires." Case 10 projected himself into the environment (becoming thus more susceptible to distant threats) and prefixed "I said" to all his repetitions and imitations. Case 11 who also showed threat hypersymbolia was echopraxic only when all people present performed the same gesture. Furthermore, as in the insulin-shock-produced aphasias, echolalia appears as the patient recovers from his aphasia, thus recapitulating the relation of the acquisition of the speech function to the development of imitation. Freud's formulation is thus given some justification in the light of this material.

In conclusion it should be emphasized that the very position of the premotor area in subserving the function of transforming and transmitting cerebral processes into the pyramidal tracts is of importance in the organization of all cerebral processes in motion, sensory as well as motor. One cannot alter a resultant of processes in motion without altering the entire equilibrium of integrative relationships. Here, too, there will finally be integrated with the biologic processes in motion, the resultants of these environment situational stimuli that determine one's conditioning.

SUMMARY AND CONCLUSIONS

1. The clinical syndromes of echolalia, echopraxia, grasping and sucking (with various types of abnormal mouth movements: mouth

opening, snapping, biting) are described in various pathologic neuropsychiatric conditions. The pertinent clinical and experimental literature is briefly reviewed.

2. The syndromes are considered as appearing in two main types of neurophysiologic disturbances: (a) in conditions due primarily to dysfunction of the *processes* of brain integration, and (b) in disorders primarily due to interruption of *pathways* such as are produced in vascular disease.

(a) Those conditions capable of disturbing brain integrative function prevent the proper organization of fine movements which flows from man's acquisition of the erect posture, speech and handedness. In these states changes of personality occur which may go on to visible organic degenerative disease or which may rest at the psychotic level. Here the echolalia, echopraxia, grasping and sucking may be automatic without modification by the deteriorated personality, or may occur in association with psychotic ideas and feelings. In these conditions the syndrome is present usually without pyramidal tract signs although language may be deteriorated to jargon with neologisms in the degenerative group. In degenerative polyglots, the patient is echolalic to the last learned language while not understanding the earlier learned tongues.

(b) Those conditions, such as vascular disease, which interrupt *pathways* leave the personality relatively intact and capable of modifying the responses. In these states there are usually associated pyramidal tract signs, aphasia and occasionally apraxia. Here the essential lesion is considered as disruption of parts of premotor area probably together with disease of the auditory cortex. Such lesions could occur in thrombosis of the artery of Sylvius in addition to other cortical arteries in the region of the Rolandic and Sylvian fissures.

3. The occurrence of the syndrome in postconvulsive states including those following insulin shock may make it indicative of a low rate of brain oxygen consumption, depending on the validity of present experimental data. In these conditions it is transitory, followed by gradual restoration of normal speech but may be superseded by psychotic ideas and feelings of a transitory toxic or permanent schizophrenic type.

4. The relation of the syndrome to the normal development of the child is indicated and the psychoanalytic implications are briefly discussed.

THE SYNDROME IN THE INVOLUTIONAL PERIOD

Here we shall examine a group of cases illustrating conditions capable of disturbing brain integrative processes *in toto*. As stressed in the previous sections, in these states changes of personality occur which may go on rapidly to visible organic degenerative disease; or, which may rest for many years at a psychotic "level" of disintegration; or, as in postepileptic confusions may clear up in a few days. If permanent, such regression may be devastating. The echolalia, echopraxia, grasping and sucking in these patients is *not* modified by the deteriorated or psychotic personality. The imitation takes on *significance* and *purpose*, as may even the grasping and sucking movements. Although the patient may be paraphasic and neologistic with jargon tendencies, pyramidal tract signs are usually not present until the deterioration has proceeded for many years. The occurrence of the syndrome in this form, in recovery from insulin hypoglycemic shock, would indicate that it is the qualitative clinical expression of a critically lowered rate of cerebral oxygen utilization, i.e., an expression of diminished cerebral energy exchange.

The involutional period is recognized to be a period of "ebb tide" in the life cycle of the individual, and more strikingly in women. Not only does the sexual apparatus begin to undergo atrophy (negative growth) but, as in growth processes generally, the entire body undergoes manifold and subtle changes which we need not enumerate here. The internist and neuropsychiatrist encounter especially at this period vasomotor crisis, "dysthroidism" of sympathetic origin, psychoses varying from mild depressions to severe melancholia and dissociated, schizophrenic states, as well as ill-defined "changes in personality" which may be the first harbingers of catastrophic degenerative disease.

In this paper we shall refer to case 7 of the previous section and present two additional cases demonstrating the tetrad of echolalia, echopraxia, grasping and sucking, as it appeared in women in the involutional or postinvolutional period observed at Bellevue Psychiatric Hospital. These patients are still alive, two in a State Hospital where they are reported steadily deteriorating, one in the custody of her family. Histopathologic correlations, therefore, are not as yet available.

CASE REPORTS

Case 1. See case 7 of the previous section (pp. 195–197) for the case history and the comments.

Case 2. A. O., admitted to the Bellevue Psychiatric Hospital November 2, 1936, was 45 years of age at the time of her admission. Her medical and neurologic history previous to the onset of the present illness was essentially negative except for the fact that when she was a child her father struck her on the head with a bottle. There was no history of familial disease.

Considering her previous personality, it is important to note that she devoted her life to the care of her father after her mother's early death, an event which had shocked her to prostration. The patient had never had sexual intercourse, and except for a brief engagement just before the menopause, there had been little or no social contact with the opposite sex. Her priest stated her confessions were without much content.

Her sister recorded that the patient's present illness began four years previously just after the menopause at which time her hair turned completely gray. She complained of pain in the legs, became restless, refused to eat various foods neglecting fruit juices and other sources of vitamin C. She was apparently afraid to eat for two years previous to admission. Her sister stated that her hands had recently begun to "clot up."

Two months before admission, her father died. Following this she became confused, garrulous, alternately laughing and crying, and complained of pain in her right thigh and leg. She imagined she saw lights.

She was admitted on October 15, 1936 to the Medical Ward of Bellevue Hospital, where she was described as "psychoneurotic" with infectious arthritis. A few purpuric areas over the right leg and left

hand were noted and the predominant blood findings were enumerated as hemorrhagic diathesis, moderate anemia, and thrombocyto-
penia. In addition she was thought to be "Parkinsonian with hyper-
tonia and hyperkinesis." A diminution of cevitamic acid in the blood
and on excretion test was found. This was thought responsible for
the "hemorrhagic diathesis" and "peripheral neuritis." However,
high vitamin diet did not alleviate the symptoms and the patient's
mental state became progressively worse. It was observed that she became increasingly depressed and reacted strongly to suggestion. There
was a slight unexplained rise in temperature. She was finally transferred to the disturbed ward of the Psychiatric Hospital. Neurologic
examination there revealed no evidence of neural involvement. The
vitamin deficiency though present was not considered etiologic, but
secondary. X-ray examination of the skull was negative.

Mentally the patient was agitated, restless, and confused. She
prayed constantly. At times she screamed: "I promise to be faithful
and loyal." Her speech had a marked religious content. She said to the
examiner: "Are you Joseph—you are Christ and I want to see my
father—Oh Christ save my soul—I have to confess something. I want
to live."

She became markedly paraphasic, but with peculiar reference to
all the examiner's objects as hers or as belonging to a member of her
family.

(Key?)—"Key to my best cellar. I am in it. The key to my sister's
house."

(Watch chain?)—"That's the watch chain that my father has."

(Comb?)—"That is my comb."

(Money?)—"That is money I might have had."

At this stage she was noted to have bilateral grasping and sucking
reflexes with marked "mimicry." Her gait became broad-based. She
showed marked echopraxia using both hands when the examiner used
one. She had many echolalia responses. Speech remained disorganized
in paraphasic directions:

(Puddle?)—"I don't recall."

(Puddle?)—"Person—woman on feet."

(Puddle?)—"Water. It will last forever."

(Puddle?)—"Puddle. Puzzle. I don't know."
(Envelope?)—"Something inside a letter."
(Frustrated?)—"Something taken from a fig."
(Watch?)—"Time—watch—blind and instaneous."

The patient continued to be confused, restless, agitated, markedly echophractic, showing disorganization of speech with bilateral grasping and sucking. She made erotic advances to the examiner. She was finally committed to a State Hospital.

Comment.—At the outset, the vitamin deficiency can be dismissed as secondary to the fear of eating which began during the menopause. High vitamin diet (both B and C) did not alleviate the condition.

The previous personality while not psychotic showed an infantile relationship to the father. At the menopause there is a definite "change in personality" which becomes accentuated and accelerated apparently by the shock of her father's death. The regression continues until there is a complete disorganization of significant relationships. Language concepts deteriorate. At this phase bilateral grasping, sucking and marked echopraxia manifest themselves. The fragmentary nature of the echolalia responses is associated with the complete disorganization of speech. It is significant that objects not hers, which she can *name,* are interpreted as belonging either to herself or to her sister. This characteristic it will be remembered is also found in case 7 in relation to the patient's daughter.

Case 3. V. A., a female, aged 45, a former professional dancer, was admitted to Bellevue Psychiatric Hospital on May 13, 1937. She had been married for three years. She was apparently well up to two or three weeks before admission except for the fact that two months previously she had become preoccupied with some freckles on her face and had them removed chemically (with salicylic acid) by a beautician. As a result, the skin of the neck was burned so severely that she bumped her head thrashing around in bed, becoming quiet only after narcotics were administered. Since the treatment she complained of "low vitality." She had been known to go on alcoholic sprees. Her menopause had begun several months previous to admission.

She had lived in New York City for eighteen years until about a month before admission when her husband took her to California by auto. She wrote home about the "scary" roads but apparently was not otherwise apprehensive. She had never before been superstitious or concerned much with religion. She had, however, smoked to great excess, consuming four to five packages of cigarettes a day, and frequently used barbiturates for insomnia. She had a history also of taking aspirin and Coca-Cola in large quantities.

After two weeks in California she began to act in a peculiar fashion. She was very fearful when crossing the street. Her husband observed her standing in the bathroom washing the bowl aimlessly with a brush. She became increasingly frightened and the husband returned with her to New York. He said: "She didn't always talk sense. We'd see some cows and she'd say 'There's some moo-moo's.' She just sat and rode and wouldn't talk. She'd eat ice cream or milk, that's all. She would move her bowels in the car and in bed. She plays with herself in bed, won't talk, nor feed, nor dress herself."

On admission the patient sat trembling and grimacing. She was mute. Occasionally she blurted out her name to persistent questioning. She appeared toxic and tremulous, was tense and resisted physical examination, with a rather pained, agonized expression on her face. Physical examination was essentially negative. Neurologically the positive findings were fragmentary echolalia and perseveration, with some palilalia, marked sucking and bilateral grasping. The left pupil was dilated and larger than the right. There were no pathologic reflexes. She was incontinent. She remained confused. She lay in bed picking her nose and masturbating. No echopraxia was noted. There was a marked aphasia.

Her responses were as follows:

(Where are you?)—"Where am I at."—"Anna"—"Anna."

(What is the trouble?)—"What is the trouble"—"Don't know."

She remained in this state for almost three weeks when gradually speech began to return. She moved around continuously making little attempt to rise from the horizontal plane. She fumbled around aimlessly with her right hand. She began to respond to questions but somewhat irrelevantly. When asked why she sucked objects, she said: "On general principles."

The left pupil remained larger than the right. Her reaction to pain was of the "thalamic" variety with a mimetic right lower facial palsy. The tendon reflexes were equal and lively. She continued to show speech abnormalities. Shown a key she called it a "glay." She repeated questions thus:

(What day is today?)—"What day is today."

(Ever take opiates?)—"Opiates."

She was irritable at times and when tested for sucking with the examiner's key said: "Don't tease me with *my* keys," thus also showing pathologic possessiveness.

She then began to confabulate and was frequently facetious. Encephalogram a week after admission showed: "A small amount of air in the ventricular system, which does not appear to be dilated, the anterior horns are vaguely visualized; the right is apparently normal. The outer pole of the left appears to be depressed with no apparent deviation from the mid-line. Cerebral sulci on right are demonstrable; sulci on left are very vague. Findings suggest arachnoiditis on left side." Ventriculography later revealed air only in the subarachnoid spaces. Ventricles were not outlined.

About six weeks following admission the patient's speech improved to the point where she was able to answer questions much more relavantly. Sucking persisted to the day of discharge. She became more active, moved around and got out of bed. She still had a dull and somewhat bewildered attitude. Six weeks after admission she was discharged in the custody of her husband to go to a private health resort.

Comment.—While in this case there are some data which suggest possible toxins such as salicylic acid, there was no evidence of reducing substances in the urine at the height of the regressive process. Neither the alcohol nor the barbiturates were used in sufficient quantities to produce a toxic psychosis. There was, however, evidence of changes relative to the menopause, namely, "low vitality," increasing tension as evidenced by the very excessive smoking. She had married late in life and when separated from her home and family, her general apprehension began. It is interesting to note that the regression goes deep enough to involve the selection of foods. She would eat only ice cream and milk. The neurological signs, such as dilated pupil, and lively reflexes, can be attributed to the arachnoiditis as evidenced by the encephalogram.

The exclusion of a toxic etiology leaves only the fact that here also an individual at the menopause suddenly underwent a severe regression with mutism, echolalia, marked grasping and sucking. Echopraxia is commonly absent when the patient is confused.

DISCUSSION

These three patients, all women, show various degrees of personality deterioration in the involutional or postinvolutional period. In each case the grasping, sucking, echolalia, echopraxia varies qualitatively and quantitatively. In the first case (case 7), the syndrome appears only in a transference relation to the patient's daughter. The grasping and biting are purposive and acquisitive in character. In this patient neologisms are present and the condition remains constant with gradual deterioration. The syndrome appears six months after the menopause. In the second case, the grasping and sucking approach more closely the classical organic type, the echolalia is fragmentary, the echopraxia being very marked. In this case the syndrome appears several years after the menopause, although nervous symptoms were present immediately following the onset of involution. The vitamin deficiency is looked on as secondary to the fear of eating, although there is a possibility that such a vitamin deficiency might produce a selective cerebral irreversible change which might then not yield to vitamin therapy. This seems unlikely in view of the fact that the vitamin deficiency was never very great so far as could be determined. There was never any evidence of neuritic changes. In the third case, the regression is much more acute and profound with a rather marked amelioration of symptoms but not with complete recovery; degenerative processes may begin acutely. The presence of a dilated pupil is ascribed to an arachnoiditis alone. Arachnoiditis frequently appears in degenerative disease. From the point of view, therefore, of the qualitative evaluation of symptoms and the neurological analysis the one feature in common in all these cases is the appearance of the degenerative disease in the involutional or postinvolutional period. The fact that these appear with different time intervals in relation to the beginning of involution and with different courses is to be ascribed to individual differences in constitution. If one looks upon degenerative disease as due to an inherent defect in the fertilized ovum, then it is to be expected that degenerative processes will occur at various periods in the life cycle when the organism undergoes diminution in somatic energy. The involutional and post-involutional period is such an epoch.

From the point of view of personality and the environmental factors which might be especially severe at this period, there is the fact that in each case some emotional shock is present. In the first case, the death of the husband; in the second case, the death of the father; in the third case, the separation from home and family. The coincidence of emotional shock and the involution may be of etiologic importance.

Cases such as the ones presented demonstrate the need for a coherent psychobiologic theory. Deterioration has to be evaluated not only from the standpoint of the natural differences in constitution, but also as to the physiologic effect of anxiety. The personality has to be looked upon as an integrative process in growth and decay. It is hence necessary to know the relationship of body, brain, and environment, not only at any given time, but also in the relation of one such period to an earlier one. At the involutional period the organism has, so to speak, to come to accounts for the anxieties of a lifetime. Any period in life when growth energy is on the wane may be more critical.

These cases show not only the developmental relationship of primitive imitation in speech and gesture to primitive movements like grasping and sucking, but also demonstrate the fact that movements like grasping and sucking cannot be attributed, in the disorganized personality, to a lesion of any single portion of the brain. The experimental removal of the premotor area and its connections may release grasping, as may also an isolated tumor in the human, as in the cases of corpus callosum tumor reported by Cramer (1936). However, isolated lesions do not produce such personality changes; consequently when grasping and sucking together with automatic imitation occur in cases of severe personality regression, one must look upon this tetrad as indicative of disorder of the brain integrative function which expresses itself in disordered function in hand and mouth activity. From the standpoint of cerebral energy exchange, in the case of the isolated lesion, the brain's energy exchange is normal, only the *pathway* is disturbed. In the severe personality regression, brain integration is abnormal while the pathway is intact. Various quantitative disturbances in brain energy exchange will result in various qualitative clinical differences. It is hence quite futile to attempt to localize grasping and sucking, echolalia, and echopraxia in such disease entities.

Finally, as to a possible relation of these cases to known degenerative disease, it will be remembered that Pick (1902, 1916) studied echolalia intensely; he regarded it as a primitive speech learning phenomenon due to disease of the temporal lobe. Echolalia in proved degenerative disease has been reported by many writers—see especially Liepmann's case report (1900) which showed atrophy of the entire brain, more marked in the dominant hemisphere and especially in the fronto-temporal region, areas normally supplied by the artery of Sylvius. Goldstein (1912–1917) believed that echolalia was a form of "transcortical aphasia" critically produced by a lesion of the motor outflow area. Whether these cases represent degenerative diseases allied to Pick's disease or whether they are indicative of a special form of degeneration is as yet impossible to state.

The "Acoustic Reflex" of Echolalia as a Manifestation of Fundamental Sonic Transformations

To reassess the meaning of this psychic "acoustic reflex" we shall begin with an analogy taken from the field of recording machines.

An ordinary phonograph record is inert until a "playing needle" is put to it while it turns upon a turntable.

In order to have recorded any voice, sonic energy was applied to the chemical substance of the record and changes made in it which would cause "revibration" or "resonance" when a proper transforming agent (the needle during turntable motion) is connected to a magnifying unit (the horn). Note also the modern anthropomorphic term "the loudspeaker."

Let us compare the record, as it comes to us "out-loud," through the "loudspeaker," with "thinking." We say: "We are thinking out loud." Now let us turn the "loudspeaker" down until the actual recording, though still being played, is inaudible at any given distance from the machine.

This situation is now comparable to "thinking to one's self," *if we assume that thinking is sonic.*

Next take our intuitive phrase: "I cannot hear myself think." Notice that we never say: "I cannot see (feel, smell, touch) myself thinking." In all the language of man, the expression is as though *thinking were a sonic quantity and quality,* however "turned down" or "turned up."

To return to our analogy: *the recording is an echo.* Today our tape-recorders provide us with swift echoes of all that we wish echoed. What has to happen to the human mind so that it becomes a sheer "reflex recorder" and so demonstrates the "acoustic reflex?" What does this prove with respect to that *sonic* transformation which we consider makes the mind? Can the "thinker" be compared to needle and record?

Examine for a moment the facts of psychoanalysis and of "free association." This technique is entirely *sonic*—and is indeed "thinking out loud." No other form of communication will suffice for real therapy. *Not even writing can produce the effect of talking freely in the presence of a transference counterforce,* so that a situation of very rapid surging of psychic forces and counterforces—as in any vibratory or "resonance" systems—takes place.

If one re-examines the cases described in the unsolved problem of the "acoustic reflex" of echolalia, one perceives this *unrestricted* surge of power between testing physician and stimulated patient. There is thus *a basic equilibrium of acoustic forces* between people—particularly on the grounds of hearing and speech, and especially when one, the patient, is helpless (the associated syndromes of infantile grasping, sucking and groping) and the other, the physician, in a position of integrity and power.

Echolalia is *not* an acoustic *reflex. It is an acoustic phenomenon between two objects,* one of external force, the other the system to be opposed, and imposed upon; it is another manifestation of a funda-mental sonic phenomenon we already know as either "direct hypnosis" or that attenuated hypnosis we call psychoanalytic transference and countertransference.

Echolalia appears—not usually in a child, though it may in the *latah* of savages—in *abnormal acoustic sytems that have lost their modifying damping effect,* i.e., their ability to modify the impact *and* rebound of a vibratory or acoustic stimulus. It thus *appears* as a "re-flex" because of its acoustic or sonic "rebound." No physiologic re-flex, however, could *reproduce* the exact complex syntax as echolalia must do to deserve the name.

Echolalia occurs not only in personalities who have lost the specific mechanism of damping of external acoustic forces, but also in the psychotic, as described, particularly with an interposed figure (the man for whom "God" had to be an intermediary, the woman for whom her daughter C— had to be present to evoke echolalia); for the psychotic person has been stripped of all defenses by that acoustic chaos which makes the psychosis.

In other words, no matter what *electrochemical mechanism of con-duction is interposed*—in the sensory "hearing" nerve or in the motor "speaking" nerve—the system behaves, in producing the symptom of echolalia, like an instantaneous "loud-speaking" recorder, *like an acoustic equilibrium in which the essential phenomenon called thinking* or "the mind" is the transformation or transducing of elec-trochemical brain processes into sonic "thought" and "utterance." The two phases of this process in echolalia would then be: (1) the conversion of the electrochemical stimulus in the auditory cortex into acoustic energy; and (2) the *instantly compelled* (because undamped) *reconversion* of the acoustic energy (thus giving it the appearance of a reflex) into speech.

The association of infantile grasping and sucking movements tells us that this is the basic mechanism of the child, and that *what hap-pens in the later growth of the brain* is an ability to dampen acousti-cally, to restrain and mold, to differentiate outer speech from inner speech, and so *to begin thinking.*

In other words, when man's brain developed its frontal lobes and its speech areas, it developed essentially complex mechanisms whereby men could not only "store" information, but also modify—and modulate—the tendency to echo each other.

The prefrontal and frontal areas seen from this point of view are interposed "modulators" of sheer acoustic forces so that force and counterforce keep up that dynamic sonic interplay which we designate by various names: "conscious thinking," "conscious awareness," "free association," etc. By virtue of the very same phenomenon, those "metastable equilibria" which growth produces in the brain operate as "ultrasonic delay lines," so that an *unconscious—because inaudible—network* exists always "underneath" or "alongside" the conscious sonic acoustic patterns in motion at any point in time.

Here, for the first time, is the possibility of ultimately achieving a true physiologic concept of the "conscious" and "unconscious" with "preconscious" representing the *transformational* phase from the inaudible "ultrasonic" to the audible, conscious sonic, as we have already described.

Chapter XIII

HEART IMAGE AND HEART MECHANISM—THE NEW SYNERGIC PSYCHONEUROLOGIC APPARATUS—THE NATURE OF THE HEART AS A RHYTHMIC NERVOUS CONTRACTILE STRUCTURE

It is by now clear that heart image and heart mechanism work together in true and quintessential synergic fashion, and that the image of the heart must, for the preservation of the individual, dominate the synergic mechanisms of the intellect. The intellect may and does vary in its inherent strength, directions, and talented coordinations; but, in order for that very intellect to survive and flourish, the *mechanism* of the heart must be conserved against external dangers at least. And yet, as we know, the internalized dangers of former external situations become much more extensively *the basis of our warning or alarm system,* as indeed it should since it is the record of all—even our own animal impulses—that has threatened, frightened and hurt us, from the stress of birth—if stress there be, forward to every separation and dismemberment danger of whatever biopsychic or psychosocial implication. In this manner we have and use "the intuitions of experience."

At the same time, the internalization of *past* dangers and defenses —to be an accurate warning system in the *present*—must be connected to a system that possesses certain neurodynamic characteristics. *To be warned means to have some intimation of the source and direction and of the distance of the danger from the boundaries of self*— particularly from the *unseen* source of danger. The sense of smell is important here to the animal but *only if it can turn its head to assess direction* and check direction against increase or decrease in the intensity of smell. In this matter, our *directional, quantitative and qualitative hearing* is supreme.

One of the prime functions of a labyrinthine-sonic system is that it gives us not only direction (like a "radar finder") but it also contributes to rotation and balance of eyes, body, and limbs in space; it contributes similarly to our sense of time and of timing, and so to the cybernetic action of our limbs for effective control: for fight or flight. *Especially the heart as mechanism must and does respond to its own image*—to the records of that image in previous similar situations and to its own current or instantaneous *sound,* as well as to its own *"palpitation,"* and *racing.* (In dreams of night terrors, the primitive jungle considerations reappear: Thus a patient, confronting and trying to assess a pack of wild lions and tigers in a night-terror dream, has such a thumping of the heart that she wonders: "Can they *hear* my heart—and *smell* my fear? Not if I *eye* them and *stare them down.*" The eye is thus *control,* while the ear and nose are *alarm;* the "eye" establishes a magic community *with* the animal, as well as upright (erect posture) power over him. The labyrinthine-sonic system also reacts to barometric pressure, and so to altitude; or depth and submergence and to temperature and so to climate. (There is a type of coronary heart pain that can be prevented by wearing ear-muffs in very cold wet weather.) Dreams of flying are, as is well known, common to people with labyrinthine disease, and *in many cases of heart pain and heart fear, the bird becomes the symbolization of death and omen.* See in this connection the famous *Raven* of Edgar Allan Poe, or the droppings of birds making patterns which the Delphian oracle utilized for predictions; or the combined night-terror image of *the harpy.* (A female patient with severe night-terror dreams of every kind, raped in a cellar by an adult male when she was five years old, had "heart-thumping wild-animal dreams" alternating with *flocks of shrieking, cawing birds,* pigeons or crows, circling around her, close to her head so that "I could not hear myself think.")

Most cogently, then, we would have to have a mechanism, a *feedback* mechanism linking together the *apparatus which makes the audible sonic aspect of the image of the heart* (labyrinthine-sonic system from cochlea to auditory cortex) and the *mechanism which makes the heart itself as a neuro-circulatory machine.*

Such a mechanism should be related to the various fluctuations *both of image and mechanism*—to symptoms of "heart beat in the ear" to "fainting" to "fear of being closed in and compressed" (claustrophobia) to "fear of being flung out and dissolved into bits" (agoraphobia)—all phenomena having labyrinthine-distance components, and beyond this to blood pressure and heart rate.

This feedback mechanism linking the labyrinthine-sonic apparatus to the heart is, as every medical student knows, the *carotid sinus* in the neck, supplied by precisely the same nerves that supply heart and labyrinthine-sonic system—namely, the 9th and 10th cranial nerves, and the similar *aortic body* in the aortic arch.

These facts enable us to construct a new "psychophysiologic apparatus" or, as we prefer to call it, an apparatus basic to the new science of sonic synergic psychoneurology.

Every well-grounded psychoanalytic and neurologically trained psychiatrist will recognize the fact that it is now possible, because of the concept of the image of the heart to create a synergic psychoneurologic apparatus equally capable of translation into psychosynergic, analytic, or neurosynergic terms.

The Nature of the Heart as a Rhythmic Nervous Contractile Structure

We have now come to the most provocative problem concerning the human heart *as a mechanism.*

The study of the sonic image of the heart, its indisputable presence in consciousness and in dreams, and the known physiologic and embryologic facts seen in this new light *force* us to the conclusion that *the heart is a portion of the nervous system which has either become interpenetrated by a contractile tissue, or has acquired a contractile quality,* the sum total resulting in that peculiar structuralization of tissue known as "cardiac muscle"—a tissue so very different in microscopic appearance and function from *both nerve and muscle.*

Nevertheless, the *facts* drive to the premise that the heart is *funda-*

mentally a migrant portion of the nervous system which fuses in the neck area of the embryo with arterial tissue. In other words, a nervous machine enters into the circulatory system. And though it now becomes the perfectly coordinated "pump" and *the* machine of the circulating blood, nevertheless a careful study of *all the phenomena* related to it tells us that *the secret of animation of the heart* lies in the fact that it is a fusion of great preformative neural tissue masses—in lower forms destined to become ganglia and cell masses of the central nervous system—with essentially contractile tissue.

All the following facts—newly illuminated by the special sonic image of the heart and the general sonic aspects of synergic psychoneurology—fit to this premise:

(1) The heart is a "perfect" machine; it "rests fully" in between each contraction; i.e., it must carry *within* its very substance a regulatory nervous function that will not permit anything less than perfect rest.

(2) The heart is "perfectly" coordinated; its very auricle, up to now, has been known to conduct nerve impulses *only* as a nerve tissue could conduct it; it would be impossible to have the so-called "ectopic focus" of auricular tachycardia, flutter or fibrelation, in any other type of muscle.

(3) The so-called "conductive bundle of His" blends into the ventricular tissue in such a way that it is difficult to separate this "nervous tissue" from the "cardiac muscle."

(4) The auricle in relation to the ventricle—and the EKG itself—indicates an electrochemical nervous transmission which dominates all "muscular" activity. The auricle really acts as an "umbrella of contractile axones" transmitting impulses from its own fused nucleus, "the sinus node," to the dendrites of the "A-V node." The fused nucleus of the ventricles which also can be viewed as much larger "contractile axones" become heavily muscularized. In brief, the general belief and teaching has been that the heart is a large special *muscular* organ which has been "joined together" and "synchronized" by special "nerve tissue"—the Bundle of His. We suggest quite a different premise, namely that the heart, formed as we know in the *nervous areas of the neck* (the vagus, labyrinthine-sonic, gill-cleft area), *is*

primarily a nervous structure which has become contractile and hence its rhythmic autonomous action. Or, in other words, the heart contains its own subsidiary "brain and nerves" within its own substance. We now comprehend why the heart embryologically "descends" from the neck area: it is part and parcel of the original sonic evolving *nervous* structure, and as its arterial components fuse, it must pass from "gill-cleft oxygenation" to "lung oxygenation." It is as though the nervous system *delegates* a large portion of itself and transforms it into a special contractile structure to *ensure* the perfect handling of fatigue. At the same time the *mechanism* of the heart, including aortic and carotid body, remains connected with the structures responsible for the *image* of the heart. The energy transformations of life and all possible coordinations—the synergic quanta operating according to the principle of synergy—are devoted to the maintenance of this *cybernetic, directional image warning of internal and external danger* (the labyrinthine-sonic apparatus, and the carotid and aortic bodies) to protect this masterpiece of nature: the human heart, to which is thus linked the great achievement of all the Gods, the human signaling system of anxiety as it steers toward its aspirations—the speech, the stance, the hand and the cybernetic-sonic thought of man.

(5) Most striking of all—next to the fact of the image of the heart in relation to the labyrinthine-sonic apparatus and the signaling system of anxiety—is the manner in which the sympathetic (excitor) nerves and the parasympathetic (depressor) nerves join the heart. The heart is joined *as though it were a part of the nervous system not as though it were an "internal organ."* For example, these "autonomic" fibers to the heart are among the general visceral efferent fibers *going out* to smooth muscle and the glands of the body. Its afferents are also among the "autonomic" fibers *going back* to the central nervous system from the internal organs. These afferent impulses from organs serve to initiate visceral reflexes and for the most part remain at a subconscious level, i.e., never penetrate to consciousness as does the sonic image of the heart.

Now, as we know, there are *three* different kinds of "autonomic ganglia" which are way stations to which the *efferent* (out going) fibers reach and "stop over." Here, another fiber carries on (the "secondary" postganglionic to the organ itself). There are three different kinds of these "way stations" (ganglia). The heart and the ciliary muscle of the eye are *the two organs* (both derivatives of the nervous system) which have their ganglia close to or within the substance of their structure. (This is true also—but only in a very limited way— for the submucous and myenteric plexuses; these are collections of nerve cells, not true ganglia, close to the substance of the tissue.)

But, *in addition to these ganglia close to the substance of the heart,* there are typical *postganglionic* fibers running from *way stations* in the head and neck, e.g., *the superior cervical cardiac nerve,* which carries fibers from the superior cervical ganglion to the cardiac plexus and so to the heart.

Furthermore, once we examine how this double sympathetic (excitor) nervous supply is distributed to the heart, in addition to the parasympathetic (depressor) vagus fibers, we realize for the first time the unique position of the heart in the *nervous scheme of the body.* For, there are therefore *four* different sets of *nerve supplies to the heart* distributed in a most curious way—curious because *there are no vagus fibers in the mammalian ventricle.*

In other words, these are the innervations:

Nerve Supply to Heart

Ventricle	*Auricle*
1. No vagus (no parasympathetic)	1. Vagus (parasympathetic)
2. Superior cardiac nerve (sympathetic)	2. Superior cardiac nerve (sympathetic)
3. Cardiac ganglia	3. Cardiac ganglia
4. "Conduction fibers" from A—V node to ventricular "muscle"	4. "Conduction fibers" from S—A node to A—V node

No other internal organ has this peculiar form of multiple innervation. None has more than *two*—sympathetic and parasympathetic; and, furthermore, no other organ thus supplied is deprived of the parasympathetic as the ventricle is deprived here.

The "cardiac muscle" can therefore not all be compared with smooth muscle, nor can it be compared with skeletal muscle.

The only known structure in the human organism—besides the heart—in which this kind of convergence of nerve tracts takes place is *within the nervous system itself.*

It is as though the "conduction bundle" represents a segment or segments of the preneural "spinal cord"—the superior, inferior, and middle cardiac sympathetic nerves would indicate an area of preneural tissue corresponding to at least three of the later segments. And the four types of heart innervation would thus have the following analogous relationships:

Spinal Cord Segment	*Heart*
1. Motor cell nuclei and motor roots	S–A Node and A–V Node
2. Visceral Efferent	*Vagus,* preganglionic to ganglia of cardiac plexus
	Sympathetic: postganglionic from cervical ganglia
3. Visceral afferent and cerebrospinal ganglia	Visceral afferents from vagus and ganglion nodosum (also possibly in sympathetic nerves)
4. Sympathetic ganglia outside the cord	Cardiac plexus ganglia outside the heart

An examination of the above chart will show that the arrangement of the vagus nerves *which are excluded from the ventricles, supplying only the auricles* and of the sympathetic nerves which do reach the ventricles make the entire nervous apparatus of the heart resemble a spinal cord segment.

The heart, then, is in part a nervous contractile structure—not only a "myocardium" but also *a cardiac myoneurium.*

Even the embryology of the heart becomes clearer from this point of view.

The heart develops as swiftly and as extensively as the brain.

In a chick embryo with five segments (23 hours), simultaneously with the extension of the head, *the entodermal component of the original head fold* is elongated into an internal tubular pocket of roughly corresponding shape; *this is the primitive foregut from which the heart develops.* Or, in other words, the brain develops from the head fold, the heart from its entodermal component. From this point on, though the "heart area" lives directly beneath the "head area," they are separated and their developments diverge except for the primitive pharyngeal membrane; at the same time, the growths of brain and heart, at this very early and critical stage, are similarly accentuated. In a chick embryo of seventeen segments (38 hours), the heart is as large, though already twisting for its ultimate descent into the thorax, as the forebrain, midbrain and hindbrain.

Curiously enough, however, a section through the pharyngeal membrane of a 25-hour embryo shows how the ectoderm of the primitive brain vesicle maintains contact up to the last possible moment with the entoderm of the foregut (heart vesicle).

At the 38-hour stage the heart can be seen developing in relation to the pharyngeal pouches and the sonic apparatus of the auditory placode.

But the brain and heart are permanently separated from each other by the closed pharyngeal membrane which later breaks through and becomes the mouth.

It is at this stage that the relationship of the heart to the three cervical cardiac nerves and to the vagus can be seen so clearly; later they get pulled down into the lung cavity.

Particularly in following the development of the vagus and of the cervical sympathetics, one can perceive that through these nerves—*no matter what twisting, coiling and descent* the heart undergoes—*it never changes its actual dynamic* (however distant) relationship to the brain, pharyngeal pouches and auditory placode.

In brief, *the heart as mechanism,* whether studied neuropsychiatrically, physiologically, or embryologically, appears to be—however "separate" its adult location and appearance—*as much of a cardiac myoneurium as a myocardium.*

*   *   *   *   *

(6) Finally of interest are the facts of the von Bezold reflex which no one can explain—namely, the *slowing* tension-lowering effect of veratrum—unless one accepts the postulate that the cardiac vagus itself contains *sensory fibers different from the pain fibers* which ascend

up the cardiac sympathetics. Or, in other words, ordinarily the "feedback" mechanisms of carotid and aortic bodies suffice to control rate and blood pressure. *But under the conditions—especially the psychic conditions—which produce the psychogenic paroxysmal tachycardias,* the vagus itself becomes *its own "feedback"* mechanism.

This new theory—supported by the fact that in the dog there is an *accessory vagus nerve* which is afferent to the aortic body from the heart—is what flows from our new approach to the heart via the sonic aspects of a synergic psychoneurology.

Stated again, ordinarily the here postulated afferent cardiac vagus *brings a periodic regulatory impulse to the brain.* This cardiac vagus impulse is different from the usual carotid body and aortic impulse which control rate and blood pressure. This cardiac vagus impulse is different from the pain fibers which go up the cardiac sympathetics. *It has a different purpose*—as our psychoneurologic study of the paroxysmal tachycardias shows. *It belongs to the entire tractus-solitarius vagus system.* It belongs to that *psychosomatic function of the vagus;* for, the motor vagus, as is well known, is the major nerve of the *deflection of tension from psychoneurologic areas to bodily organs,* and so also *to the heart.*

In order for the motor vagus—in its deflection of tension *to* the heart not to become *too* inhibitory, it must have a countermechanism, a *psychosomatic feedback* from the S—A node itself at all times, so that the heart does not stop out of, say, sheer terror. The carotid and aortic bodies cannot suffice for this purpose; the demand is too immediate upon the vital S—A node itself.

When, therefore, a paroxysmal auricular (or ventricular) tachycardia sets in, neither pressure upon the carotid body in the neck or on the eyeball nor even mecholyl suffices. (It is terribly cruel to give mecholyl to a patient with paroxysmal tachycardia.) The reason is quite simple.

The psychic fear of dismemberment is so deep, so primitive, that the deepest and most primitive—and "foolproof"—of all cardiac mechanisms sets in. The "feedback" mechanism—before this entrusted to carotid and aortic body—now *is in the nodal tissue itself and is conveyed by the hidden afferent vagus.* This nerve, up to now unsuspected as such, is always a *psychosomatic feedback cardiac mechanism*. In great terror *it* takes over. And, ordinarily when the terror has subsided, then and only then are the carotid and aortic bodies allowed once more to act.

In support of this new theory we offer all the material here studied with reference to the image of the heart.

It is not possible otherwise to explain the von Bezold "reflex" with veratrum. It is not possible otherwise to explain the psychoneurologic phenomena of the paroxysmal tachycardias.

Nature appears again to have been wiser than man. Her synergies protect the instinct to survive. The heart *must have* its own built-in psychoneurologic regulatory apparatus.

Otherwise we should not have survived.

*   *   *   *   *

Finally in this connection I can offer one piece of research done by the late Dr. Milton M. Abeles and myself over twenty years ago—a study which is here reproduced in full.

ELECTROCARDIOGRAPHIC CHANGES DURING ENCEPHALOG-RAPHY (20 CASES)

CLINICALLY, pulse changes and other signs of vagus effects such as vomiting, pallor, sweating and variations in blood pressure have often been noted, during the injection of air in encephalography. In addition, there may be usually a slight rise in temperature, meningeal signs, headache and, during the passage of air upward, pain along the nerve roots.

The pulse changes have been described by various authors. In a typical description by Krause (1930), he points out that the pulse becomes slower, arhythmic, small and weak and that pulse as well as accompanying respiratory changes for the most part soon disappear. Pancoast and Fay (1929) state that the slowing of the pulse to 60 beats per minute is not uncommon. A number of observers have reported an initial acceleration of the pulse rate. Juzelevsky (1930–31) describes a case in which the patient's pulse could not be felt and the patient appeared to be on the verge of collapse. In almost every case of encephalography, however, there are minor signs of shock probably due to vagus stimulation.

Since we were unable to find in the literature any but clinical observations of the pulse changes, it seemed probable that simultaneous electrocardiography would yield further valuable information.

TECHNIQUE

The patients were prepared by omitting lunch and giving a hypodermic injection of Magendie's Solution m. vii and Hyoscine gr. 1/150, from half to three quarters of an hour before beginning the procedure. The patients were all in the sitting position in the encephalographic chair. Entry into the subarachnoid space was made *via* the lumbar route. At the same time the limbs were prepared for electrocardiography and a control electrocardiogram taken. In three cases, a record was taken every 10 minutes from the outset, at the first injection of air. In the remaining cases, tracings were obtained during the period when the pulse began to decrease in rate, and at intervals when the changes in pulse indicated that the more accurate record was necessary. The technical facilities at our disposal were such that continuous records were not feasible. Blood pressure was observed but not correlated with simultaneous electrocardiograms. Our readings, however, tended to confirm the already established facts, that the blood pressure rises during the injection of air and then gradually falls to normal within eight to thirty-six hours (Meyer, 1932). Pulse rates were noted in each case at 15-minute to 30-minute intervals for as long as the pulse remained below 60 *after* the injection of air was discontinued. This, of course, varied with the individual case.

RESULTS

To summarize the results listed in Table 1, it may be pointed out that the most frequent electrocardiographic change was that consequent upon stimulation of the pacemaker, i.e., in thirteen cases. Of these, at one or another time during the procedure, seven showed sinus arhythmia, five showed sinus bradycardia, two phasic sinus slowing, three sinus tachycardia, and two showed a combination of

TABLE 1.—ELECTROCARDIOGRAPHIC CHANGES DURING ENCEPHALOGRAPHY.

No.	Age.	Electrocardiographic changes.	Positive encephalographic findings.	Blood pressure.	Spinal fluid pressure (water).	Fluid/Air ratio.	Diagnosis:
1	19	Marked S.A. Occa. V.E.S. L.V.P. P_2 and P_3 inverted. Suggests interference with nervous mechanism	Cortical atrophy (left parietal).	100/90	110 mm.	125/95	Idiopathic or post-traumatic epilepsy.
2	12	S.A. In records Nos. 2 and 3 the Q-R-S waves are of lower voltage than in record No. 1 before encephalography	Normal	120/80	Low	102/82	Idiopathic epilepsy.
3	49	Migration of the pacemaker in Lead 3	Air in subentorium. Cortical markings on both sides exaggerated	112/86	120	190/145	Idiopathic or post-traumatic epilepsy.
4	46	No appreciable change during injection of air. R_3 low	Normal	140/90	90	185/145	Idiopathic epilepsy.
5	20	Slight S.A. accentuated during encephalography with the production of bradycardia	Cortical atrophy (right parietes (?))	115/70	70	145/110	Idiopathic epilepsy.
6	8	Considerable S.A.	Sl. enlargement of 3d and 4th ventricles. Basal cistern dilated	110/80	Low	90/70	Idiopathic epilepsy.
7	13	First record: S.T. rate 165/min. The second record showed periods of phasic sinus slowing with an A-V nodal rhythm	No air in vent. system. Cortical markings good	100/80	60	120/115	Diffuse degen. Cerebral disease. (Congenital).
8	8	S.A.	Hugely dilated vent. system—symmetrical	124/80	150	......	Degenerative disease marked int. hydrocephalus.
9	41	Migration of cardiac pacemaker between the S-A and A-V nodes. Periods of S.A. with transitory nodal rhythm	Normal	110/60	100	......	Post-traumatic encephalopathy.
10	40	Rate 48/min. 2 hours after encephalography	Subarachnoid markings exaggerated and basal cistern enlarged	140/80	Low	200/165	Traumatic encephalopathy.
11	54	Sinus bradycardia, rate 48/min. R and T lower in second record than in first	Moderate dilatation of vent. Much air in subarachnoid space	150/90	Low	260/210	Traumatic encephalopathy. Lues?
12	55	Low voltage in all leads. L.V.P.	Mod. dilatation of the vent. system. Much air in subarachnoid spaces.	140/80	Low	330/245	Alzheimer's disease.
13	34	Bradycardia of 50-60/min. Main deflection shows widening. Notching in all leads. T_1 inverted. R-T transition slightly abnormal in Leads 1 and 3	Slight asymmetry of lat. vent., left larger than right 3d vent. normal	112/76	100	150/125	Traumatic encephalopathy.
14	28	S.T., rate about 135/min. In Leads 2 and 3 rate slower with periods of sinus slowing, too far apart to be regarded as respiratory. Probably a form of sinus depression	Unusual collection of air in subentorium bilaterally. Otherwise normal	......	160	145/115	Traumatic encephalopathy? Hysteria?
15	41	Marked bradycardia, 60/min. Shallow T in all leads	Slight depression of left lateral vent. Air over left cortex	188/133	230	98/83	Oxycephaly. Pituitary tumor.
16	42	Left vent. preponderance	Vent. not outlined. Much air in subarachnoid space	120/90	110	......	Left frontotemporal. Neoplasm.
17	45	Sinus tachycardia, 100/min.	Intervent. septum displaced to right; left vent. displaced downward. Cortical markings absent on left. Much subtentorial air bilaterally	130/90	120	105/90	Left temporal neoplasm.
18	3½	S.A.	Symmetrical and enormous dilatation of entire vent. system	......	60	250/220	Congenital communicating hydrocephalus.
19	56	No change	Symmetrical dilatation of the vent. system and much air in subarachnoid spaces	200/110	160	200/180	Cerebral arteriosclerosis.
20	35	A.F. and nodal rhythm	Slight dilatation of the vent. system. A little air in the subarachnoid spaces	100/70	220	125/115	Brain tumor? Pleuriglandular syndrome.

KEY: S.A. = Sinus arrhythmia; V.E.S. = ventricular extrasystole; A.F. = Auricular fibrillation; L.V.P. = Left ventricular preponderance; S.T. = Sinus tachycardia.

these changes. The next most frequent variations was that consequent upon migration of the pacemaker. Of these, one showed auricular fibrillation (though impure flutter was seriously considered), two showed migration of the pacemaker between the S—A and A—V nodes. Next in frequency were changes indicative of dominance of the A—V node or lower ventricular foci. Of these, there were three cases of transitory nodal rhythm and one case of ventricular extrasystole. Five cases showed no appreciable change. In six cases the bradycardia lasted for six hours and then gradually returned to normal.

From these records, the conclusion may be drawn that the majority of the changes are to be attributed to excessive vagus stimulation. This is correlated with the other clinical manifestations of vagus origin. In the one case in which auricular fibrillation occurred, this change appeared immediately coincident with the first withdrawal of 15 cc. of spinal fluid, before any air had been injected. What the mechanism in this instance was, we we are unable to say. It may have been due to a sudden change in intracranial pressure.

In view of these changes, it is interesting to consider whether or not, interference with the conduction mechanism of the heart might possibly be a factor in encephalography death, especially in those cases where the difference between the amount of fluid removed and air injected is very small and theoretically too little to accommodate air expansion or air irritation. The following case of encephalography death is of interest in this connection.

CASE ABSTRACT

A man, aged 55, was admitted to the Mount Sinai Hospital on September 29, 1928, with the complaint of weakness in the left upper and lower extremities of six months' duration, together with failing vision and personality changes.

Examination. Showed apathy, mental torpor, pyramidal tract signs and weakness on the left side, coarse tremor of fingers of the right hand, and bilateral papilledema and hemorrhages. The blood pressure was 140/85. Laboratory findings were negative. The clinical diagnosis was neoplasm of the right cerebral hemisphere, post-

Rolandic in location. Cardiac rate and rhythm normal. Heart sound of poor quality.

Course. On October 5, 1928, at 3.00 P.M., encephalography was performed; 100 cc. of fluid was removed and 100 cc. of air was injected. The patient became ashen and cyanotic. At 6.10 P.M. the pulse was 40. Hands cold. At 11.00 P.M., the patient was in complete coma, breathing stertorously and moribund. The clinical impression at that time was questionably that of hemorrhage into a neoplasm. The next day at 8.20 A.M. the temperature mounted to 107 and the pulse was imperceptible. The patient died 15 minutes later, approximately seventeen and one half hours after encephalography. The left cerebral ventricular system had been well visualized, was displaced to the left and was moderately dilated. The third ventricle was visualized and displaced a distance of $\frac{1}{2}$ inch. No autopsy was obtained.

Inasmuch as anatomic verification of the brain's condition was not possible, it cannot be stated with certainty that there was not a hemorrhage into a neoplasm. However, the lapsing into coma eight hours after encephalography together with the profound bradycardia and obvious cardiac death makes it necessary to consider the possibility of excessive vagus stimulation in a patient in the sixth decade of life and whose heart sounds were recorded as weak.

SUMMARY

Twenty cases of simultaneous encephalography and electrocardiography are presented with a study of the changes in the cardiac conduction mechanism. The most common changes are those consequent upon stimulation of the pacemaker through the vagus: sinus arhythmia, sinus bradycardia, phasic sinus slowing, sinus tachycardia, migration of the pacemaker between the S—A and A—V nodes, transitory nodal rhythm. In one case ventricular extrasystole was observed and in another auricular fibrillation. In one fatal case following encephalography the death was probably cardiac and followed the excessive injection of air with subsequent bradycardia and collapse at that period when most cases begin to show a return to normal rate. The findings are correlated with other clinical manifestations of vagus stimulation.

It will be observed that there can be no other explanation of the bradycardia and tachycardias and block obtained when the brain spaces are filled with air.

These cannot be due simply to different "gradations" of motor inhibition. They can, however, be very clearly seen as the result of interference with a *cardiac afferent vagus mechanism* which registers its controlling influence *in the fourth ventricle of the brain at the level of the tractus solitarius.*

For this reason, to fill the ventricles of the brain with air is to upset *the pacemakers within the heart.*

It will be the task of cardiac physiologists to prove or disprove this theory. In so doing, however, they must take into account not only the von Bezold "reflex" but also the fact that there exists an image of the heart which, in no small measure, controls our lives.

Chapter XIV

SUMMARY—PERSPECTIVES

PART I

(1) With respect to the problem of "heart attack," the principle of synergy in psychoanalysis is introduced as the dominating neuropsychic force determining immediate survival and ultimate longevity. The basic synergy of the postnatal ego centers around the image of the heart and its dynamic relationship to the rest of the ego. Together with the later synergies inherent in heterosexual identification and the nature of one's talents, the image of the heart influences—as any foundation influences a subsequent dynamic structure reared upon it—the directional activity of the ego.

(2) The principle of synergy marks an advance in psychoanalytic theory; strictly speaking we do not analyze a vague "psyche"; we analyze the various ways in which trends and inherent drives "work together," i.e., the way they *synergize*, specifically in each individual, and universally in the race of Man, either psychosomatically in problems of longevity on the one hand or psychoculturally in problems of true self-definition and direction, on the other. Psychosynergy enriches and advances psychoanalysis in the tradition established by Sigmund Freud, the trained neurologist and psychiatrist.

(3) Central to the principle of psychosynergic dynamics is a new view of the human heart as having—however vague and unorganized in the waking state—psychic representation. In contrast to all other internal organs which are "separated" from consciousness in an autonomy, the heart does produce its individually highly variable image *sonically* via a special synergic mechanism for hearing the heart beat, *ryhthmically* via the pulsatile expansion and contraction of arteries

239

throughout the body, and under certain conditions *volumetrically* by the "dimension" of sensations produced within the chest during effort and alarm.

(4) The image of the heart appears in dreams as a rigid-walled container or mechanism in response to the wish for magic cardiac standstill such as an hourglass, pump, chugging engine, compartmentalized flask, or as a watch—"the ticker." The image of the heart only deceptively and secondarily takes on the aspect of a "uterus" as a reflection of the intrauterine past when the mother's heart and lungs "carried" the circulation of the foetus. Hence the image of the heart has been primarily interpreted as "intrauterine fantasy" whereas such fantasy is its secondary import, at most.

(5) The first "act" of birth and therefore of the postnatal ego—namely, the ending of the umbilical circulation and the closure of the foramen ovale—is that of the completion of "heart independence." The image of the heart thus exists at the very root of the postnatal ego and, in many ways, the image of the heart may be said to "branch" into the growing ego. In some dream images of the heart, the timing of the circulation is portrayed (the hourglass symbol) and the air-inlet is closed; in others the air-inlet and breathing crises are portrayed (flask with very long neck); in still others, the "branching soundtrack" of the image of the heart and its rhythmic sonic force appears (the chugging engine).

(6) The problem of anxiety is greatly simplified by this approach. Anxiety may now be defined as the dyssynergy between the image of the heart (with all its sonic branchings) and the rest of the ego—the heart image "recoils" and tends to become too organized, in extreme cases to be suppressed and appear in dreams.

(7) The "psychosomatic syndromes" may, in this sense, be seen as defenders of the heart. An example is given of a case with an entire galaxy of such syndromes, the last to appear being anginal pain.

(8) This definition of anxiety brings a new orientation to the problem of premature coronary death and of paroxysmal auricular tachycardia (the "neurosis of the runaway heart") whose rate regresses to the rapid intrauterine foetal heart rate. Both syndromes predominate in men particularly up to forty years of age.

(9) In certain situations—in symbolic language—"the heart is the child." In men this may become one of the elaborations of the "pregnancy fantasy" in accord with another male childhood notion that the baby is born by emerging in the precordial area between the mother's breasts.

(10) This orientation fits to recent U.S. Army statistics showing *gross* coronary disease in 77.3 per cent of 300 males with an average age of 22.1 years, indicating long-standing cardiac stress and strain.

(11) The psychosynergic function of the image of the heart is dramatically illustrated in its relationship to sleeping and dreaming, verifying Freud's dictum that the dream is the guardian of sleep. In "night terrors" the human child awakens in response to· the dyssynergic "palpitations" of the heart; in "day terrors," the human adult may go into sudden inhibitory sleep to achieve the magic cardiac standstill of intrauterine fantasy. Taken together with the phenomenon of paroxysmal auricular tachycardia, this indicates the involvement of the cardiac conduction mechanism and psychic injury to the arteries supplying the heart in very severely traumatic situations.

(12) Against these basic considerations, the premise is offered that premature coronary death in relatively young men is the result of a most severe though masked continuous onslaught against the child—pressures which produce too organized, too invasive and pervasive an image of the heart and its derivatives. The major preoccupation of such individuals is defense of the heart at all costs.

(13) The costs are high. The basic defense is a very intense identification with mother which can lead either to partial or complete transvestism. Most males—destined to "coronaries"—make a late "normal" heterosexual identification to cover up; they have as a consequence almost daily "success or hero" fantasies (not to be confused with creative imagination) about which they are very secretive since they are dimly aware of their connection with underlying partial transvestism and very primitive oral impulses. This internal eruptive dilemma—the "healed split-identification"—makes them denunciative of all psychologic approach before their first attack—and may bring about their subsequent and fatal attacks.

(14) In the "coronary," the basic character traits (whatever the individual variation) are each specific primary defenses against this deep conflict. These traits are: (a) a peculiar *controlled tension* the manifestation of a constant necessity to revise infantile magic thinking; (b) a *physical hurry* including a highly individual "hurrying gait," a kind of atoning advertisement of their "interest, command and efficiency"; (c) a constant need for either or both "self-purification" or "immunity from accusation," side by side with tendencies to conniving or conspiracy and to evasion or deceit; (d) these conditions and activities—essentially the exercise of a *fatal magic*—reinforce the secondary defenses of "superrealism and superpaternalism"; (e) caught in the toils of such clashes, talent suffers; the man who dies a premature coronary death generally has a personality the very antithesis of the creative artist; premature coronary attacks are most common in certain types of professional workers.

(15) Physiologic research must take these factors into account; the importance of an *abnormal* cholesterol metabolism increases—since patching is unavoidable.

(16) The life, the work, the death of Edgar Allan Poe illustrate all these factors; they show too the violent necessity, to Poe, for drugs and alcohol to "allow" passage to whatever creative impulses so afflicted an individual may have. The addiction to nicotine is no exception and plays its cumulative role in the disease.

(17) Further study of the sonic image of the heart is pursued, particularly as manifest in dreams but also including projection to external real objects such as a "chime clock."

(18) The sonic image of the heart bears a relationship not only to "chiming" but also to "rhyming" as pathology in the "clang association" of mania.

(19) The "stroke" and the fall of blood pressure which follows "stroke" is tentatively seen as the collapse of the sonic signaling system of anxiety.

(20) If the function of dreams is to guard sleep, then sleep has the prime purpose of releasing the sonic image of the heart from its synergic compounding with the other more definitive images of the ego. In this way the heart normally rests; the dream image of the heart

usually presents the sharp wish for magic cardiac standstill; conversely "night terrors" demand awakening; in the latter event the daytime injury to the sonic image of the cardiac mechanism—the synchronizing tissue—can only be discharged by "frightening animals" or "taboo fears of things," as is also manifest in certain deliria—intensities of stimulation which demand awakening.

(21) Several dreams of the disguised heart image (frequently fused with symbols of the genitals) are recorded: (a) two dreams of a man after a coronary attack with permanent alteration of the electrocardiogram; (b) a dream indicating pregnancy and the formation of the forerunners of the heart; (c) a dream of a rheumatic patient with severe ejaculatio praecox.

(22) In all of the above dreams the cardiac mechanism, particularly the pacemaker-synchronizer action, is symbolized as a small "leaping animal"; mouse, cat, bullfrog. These symbolizations fuse heart with genital or both "heart" and "genital" with "unfinished child."

(23) The cardiac pacemaker-synchronizing tissue appears to be neurosexual in nature, connected with the neural sonic tissue embryologically and functionally (the vagus) and with the sexual system. This may be sexually symbolized or fused with sexual symbols.

(24) In its neurosexual derivation and function, the cardiac pacemaker-synchronizing tissue—together with the respiratory sonic mechanism of the head and neck—becomes the mechanism of sexual, cardiac, and therefore individual animation; hence its dream symbolization as a "leaping animal," leaping either into or out of a "moving enclosure," i.e., into or out a body either in the motion of growth, of intercourse or of death. The "leap" seems to signify the "leaping" transition out of the inanimate into the animate or vice versa. In particular, it fuses with genital symbols.

(25) A case of "voodoo death" is briefly redescribed from Cannon's work—a death, the result of eating a taboo animal; its relation to the known occurrence of paroxysmal ventricular tachycardia, the result of terror, is mentioned and interpreted as the futile "flight of the heart," with the rest of the body immobilized in an acute helplessness. Psychically the eaten taboo devours the eater. (Slowly deteriorating schizophrenic catatonia with its slow heart can be evaluated as a

chronic voluntary muscular counterbalance to a paroxysmal ventricular tachycardia, so that the schizophrenic heart slows and is spared over a long time as opposed to the "running heart" and quick death of a masked ventricular tachycardia.) Neurophysiologically, the breaking of the taboo may be interpreted as disrupting the sonic integrity of the pacemaking-synchronizing cardiac controls.

(26) The "case of the clock chimer" is described in the case of an artist, three times analyzed before he discovered, or rather rediscovered that he, like his father before him, had paroxysmal auricular tachycardia. His severe sexual impotence and creative inhibition began with his first unrecognized attack and the usual analytic theory of inborn "passivity" was used with some improvement but little effective permanent force. His entire ego had become dyssynergic as a result; he discovered that he took not the image of castration but the image of cardiac death—and sacrificial impotence—to bed with him. "The Image of the Heart" helped to achieve a complete restoration of his sexual and creative powers. His symptom—his need to "make all the clocks chime together"—became clear to him as a technique of projecting and perfecting "the sonic image of the heart," so that he might in accord with the principle of synergy assure himself that his cardiac pacemakers and synchronizers were faultless. With this insight his sexual powers were released from the grip of anxiety.

(27) The cases described include a proven coronary, a known rheumatic cardiac, and a case of paroxysmal auricular tachycardia. No matter what the difference in cause, the sexual disturbances and the dreams all obey the basic principle of psychosynergy and portray the sonic image of the heart.

(28) Both in psychophysiologic terms, as seen in sleep, dreaming, and "night terrors"—where the sonic roar of the circulation in the ear becomes "the lion"—and in neurophysiologic terms, in which the vagus is an important visceral component of the sonic system, the image of the heart appears to hold the key to consciousness because it is in dynamic equilibrium with the cardiac pacemaking-synchronizing mechanism. The image of the heart appears to influence waking and sleeping in a fashion tentatively outlined as follows:

(a) When the image of the heart "compounds" itself with reality, it "engages" the external world once more; we awake.

(b) When, during waking, the image of the heart tends to "retract," we experience anxiety; during sleeping and dreaming, a severe day-time stimulus to the image of the heart will be dreamt out as the "leaping animals" of night terror—a condition which demands waking and crying out for help, i.e., engaging reality in order to compound and dilute the sheer symbolic power of the sonically stimulated dream imagery of the heart.

(c) When the image of the heart is able to be "released," or rather to release and relinquish the image of the external world, we fall asleep.

(29) And finally, in this last formulation, we have the explanation for the well-known involuntary "jumping" of the entire body just before falling asleep, particularly after a stimulating day. For a long time it has been known that this reflex phenomenon recapitulates the hiatus of birth—that moment when the foetal heart "leaps" to its lifelong independence and the lungs fill with air. The "jumping" thus wakes us, as we are on the verge of sleep, on the verge of relinquishing for a while the image of the world to rest the heart whose sleep sentinel is the dream.

(30) Freud never succeeded in penetrating to the actual nature of anxiety, though he understood and described its dynamic effects more completely than anyone in history. His final statement was that anxiety is the original reaction to helplessness in the traumatic situation, in which external danger and internal danger, reality peril and instinctual demand coincide. In terms of the ego, anxiety is thus capable, as Freud showed, of producing the universal characteristic dividedness of the neurosis, all the way from contradictory attitudes to a true "split" in the ego. So fundamental is anxiety.

(31) And yet, Freud completely missed the implications of the sonic image of the heart. The concept of anxiety as dyssynergy between the image of the heart and the rest of the ego *simplifies and resolves* a great many theoretical and practical confusions.

(32) The sonic image of the heart is part and parcel of *an internal sonic system* existing diffusely all over the body both in its depths

and on its skin surface. In this way the sonic image of the heart is in dynamic equilibrium with the rest of the ego and with the heart itself —*as mechanism.*

(33) This is why "anxiety"—dyssynergy—"rings the warning bell" at the approach of any threat to limb, head, genital, or diffuse skin integrity; there is a *limb-artery* synergy, as well. Therefore, the well-known "separation danger" which triggers anxiety is always dismemberment-danger psychically.

(34) The mind is a sonic phenomenon; the heart image is a portion of the synergy of the sonic forces that make up "mind." In contrast to "classical neurology" which views man as an *addition of reflexes which govern muscles,* synergic psychoneurology views man as an always individual *dynamism of synergies governing movements.*

(35) In the sphere of somatic and psychic growth, synergic psychoneurology views the brain as the expression of integrated force and is thus concerned with the maintenance and *delivery of power* as well as with the *cybernesis of pattern.* The *heart as mechanism* serves the maintenance and delivery of power; the *heart as image* serves the cybernesis of pattern.

(36) The sonic image of the heart is connected intimately with the signaling system of anxiety—of which *words* form a sonic and audible nucleus, central to all thought structure, however elaborated.

(37) The history of words shows a constant cross reference between the names for "heart-limb-memory-mind-anxiety." In spite of centuries of ignorance (before the work of Harvey in 1628—and since) of the heart's *work,* the history of language indicates that the sonic image of the heart—not as a rationally perceived object but as *an internal image*—is a keystone of thought and the dynamic sonic center of the signaling system of anxiety.

(38) The reason why the sonic image of the heart was, up to now, not recognized, is because the signaling system of anxiety is created as a substitute for heart-fear *before* there can be a designation—in words—for the image of the heart. The threat of dismemberment is so overwhelming to an infant (in the incompletely myelinized state) that it can onlf be expressed by heart-fear, flight of the heart, waves of panic, *which in turn must be repressed* together with certain impulses

that trigger it. This is why the "superego" represents the achievement and ideal as well as the steersman and repressor. Growth of the neo-ego shifts the emphasis from archi-ego impulse and terror to neo-ego achievement and aspiration. As part of this shift, the phonosonic signaling system of anxiety is created in the development of speech, erect posture and handedness. In brief, conscience sits in judgment on the fear-makers; a sense of reality and rational thought (the secondary process) chain the irrational impulse of the dismembering rage and act as buttress against the recoil of dismemberment terror. A very high degree of synergy is thus established, compared to lower animals. The heart is defended by the plastic powers of mobilization which follow upon "good superego" formation, i.e., permissive as well as judicious, economic as well as cybernetic. Conscience may be severe but the heart is saved. Nature protects its miracle: the heart and the brain of man. The psychosomatic syndromes may be regarded as "defenders of the heart."

(39) The "coronary character" *before the attack* betrays all the signs of a psychically poorly fused archi-ego and neo-ego underneath all the "dynamic executive drive" of such persons. Each "split" brings with it an assault upon heart and arteries from childhood forward. Secret transvestite traits exist and mask by inverted defenses the dyssynergic image of the heart. The transvestite thus appears in a new light; the sexual threat of dismemberment becomes intolerable to the life of such people; open transvestism may progress to surgical self-mutilation and paranoia; covert transvestism and bachelorhood may persist until a plunge into sudden marriage and equally abrupt coronary death.

(40) Repression, particularly the "primal" type, takes on new importance. In infancy, because of incomplete nervous growth and organization, the sonic image of the heart becomes too easily dyssynergic, produces severe anxiety, and must become repressed in part by growth itself. The "superego" which forms is conservative therefore; it is a steersman-repressor, as part of its functioning "ideal" and "judgment." The steersman is cybernetic. The repressor is economic. The steersman watches and warns, and serves the synergy of the ego by its access to both vision and the retracting image of the heart. The

repressor restrains and redistributes, and serves the synergy of the ego by its control of archi-ego dismembering impulses (sadism) and dismemberment terror (masochism) which leash and lash the mechanism of the heart. This is the well-known "pact" between the ego and the id—in our terms, between neo-ego and archi-ego.

(41) The differences between "primal" repression and "subsequential" repression become clear. Primal repression has its gravitational effect and "draws down" subsequent repression to the earlier levels of "fixation" because it is the result of the *fundamental anxiety of psychic growth*—the "pact" between archi-ego and neo-ego; the "superego" forms—as steersman-repressor—because of the cybernetic-conservative necessities which preserve the heart. The *primal* repression may have been severely excessive; the task of analysis then is to prevent, where possible, the oversevere gravitational effect upon subsequent life. From the standpoint of longevity, analysis must follow "the track of the heart" along the "nodal points" of excessive aggression become transformed into constricting repression. The therapeutic approach must always be, therefore, to restore and improve *synergy*.

(42) The neurotic fear of "heart stop" is traced to this fundamental aggression, at the very beginning of "superego" formation, of *symbolically wishing to destroy both heart and genital of father*—i.e., the archi-ego wish to dismember and destroy the body and authority of reality. It interprets "threats" *from* the father in this dismembering and heart-stopping light, and the *severe anxiety preceding superego formation* is thus reflected later as the terror of "heart stop," in much milder but nevertheless derivative form. *In severe enuretics, this form of anxiety is particularly intense; their raging defiance against authority produces all the masochistic variations* of "block" and "collapse"; they are apt to suffer severe neurotic depression as a result; this coincides with a deceptive "cooperativeness," the reflection—in the case of the male—of an intensely hostile identification with mother and a refusal to become an authority if that means changing identification to that of acceptance of the father. As all analysts know, in the place of a willingness to accept and become an authority in the real adult sense of the term, these former enuretics have severe "anal-sadistic and masochistic" obsessive-compulsive mental habits of op-

erating in life; a violent exhibitionism covers this trait; severe anxiety returns when this is exposed, as it must be, to bring about any degree of real synergy of the ego; as one would expect, from what has been said of heart-genital imagery, these patients, male and female, are apt to be sexually impotent, episodically. This group of patients (former severe enuretics) are particularly vivid examples of the role of the sonic image of the heart in that *dyssynergy* we call anxiety.

(43) The paroxysmal tachycardias, both auricular and ventricular, in men and women, show all the phenomena that have been described in exquisite and pure form. Here too, the fear of "heart stop" in relation to decapitation-dismemberment phenomena is utterly clear. The hiatus of birth and the later fusion of archi-ego and neo-ego are to be seen in the raging aggression so easily released and so violently "boomeranging." The characteristic juncture and synergic fusion of the image of the heart and the image of the genital is broken into by the rape-murder threat; and the image of the heart consequently "breaks away" into a "run"—the "runaway heart."

Apart from *proven organic disease* of the heart, it would seem that most, if not all, other cases of paroxysmal tachycardia should be given the benefit of psychosynergic study and if necessary analytic therapy.

(44) A study of Edgar Allan Poe's *The Tell-Tale Heart* in relation to his own severe dyssynergy illustrates the startling derivative imagery to which the dyssynergic sonic image of the heart gives rise. The entire problem of premature cardiac death and thus of human longevity is laid bare. There can be little doubt that the synergies of art are useful "releases" to the tensions of terror and aggression. The synergic exercise of talent is thus a compulsion as well as a desire, a relief as well as cultural interpretive enhancement, and an indispensable "unburdening of the heart."

PART II

(45) To re-evaluate the heart's role, brain-mind relationships must be reconceived. The basic principle of synergy in a new and synergic psychoneurology supersedes the reflex as a fundamental principle of "classical neurology." Indeed, one is logically forced to challenge the assumption that "classical neurology" is at all a complete science. The

division between "psychology" and "neurology" is not only spurious, *it is primitive.* All that is necessary to make progress here is to conceive of *a genetic neurology*—the growth concept of nervous action we have already evolved—to go hand in hand with a *genetic psychology.* The net achievement is a *psychoneurology;* yet, not a *genetic* psychoneurology; rather a *synergic* psychoneurology because the *meaning* of the genetic aspects of the component psychology and neurology, as their genetic functions fuse, is *synergy.* If this be true, "psychoanalysis" is only an expression of synergic psychoneurology and "classical neurology" is only a part-science.

(46) Thus, the basic premise of a synergic psychoneurology is that transformational activity by which, constantly, *brain becomes mind.* From this point of view, the "reflex" as well as "the complex" must be re-examined. The neural "reflex" is only one part aspect of *psychic* cybernesis and adaptation; the psychic "complex" is only one—however important—expression of *neural* dynamics, growth, and evolution, e.g., infantile myelinization, the erect posture, speech area, handedness. Similarly, the *basic unit of a synergic psychoneurology* is not a number of "reflexes" nor "complexes" but rather the synergic quantum, the unit of transformational energy, *the building block* by which the nerve cells of brain and cord build psychoneurologic dynamic structures of communication and control.

(47) The synergic quantum, the transformational building block by which brain is built into mind—and by which, conversely, mind influences brain—bears all the characteristics of a *sonic* quantum; the electrochemical milieu is *transduced*—as in electroacoustic transducers—into sonic energy. This transduction of energy enables us to link together synergically the genetic aspects of the growth concept of nervous action with the genetic aspects of psychoanalysis. The tension-relaxation equilibrium which, we showed in evolving the growth concept of nervous action, *governs life itself, including heart action,* also functions as a "metastable equilibrium" which makes possible the psychic phenomenon of *repression.* In this way the genetic *neural* thermodynamic tension-relaxation equilibrium, by its metastable action, behaves as a *psychic* "ultrasonic" delay line. In repression the sonic "audible" becomes the sonic "inaudible"—or *ultrasonic* which,

curiously enough also belongs to the pain-pleasure system. In this way synergic psychoneurology makes coherence out of theoretic chaos; an entire new field for investigation—the field of psychoneurological transformation—comes into existence.

(48) Here, finally, the sonic image of the heart—either in that synergy with the rest of the ego which is "security" or in that dyssynergy which is "anxiety"—takes its place both in physiology and psychology. The ego is first and foremost a body-surface phenomenon, as Freud showed; the sonic image of the heart—its miniature image in the ubiquitous *pulse* in the body surface and its acoustic vibratory aspects throughout the network of arteries and arterioles—may now be seen to be part of a totally synergic sonic-ultrasonic perceptive field of the ego. The definition of "anxiety" as dyssynergy between the image of the heart and the rest of the ego may now be seen to have a sharp, tangible, and measurable reality, not only in the hearing of the heart beat and in the feel of its "palpitation" but also in the entire enveloping skin surface itself—the sonic tissue envelope of the body which is the fundament of the ego.

(49) Paroxysmal auricular tachycardia *occurs actually at birth,* as well as later on in adult life, *when the very same dismemberment threat to the body-surface psychic integrity* produces the identical tachycardic response. "Waves of panic" tell us that what is involved is the transitional period from the unmyelinized to the myelinized state.

(50) *Proof* of the validity of this concept of sonic-ultrasonic dominant forces determining psychoneurologic action, both in the metastable repressional equilibria and in the actual growth and metabolism of brain and body, is given by the equations which are both thermodynamic and sonic. In both equations, the nervous system comes to be the expression of integrated acoustic force.

(51) Further evidence of the importance of the sonic-ultrasonic neural forces in living things and in man is the operation of the specifically evolved labyrinthine-sonic system of direction, balance and hearing—the latter dealing, through the cochlea, with the *audible* "band" of the acoustic vibrational spectrum; it is thus linked to problems of deafness. Here again the relationship to the heart comes di-

rectly into play; during fatigue we not only hear the heart beat, we feel it diffusely; vertigo, which is so common as the result of maso-chistic overexertion, is also the harbinger of coronary spasm and closure; the labyrinthine-sonic system shares the ninth and tenth nerves with the heart "feedback" mechanism—the carotid and aortic body; and finally the labyrinthine-sonic system provides—in addi-tion to the sense of vibration in general—the sonic nucleus of thought. The general importance then of the tractus solitarius to the sonic-ultrasonic ego becomes enormous. This fits finally to our claim that there are only four special senses—that taste is not a primary sense and does not usurp the tractus solitarius. Here in the sonic-ultra-sonic ego barrier is the principle which, as Freud predicted, goes "be-yond the pleasure principle." From this same labyrinthine-sonic sys-tem—which physiologically and psychologically belongs to the diffuse body surface and to "stretch reflexes"—stems quite appropriately the word-signaling system of anxiety.

(52) Even in the strictly "neurologic sphere," the so-called "echo-lalia"—or "acoustic reflex"—teaches us that *thinking is sonic*. The clinical syndromes of echolalia, echopraxia, grasping and sucking be-come clear in illustrating *the sonic mind*. Ordinarily we do not echo because we *counter* the tendency; all thinking has echo or sonic repe-tition as a foundation. But what emerges, more important, is that a study of this "acoustic reflex" shows how, *under the sonic network of consciousness, there lies the vast "ultrasonic network"* designated as "the unconscious." It shows us the *origin* of thinking: first the infant echoes; and only as he learns, because he becomes "ultrasonically" equipped to repress, does he acquire the transformational ability to mold the sonic echo. That modification is called *thinking*. The entire technique of psychoanalysis is based—as a sonic technique—upon the interplay of these factors.

(53) Finally, in regard to heart mechanism itself—as suggested by all the implications of the discovery of the heart image—one is forced to the premise that the heart is a portion of the preneural tissue, of the "animation mechanism" of the embryo; this "preneural" mass has become interpenetrated by a contractile tissue, producing a net resultant cardiac tissue different from *both nerve and muscle*. For

this we suggest the term: *cardiac myoneurium*. (A patient worrying about his heart "giving out" is generally one who, among other things, thinks of "heart muscle" as though it were "leg muscle"; considerable relief follows the explanation of not only the perfect synergy of the heart but also the unusual durable character of cardiac myoneurium.) The heart is "supplied" by nerves as no other internal organ is; it may be said to have its own "brain." Its embryology supports this idea of a development from preneural masses. Ultimately also, it would appear that the vital "nodal tissue" of the heart must have its own "feedback" mechanism within the vagus; indeed, the embryology of the vagus points in this direction, as do all the psychic phenomena of the paroxysmal tachycardias.

If the heart makes its sonic image everywhere on the skin surface, within the chest, and via the labyrinthine-sonic system and in the word-signaling system of anxiety, it is because the heart is a sonic and synergic psychoneurologic machine of special contractile quality.

PERSPECTIVES

The perspectives of this new transformational science of synergic psychoneurology—designed to bridge the gap between psychoanalysis and neurology—are manifold; further possible developments are beyond the scope of this first statement. However, a few things may be remarked upon very briefly now:

A. THE TREATMENT OF ANXIETY BY THE RESTORATION OF SYNERGY

It is clear from our definition of anxiety that it cannot be treated successfully by any attempt to locate "troublesome impulses from the id" or by "wild symbolisms." The patient who has anxiety must first of all accept the fact that he is not and can not be *immune* from dyssynergic crises. *The restoration of synergy is the issue;* in mental disturbances—particularly in those with previous histories of "nervous breakdown"—the restoration of synergy may be a difficult and lengthy process; there are furthermore situations in life in which a husband's character, say, may precipitate perpetual dyssynergic conditions within a wife—and vice versa; so too with parent and child.

But, whatever the cause of dyssynergy—birth trauma, severe growth disturbances, hazardous oedipal transition, enuretic "blame and shame," situational stress—the issue is still restoration of synergy. This is really what is meant by "working through."

This book has been written in an attempt to forge a new advanced psychodynamic instrument equally neurophysiologic in our fight against the "burdens of the heart"—as well as perhaps to develop a technique that may have some bearing upon problems of longevity itself; and surely to prevent, if possible, premature coronary death. Yet, synergic psychoneurology must become important also in the great group of neurologic dyssynergies: epilepsy, multiple sclerosis, amyotrophic lateral sclerosis, etc., as well as the psychoses themselves where "heart and mind" are so alienated the one from the other.

B. AN INSTITUTE FOR THE STUDY OF PSYCHOCARDIOLOGY AND SYNERGIC PSYCHONEUROLOGY

It will be clear, therefore, that the ordinary "psychoanalytic institute" cannot handle these newly perceived specific problems of psychocardiology in which cardiologist and synergic psychoneurologist must meet. The solution to "coronary death" is more urgent than the customary confused "psychosomatic" approach will permit.

Synergic psychoneurology emerges as *the* science of what psychoanalysis has so long called "the psychophysiologic apparatus."

Moreover, the special sonic-ultrasonic aspects of synergic psychoneurology alone require trained biophysicists; the cult of "orthodoxy" in psychoanalysis, valuable as it has been historically, is simply not equipped theoretically or practically to solve these problems.

The great work of Sigmund Freud was not meant to be fettered by limitations inherent in the tendency to clinical verbiage or verbalism; he pointed to the future himself in *Beyond the Pleasure Principle* as one of quantitative psychoneurologic concepts.

Synergic psychoneurology (which introduces psychocardiology) and its obvious relationships to the modern sciences of cybernetics and sonics takes the great legacy of Freud into promising regions of the future.

Appendix

APPENDIX I

Of interest perhaps is the following technique of deriving a simultaneous record of alpha wave: Q-R-S complex from the body surface. The original publication (done under a grant by the Israel Abrahamson Fellowship Fund of Mount Sinai Hospital) is here reproduced in full. Its theoretic and practical potentialities must be commented upon more fully in a later work. The article follows:

The Electro-encephalo-cardiogram[1]

INTRODUCTION

Increasingly the neurophysiologist is being confronted with problems of the total *integrative* action of the central nervous system in relation to somatic change. Hence, there is an increasing need for experimental methods to measure the variables of total integration. This paper is intended to report briefly a method for measuring simultaneously changes in the electrical potentials of the heart and cerebral cortex.

In both neuropsychiatric and general medical problems the interrelated activity of cardiovascular and nervous tissues is of considerable importance; to date, however, methods for measuring the *relationship* at any time have not been available. In general medicine, with instances of coronary disease, the effect of anxiety on the heart is of

[1] Reprinted from *The Journal of Nervous and Mental Disease*, Vol. 91, No. 6, June 1940.

257

enormous importance. In anxiety, for example, one can observe (and one ought to be able to measure *simultaneously*) the following changes:

(1) The alpha wave of the electroencephalogram disappears.

(2) The heart rate and pulse pressure alter with corresponding changes in peripheral vascular dilation and the output of heat and moisture from the skin.

Clinically there is tendency to separate the alterations in cardiac electric rhythms from those in the nervous system and to treat the heart as though it were autonomous. It must be emphasized that the heart and vascular system are not strictly autonomous; the sinus node and even the auriculo-ventricular node normally operate under central influence via the vagus. Abeles and Schneider (1935) demonstrated some of the electrocardiographic changes during the injection of air into the subarachnoid spaces of the neuraxis.

In this communication two sample records are presented from the same subject showing that it is possible to record from a single ink-writing pen the alpha or beta waves of the cerebral cortex and the Q-R-S complex of the cardiac conduction system.

TECHNIQUE

The method used was relatively simple. The apparatus consisted of suitable electrodes, amplifiers of the Garceau (1934) design and a Brush crystal recorder with an ink-writing pen. The subjects were normal adults inclosed in a properly shielded compartment.

RECORDS AND COMMENT

Figure I shows the relation of the Q-R-S complex to the alpha and beta waves of the cerebral cortex. These records were obtained by placing one lead over the occiput and the other over the bony prominence of the seventh cervical vertebra. It is a simple way of measuring simultaneously the effect of any experimental variable (drugs, etc.) on the cerebral and cardiac electrochemical potentials.

Physiologically one might say at first glance that this simultaneous record has no more significance than the mechanical feat of recording two independent electrical events from the same needle, and, that the ratio thus made evident between the encephalic and cardiac rhythms (5-6 alpha to 1 Q-R-S complex and 25-30 beta to 1 Q-R-S complex) is nothing but the comparison of two regularly recurring independent rhythms.

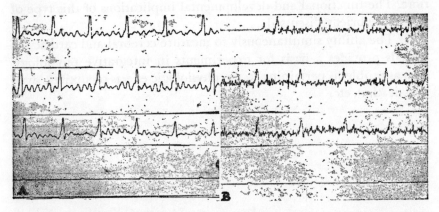

FIGURE I.—Showing the Relation of the Alpha and Beta Waves of the Electroencephalogram to the Q-R-S complex of the Electrocardiogram.

(A) Alpha: Q-R-S Ratio   (B) Beta: Q-R-S Ratio
The time signal is in seconds.

However, from the viewpoint of a truly *integrative* neurosomatic physiology, it is clear that the various tissues of the body, though each enjoys some "autonomy," stand in dynamic relationship to each other, all co-ordinated and integrated by the activity of the nervous system. In addition to the momentary functional integrations, there is another *developmental* relationship between these ratios which is of value for purposes of measurement. Due to the progressive *increase* in cortical wave frequency up to twelve years of age, as shown by Lindsley (1936), and the progressive *decrease* in heart rate as age advances, *the ratio of cortical wave frequency to heart rate constantly increases, from birth to twelve to sixteen years of age.* Thus in infancy, at about four months of age, there are three to five alpha waves per second as compared with approximately two heart beats per second. After sixteen years of age the ratio is stabilized at the value demonstrated in Figure 1. The cortical-cardiac frequency ratio is therefore *indicative of a state of growth.* (The beta waves likewise show a growth increase in frequency proportional to that of the alpha waves.)

SUMMARY

(1) The electro-encephalo-cardiogram is presented for the first time. The functional and developmental implications of this type of record are briefly discussed.

(2) The ability simultaneously to measure cerebral and cardiac potentials provides a basis for experiments in integrative physiology, such as problems pertaining to the physiologic effects of anxiety, drug intoxication, etc.

References

REFERENCES

Abeles, M. M. and Schneider, D. E. (1935), Electrocardiographic Changes During Encephalography. *Am. J. Med. Sci., 190*:673.

Allen, W. F. (1922–1923), *J. Comp. Neurol., 35*:198, 275.

Barr, M. W. (1898), *J. Nerv. & Ment. Dis., 25*:20–30.

Bateman, F. (1870), *On Aphasia.* London: J. Churchill & Sons, p. 110. Sec. ed., 1890, p. 213.

Bender, L. and Schilder, P. (1933), *Arch. Neurol. & Psychiat., 29*:990.

Benedict, F. G. (1920), *Proc. Nat. Acad. Sci., 6*:7–10.

Betlheim, S. (1924), *Jahrb. f. Psychiat., 43*:226–234.

Bieber, I. (1936), Grasping and Sucking. *J. Nerv. & Ment. Dis., 85*.

Bierring, E. (1931), *Standard Metabolism of Boys.* Copenhagen: Levin & Munks-Gaard.

Bonaparte, M. (1949), *The Life and Works of Edgar Allan Poe.* London: Imago Publ. Co.

Bromberg, W. (1934), *Am. J. Psychiat., 91*.

Costen, J. B., Clare, M. H. and Bishop, G. H. (1951), *Ann. Otol., Rhinol., & Laryngol., 60*:591.

Cramer, F. (1936), *Bull. Neurol. Inst. N.Y., 5*:37–60.

Cushing, H. (1903), *Bull. Johns Hopkins Hosp., 14*:71–78.

Dameshek, W. and Meyerson, A. (1935), *Arch. Neurol. & Psychiat., 33*:1–18.

Darwin, C. (1890), *The Descent of Man.* New York: Appleton & Co.

Dromand (1905), *J. of Psychol.*

Eideken, J. (1943), *Am. J. Med. Sci., 205*:52.

Enos, W. F., Holmes, R. H., and Beyer, J. (1953), Coronary Disease among Soldiers Killed in Action in Korea. *J. Am. Med. Assoc. 145*:1090.

Fenichel, O. (1941), *Problems of Psychoanalytic Technique.* New York: Psychoanalytic Quarterly, Inc.

Foley, J. O. (1945), *Proc. Soc. Exper. Biol. & Med., 60*:262.

Freud, S. (1900), *The Interpretation of Dreams.* The Complete Psychological Works of Sigmund Freud, Vols. 3 & 4. London: Hogarth Press, 1953.

—— (1920), *Beyond the Pleasure Principle.* London: Hogarth Press, 1922.

—— (1923), *The Ego and the Id.* London: Hogarth Press, 1949.

—— (1925), A Note Upon the "Mystic Writing-Pad." *Collected Papers, 3*:175–180. London: Hogarth Press, 1950.

—— (1926), *The Problem of Anxiety.* New York: W. W. Norton, 1936.

—— (1932), *New Introductory Lectures on Psychoanalysis.* New York: W. W. Norton, 1933.

—— (1939), *An Outline of Psychoanalysis.* New York: W. W. Norton, 1950.

Fröschels, E. (1917), *Münch. med. Woch., 1*:23.

Fulton, J. F. (1934), *Arch. Neurol. & Psychiat., 31*:221.

Garceau, E. L. and Davis, H. (1934), An Amplifier, Recording System, and Stimulating Devices for the Study of Cerebral Action Currents. *Am. J. Physiol., 107*:305.

Gibbs, F. A., Davis, H., and Lennox, W. G. (1935), *Arch. Neurol. & Psychiat., 34*:1133.

Goldblatt, H. (1941), *Hypertension.* Philadelphia: University of Pennsylvania Press.

Goldstein, K. (1912–1917), *Ergeb. d. Neurol. u. Psychiat., 2*:349.

Gowers, W. (1888), *Textbook of Neurology.* Philadelphia: Blakiston.

Grasse, J. (1934), *Arch. f. Psychiat., 102*:689–705.

Guggenheim, L. (1948), *Phylogenesis of the Ear.* Culver City, Calif.: Murray and Gee, Inc.

Halliday, J. C. (1940), *Ohio J. Sci., 40*:337.

Hayes, E. R. and Elliot, R. (1943), *J. Comp. Neurol., 76*:227.

Herrick, C. J. (1926), *A Survey of the Origin and Biologic Significance of the Cerebral Cortex*. Chicago: University of Chicago Press.

Hobohm (1908), *Jahrb. der Hamburg. Stattskrankenanst., 13*:227–241.

Hollingworth, L. S. (1917), *J. Educ. Psychol., 8*:212–219.

Hunt, J. R. (1909), *J. Nerv. & Ment. Dis., 36*:322.

Juzelevsky, A. (1930–1931), Ueber die Gefahren and Komplikationen bei der Encephaloventriculographie, über Prophylaxie und Therapie. *Beitr. f. klin. Chir., 151*:48.

Keschner, M., Bender, M. B., and Strauss, I. (1936), *Arch. Neurol. & Psychiat., 35*:572–593.

Kiesow, F. (1894, 1896), *Philos. Stud., 10*:329; *12*:465.

Krause, F. (1930), Cerebrale Krankheiten des Kindesalters in typischen Encephalogrammen. *Ergeb. d. inner. Med. u. Kinderheilk., 37*:333.

Kubliako (1902), *Arch. f. ges. Physiol., 90*:461.

Liepmann, H. (1900), *Neurol. Centralblätt., 19*:389–399.

Lindsley, D. B. (1936), Brain Potentials in Children and Adults. *Science, 84*:354.

Meredith, H. V. (1935), *Univ. Iowa Stud., 11* (No. 3).

Meschede, F. (1897), *Allg. Zeitshcr. Psychiat., 53*:443–454.

Meyer, A. (1932), Das Verhalten des Blutdrucks bei der Encephalographie. *Klin. Wchnschr., 11*:1873.

Oehrwall, H. (1891), *Skand. Arch. Physiol., 2*:1.

Oliver, W. A. (1934), *Calif. & West. Med., 41*:328–330.

Pancoast, H. K. and Fay T. (1929), Encephalography: Roentgenological and Clinical Considerations for Its Use. *Am. J. Roentgen., 21*:421.

Pfaffman, C. (1951), *Handbook of Experimental Psychology*. New York: Wiley & Sons.

Pick, A. (1902), *Jahrb. f. Psychiat., 21*:282–293.

—— (1916–1917), *Fortschr. d. Psychiat., 4*:34–42.

—— (1924), *Klin. Wchnschr., 3*:662.

Raymond (1888), *Mem. et comt. rend. de la Soc. d. Sci. med. de Lyons, 28*:12–19.

Richter, C. P. and Hines, M. (1934), *Monograph, Assoc. Research in Nerv. & Ment. Dis., 13*:215.

Romberg, M. H. (1842), *A Manual of the Nervous Diseases of Man.* Tr. E. A. Sieveking. Vol. 2, 1853, p. 430.

Rosen, S. (1951), *Ann. Otol., Rhinol., & Laryngol., 60*:657.

Scammon, R. E. (1930), *The Measurement of Man.* Minneapolis: University of Minnesota Press.

Schneider, D. E. (1938a), The Clinical Syndromes of Echolalia, Echopraxia, Grasping and Sucking. *J. Nerv. & Ment. Dis., 88*:18–35, 200–215.

—— (1938b), Further Studies of the Syndrome of Echolalia, Echopraxia, Grasping and Sucking. *J. Mt. Sinai Hosp., 5*:536–544.

—— (1940), The Electro-Encephalo-Cardiogram. *J. Nerv. & Ment. Dis., 91*:742–744.

—— (1944), The Growth Concept of Nervous Integration: V. The Theoretic Formulations and the Basic Equations for the Relations of Heart Production, etc. *Growth, 8*:43–50.

—— (1950), *The Psychoanalyst and the Artist.* New York: International Universities Press, 2nd ed., 1954.

—— (1949), *The Growth Concept of Nervous Integration.* New York: Nerv. & Ment. Dis. Monograph, No. 78.

—— (1952), Psychosomatic Implications of a New Theory of Taste and Hearing: Psychosurgical Perspectives. *J. Hillside Hosp., 1*: 156–165.

—— (1953), The Psychophysiology of the Sonic System. *J. Nerv. Ment. Dis., 118*:494–515.

—— (1954), The Image of the Heart and the Synergic Principle in Psychoanalysis (Psychosynergy). *Psa. Rev., 41*:197–215.

Schuster, P. and Pineas, H. (1926), *Deutsche Ztschr. f. Nervenheilk., 91*:12–56.

Schwartz, H. G. and Weddell, G. (1938), *Brain, 61*:99.

Serin, Mlle. (1922), *Bull. de la Soc. Clin. de Med. Ment., 10*:224–227.

Sterling, W. (1932), *Rev. Neurol., 1*:144–145.

Strauss, I. and Keschner, M. (1935), *Arch. Neurol. & Psychiat., 33*: 986.

Strongin, E. I. and Hinsie, L. E. (1938), Parotid Secretory Rate in Schizophrenic Patients. *J. Nerv. & Ment. Dis., 87*:715.

van Bogaert, L. (1934), *J. Nerv. & Ment. Dis., 80*:48–61.

Waelder, J. Hall (1935), The Analysis of a Case of Night Terror. *The Psychoanalytic Study of the Child, 2*:189. New York: International Universities Press, 1946.

Walshe, F. M. R. and Robertson, E. G. (1933), *Brain, 56*:40.

Wetzel, N. C. (1937), *Growth, 1*:6–59.

Wilburne, M. and Mack, E. G. (1954), *J. Am. Med. Assoc., 154*:1337.